Study Guide

TO ACCOMPANY

Physics

BY PAUL A. TIPLER

Granvil C. Kyker, Jr.
ROSE-HULMAN INSTITUTE OF TECHNOLOGY

WORTH PUBLISHERS, INC.

Study Guide
to accompany
Physics by Paul A. Tipler

Printed in the United States of America.
ISBN: 0-87901-055-X
First printing, January 1976

Worth Publishers, Inc.
444 Park Avenue South
New York, New York 10016

For Penny and Peggy and Dorothy

Preface

How do you study physics? There isn't any one answer, of course; you have to find and develop the system that works best for you. The important thing is that you continue to improvise until you find it, and that you keep with it throughout the course. In this Study Guide, written to accompany Paul A. Tipler's Physics, I have tried to put together several kinds of materials that will help you to do this.

Each chapter of this Study Guide was written to be read with the chapter in the Tipler textbook. The organization of each chapter is described below.

1. Chapter Summary. These summaries tie together the important physical ideas and techniques discussed in the text chapter.

2. Check List. This is a list, for quick review, of the new or important terms, concepts, etc., that you should have become familiar with in reading the text.

3. True or False? Many true-false questions are provided, related directly to points made in the chapter.

4. Questions. These questions require more thinking than the true-false questions do. Most are conceptual, although simple numerical questions are also included.

5. Examples. Several examples are provided for each chapter. They range in difficulty from medium-easy to hard and require that you apply one or more of the concepts developed in the text. Most of the examples have numerical answers, although a few derivations are included in chapters whose content is essentially technical.

6. Answers. Answers to all the questions and examples in Sections 3, 4, and 5 above are given - my answers, at least.

The most important resource you have in studying physics is your instructor; you should assume that he is always ready to answer the questions that you will certainly have. First, though, do your part by pinpointing just what your question is. If you can get your difficulty down to the point of "right here is where you lost me," it will save you and your instructor a lot of time and frustration; it will usually get you a clear, and really helpful, answer; and often, in the process of doing this, you will find that you've cleared up the difficulty for yourself.

Identifying just what your problem areas are is one of the ways in which this Guide can help you study physics. Start working through each chapter of the Study Guide as soon as you have finished your first reading of the corresponding textbook chapter. The chapter summaries are intended to help you bring things together in your mind after studying them in detail in the text, in lectures, and in homework assignments. Together with the check lists, they also provide a quick and convenient review of the chapter. Where a few of the fundamental equations best express parts of the physical content of the chapter, they are also included in the summary. It isn't necessary to memorize them; physics students as a rule spend too much time memorizing equations. After you've studied the text chapter in detail, you'll find you've learned (not memorized) many of the equations in the chapter summaries. What you can't do with the chapter summaries is try to use them as a substitute for concentrated study of your text.

To use the check lists, close your eyes and imagine yourself, on a quiz, confronted with a question like "in a sentence, identify or explain..." each item. Could you do this without fumbling around for very long? If not, look it up.

The true-false and verbal questions - Sections 3 and 4 - are also meant primarily for review and self-examination. Almost all the true-false questions are answered directly somewhere in the text chapter. A few of them are subtle; none were intended to be ambiguous. But you are bound to read some of them differently than what I had in mind when I wrote them. This really doesn't matter; no one is grading you. To try to make them more useful, however, I've included - for all the "false" and many of the "true" answers - a sentence of explanation with the answer. The questions in Section 4 call for written answers - a sentence or two each, perhaps - and in most of them you need to think a little past exactly what's said in the chapter and put a couple of different ideas together.

Probably the most demanding and rewarding part of your study of physics is learning to apply the ideas and equations you encounter to the solution of specific physical problems. At some point you are likely to feel "I understand the theory - I just can't do the problems." Sorry, it just isn't so. In this case, the medium really is the message: until and unless the physical ideas you are studying become tools that are yours to apply to concrete situations, you haven't really learned them.

Learning to work problems requires skill and drill. One of the unique features of the Tipler textbook is the set of exercises after each chapter. There are many simple exercises there. Most are quite direct applications of just a few ideas discussed in the chapter, and all the odd-numbered ones are answered. Do a lot of these - almost certainly more than you are required to do for homework. This is what I mean by "drill." When you come across a particular point or technique that you're not clear on, do as many of the exercises relating to that topic as you can find time for.

The examples in Section 5 of each chapter of this Guide are designed to help you to acquire skill in attacking more complex problems. The examples, most of them, are not very easy. Their solutions are presented in three parts, each separate from the others. This purposely makes them inconvenient to read right through, as you would the worked examples in the textbook - so don't, that's not what they're for. Try first to set up and work each example without reference to the solution. If you have difficulty, look back in your text - or in the chapter in the Guide - and try to identify just what the applicable principles and techniques are; how do they apply to the stated situation? If it still isn't clear how to attack the problem, then read the first partial solution only. Usually, this states the appropriate principle and provides a few clues as to how it applies. At this point, try again to do the problem.

If you need more help, read the second part of the solution; typically this finishes setting up the problem but leaves you to work it through. For each of the examples - or, at least, each one that isn't transparent to you - try to do as much of the solution on your own as you can. You will find that a little help in setting up the problem will enable you to do many examples that might otherwise stump you - and also that you will gradually become able to spot those first steps for yourself.

Finally, there are occasional "digressions" on mathematical subjects. These are meant just for reference.

One last bit of advice: try, throughout the course, to keep the forest in view behind all those trees. There is a coherence, an overall continuity, to all the various things you will find yourself working at, and keeping in mind these interrelationships will make all the details a good deal more intelligible - may even make them fun.

I am grateful to Paul Tipler for suggesting this project to me, for his continuing advice and very helpful suggestions, and most especially for writing a textbook that has been a joy to work with. And above all, I must express my gratitude to my wife, Penny, and my two daughters, for the support that made this effort possible, and for putting up with my preoccupation with it.

Granvil C. Kyker, Jr.
Terre Haute, Indiana

Contents

CHAPTER 1
Introduction

1.1 CHAPTER SUMMARY

The subject of this text is "classical" physics. This is our understanding of
the physical world as it had developed through, roughly, the end of the last
century. Although it fails on the very small scale - atomic or smaller - and
at very high speeds, classical physics is a wholly adequate description of
phenomena in the range accessible to our senses, and it provides the conceptual foundation for the theories of modern physics.

The laws of physics are quantitative generalizations of experimental
observations, usually best expressed as mathematical equations. These relate
physical quantities based on measurement - mass, force, electrical charge,
temperature, etc. - and are meaningful only if the quantities are expressed in
terms of appropriate <u>units</u>. The universal standard system of units is that
based on the meter, the kilogram, and the second; units for other mechanical
quantities are derived from these. (Some use is made of other unit systems,
depending on convenience.) In a physical equation, the units of quantities
multiply, cancel, etc., just as algebraic quantities, and equations correspondingly must relate quantities in a way consistent with their dimensions.

A review of the elements of trigonometry is found in the text. A very
useful approximation for <u>small</u> angle θ is

$$\sin \theta \cong \tan \theta \cong \theta$$

with θ measured in <u>radians</u> only. Approximations to small quantities are
useful in many physical problems; another follows from the binomial expansion:

$$(1 + x)^n \cong 1 + nx$$

for x much less than 1.

1.2 CHECK LIST

meter	SI units
kilogram	British system of units
ampere	radian
kelvin	binomial theorem
unit	conversion factor
dimension	sine
fundamental vs. derived units	cosine
classical vs. modern physics	tangent
metric system	small-angle approximation

1.3 TRUE OR FALSE?

_____1. Two quantities of different dimensions may be added, but not multi-
         plied, in a valid physical equation.

_____2. All conversion factors are equal to 1.

_____3. Classical physics fails to describe systems on an atomic or smaller
         scale.

_____4. The fundamental definitions of the meter and the second are in terms
         of the size and period of the earth's orbital motion.

_____5. In the mks system, units of force, momentum, and such are defined in
         terms of the units of mass, length, and time.

_____6. In general, units of force, momentum, etc., are derived from funda-
         mental units of mass, length, and time.

_____7. In the British system, the unit of force is defined in terms of the
         earth's gravitational pull on an object.

_____8. An angle is a dimensionless number.

_____9. Two quantities with the same dimensions must be measured in the
         same units.

_____10. 360 degrees is the same angle as π radians.

_____11. The quantity $\sin \theta$ is approximately equal to θ, for θ small, only
         with θ measured in radians.

_____12. For small θ, $\cos \theta$ and $\tan \theta$ are approximately equal.

_____13. The binomial expansion is an infinite series of terms, unless the
         power n is a positive integer.

_____14. For small x, the quantity $(1 - \sqrt{1 - x^2})$ is approximately equal to x/2.

1.4 QUESTIONS

1. What properties should an object or a system have for it to be a
    useful standard of some physical quantity (as length, time, etc.)?

2. Acceleration - such as the acceleration due to gravity, g - has
    dimensions LT^{-2}; those of velocity are length per unit time. The
    velocity of an object which has fallen a distance h under gravity is
    either $v = \sqrt{2gh}$ or $v = (2gh)^2$, you can't remember which. Which one
    must it be?

3. Find the conversion factor relating mi/h to m/sec.

4. The period of a pendulum clock is $T = 2\pi\sqrt{L/g}$, where L is the length
    of the pendulum and g the acceleration due to gravity. This apparently
    relates a time measurement to the standard of length in terms of which
    L was measured. But length and time are supposed to be independent
    fundamental quantities. Comment.

5. You can estimate the distance of an object, whose size you know, by
    comparing its apparent size to that of your thumb held at arm's length,
    and relating them by simple proportion. When you do this, on what
    length standard is your distance measurement based?

6. Imagine blowing up a spherical balloon (the volume of a sphere is
    $\frac{4}{3}\pi R^3$). If you increase its radius by 5%, by how much is the volume

increased? Estimate the answer by an appropriate (binomial) approximation, and compare it to the exact result.

1.5 ANSWERS

True or False?

1. False - in appropriate circumstances they may be multiplied (speed times time gives distance), but it makes no sense to add different quantities.

2. True - in the sense that "5280 ft/mi" may be thought of as 5280 ft divided by 1 mi, which is plainly 1.

3. True.

4. False - they are defined in terms of the wavelength and frequency of certain spectral lines; the second was originally defined as a fraction of the earth's orbital period.

5. True.

6. False - one may equally well take some other mechanical quantity (such as force, in the British system) as fundamental.

7. True - this is weight.

8. True - its definition amounts to a ratio of lengths.

9. False - it must be true the other way around, but time can be measured in seconds, years, fortnights, or other units, for instance.

10. False - 360 degrees is 2π radians.

11. True.

12. False - for small θ, $\cos \theta$ approaches 1.

13. True.

14. False - this would work out to approximate $x^2/2$.

Questions

1. Plainly it should be invariable, not subject to change with time, and as nearly as possible independent of extraneous conditions. It should be such that comparison of measurements is relatively straightforward and possible at different places without physically carrying the standard around. Convenience of use is perhaps more important for secondary than primary standards.

2. The expression $\sqrt{2gh}$ has dimensions

$$\sqrt{(LT^{-2})(L)} = \sqrt{L^2T^{-2}} = LT^{-1}$$

which are appropriate for velocity; those of $(2gh)^2$ are

$$\left[(LT^{-2})(L)\right]^2 = L^4T^{-4}$$

which aren't; so the former must be the correct expression.

3. $\left(\dfrac{1 \text{ mi}}{\text{hr}}\right)\left(\dfrac{5280 \text{ ft}}{1 \text{ mi}}\right)\left(\dfrac{0.3048 \text{ m}}{1 \text{ ft}}\right)\left(\dfrac{1 \text{ min}}{60 \text{ sec}}\right)\left(\dfrac{1 \text{ hr}}{60 \text{ min}}\right) = 0.447 \dfrac{\text{m}}{\text{sec}}$

4. There is nothing fixed about the choice of length and time as fundamental quantities, at least in principle; one could just as well take acceleration as fundamental along with length and derive the unit of time. In terms of the ordinary system of units, however, a pendulum clock doesn't tie the length and time standards together, because the time standard has been used, implicitly, in the measurement of g.

5. On the length of your arm and thumb - or on whatever standard you measured them against.

6. $V + \Delta V = \frac{4}{3}\pi(R + \Delta R)^3 = \frac{4}{3}\pi R^3 (1 + \frac{\Delta R}{R})^3 \simeq \frac{4}{3}\pi R^3 (1 + \frac{3\Delta R}{R})$

$V + \Delta V = V(1.05)^3 \simeq 1.15\ V$

the exact result is $(1.05)^3 V = 1.1576\ V$ instead of $1.15\ V$.

CHAPTER 2
Motion in One Dimension

2.1 CHAPTER SUMMARY

We begin by considering the motion of a particle in one dimension. By "particle" we simply mean an object small enough, in the context of a particular problem, that we don't worry about its size and structure. Call the position of the particle x; as it moves, x changes as a function of time. If in the interval from time t_1 to t_2 the particle moves from x_1 to x_2, we define its average velocity as

$$v_{av} \equiv \frac{x_2 - x_1}{t_2 - t_1} = \frac{\Delta x}{\Delta t}$$

Note that v_{av} may have either sign, depending on which way the particle is going. If we imagine an x-vs.-t graph of the particle's motion, v_{av} would be the slope of a line drawn between (t_1, x_1) and (t_2, x_2). If the velocity is constant, the graph would be a straight line expressed by $x = x_0 + vt$.

If velocity is not constant, then v_{av} depends on the time interval chosen. We can define the instantaneous velocity at a particular moment by imagining that we take the average over an extremely short time interval; this is called a derivative:

$$v \equiv \frac{\text{limit}}{\Delta t \to 0}\left(\frac{\Delta x}{\Delta t}\right) = \frac{dx}{dt}$$

On an x-t graph, v is the slope of the line tangent to the graph at the moment in question.

If v is not constant in time, we define the <u>acceleration</u> of the particle, in turn, as the rate at which its <u>velocity</u> is changing:

$$a_{av} \equiv \frac{\Delta v}{\Delta t} \qquad \text{and} \qquad a \equiv \frac{\text{limit}}{\Delta t \to 0}\left(\frac{\Delta v}{\Delta t}\right) = \frac{dv}{dt} = \frac{d^2 x}{dt^2}$$

instantaneously. The acceleration would be the slope of a graph of <u>velocity</u> vs. time.

Given the position of a moving particle as a function of time, we have defined its velocity and acceleration. We may also consider the inverse problem: given the velocity, find x(t). This amounts mathematically to finding the function whose time derivative is the given v(t) - that is, the antiderivative of v(t). The physically important situation, since acceleration is the quantity given by dynamical laws, is to solve for v(t) <u>and</u> x(t) of a particle whose acceleration is given; this requires finding an antiderivative twice in succession. The antiderivative of a given function is always arbitrary within an additive constant; thus the solution depends on the initial conditions of the particle's motion. Finding an antiderivative is related to the problem of <u>integration</u> - finding the area under an arbitrary curve. If, for instance, x(t) is the antiderivative of v(t), the area under the v(t) curve between t_1 and t_2 is just $x(t_2) - x(t_1)$.

A most important practical case is that of a motion with <u>constant</u>

acceleration, for instance, that of a particle falling freely under gravity. If the acceleration is a_0, we find for this case

$$v = v_0 + a_0 t$$
$$x = x_0 + v_0 t + \frac{1}{2} a_0 t^2$$

if x and v, respectively, are the position and velocity at time t = 0. If more convenient in a given case, we may obtain other relations describing the same motion by eliminating one or another variable:

$$v^2 - v_0^2 = 2a_0 (x - x_0) \qquad \text{or} \qquad v_{av} = \frac{1}{2}(v + v_0)$$

for motion with constant acceleration.

2.2 CHECK LIST

$g = 9.80 \text{ m/sec}^2 = 32.2 \text{ ft/sec}^2$	differential
particle	second derivative
displacement	acceleration
velocity	initial-value problem
average and instantaneous velocity	antiderivative
average and instantaneous acceleration	integration
derivative	definite integral
acceleration of gravity	

2.3 TRUE OR FALSE?

____1. A particle is necessarily a very small object.

____2. Extended or complex objects are treated as systems of many particles.

____3. The average velocity of a particle is always a positive number.

____4. If a particle's average velocity over a certain time interval is zero, it has been at rest during the interval.

____5. Velocity is expressed in units of distance times time.

____6. Instantaneous velocity is defined as the average velocity calculated over a vanishingly small interval of time.

____7. If a particle's instantaneous velocity at a certain instant is zero, it is at rest.

____8. A particle whose motion is given by $x = Ct^2$ (C is a constant) is moving with a constant velocity.

____9. If the average acceleration of a particle over a certain time interval is zero, its velocity has remained constant through that interval.

____10. If the instantaneous acceleration of a particle is zero at a certain instant, its velocity is constant.

____11. A particle whose motion is given by $x = Ct^2$ has a velocity given by $v = 2Ct$.

_____12. The particle in the last question has a constant acceleration
a = 4C.

_____13. Over a certain time interval, the velocity of a particle changes
from v_1 to v_2; its average velocity over the interval is therefore
$\frac{1}{2}\left(v_1 + v_2\right)$.

_____14. If at a certain moment a particle's acceleration is positive, its
velocity is also positive.

_____15. A particle has a constant velocity v_0; its motion then is given by
$x = v_0 t$.

_____16. The derivative of the derivative of a function is called its
antiderivative.

_____17. The "initial-value problem" consists of finding a particle's
velocity and acceleration at time t = 0.

_____18. The area under a graph of velocity vs. time, over a given time
interval, is the distance the particle has gone in that interval.

_____19. The area under a graph of acceleration vs. position, over some
interval, is the particle's average velocity during that interval.

_____20. A particle falling freely near the surface of the earth moves with
a constant acceleration downward.

2.4 QUESTIONS

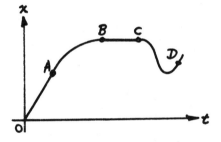

1. In the graph, sketched at right, of the
position of a particle vs. time,
   (a) Over what interval(s) is the particle's
   velocity apparently zero?
   (b) Over what interval(s) is the particle's
   velocity apparently constant?
   (c) Over what interval(s) is the particle's
   average velocity less than zero?

2. In the graph of question 1,
   (a) Over what interval(s) is the particle's acceleration apparently
   zero?
   (b) Is there any interval over which the particle's acceleration is
   obviously not constant?

3. A certain particle's motion is given by $x = a + bt + ct^2$. Is it
moving with a constant acceleration? Either way, explain.

4. (a) Can a particle whose velocity is zero still have a nonzero
   acceleration?
   (b) Can a particle's speed be changing if its acceleration is zero?

5. An elevator is (a) moving upward, (b) moving downward, (c) at rest
when a bolt falls off its underside. Other things being equal, in which
case does the bolt hit the bottom of the shaft with the highest speed?

6. At some instant, a car's velocity is 15 ft/sec; 1 sec later, it is
11 ft/sec. If the particle's acceleration is constant, what was its
average speed over the interval? How far did it go? Can you answer
these questions if the acceleration is not constant?

2.5 EXAMPLES

1. A car driving along a straight road proceeds at 30 mi/h for the first 2 mi, stops for 1 min, and continues at 90 mi/h for the next 3 mi. Neglecting the time required for it to accelerate and decelerate, what was its average velocity?

2. A car is traveling at 12 m/sec along a straight, level road. The driver suddenly sees another car ahead in his lane, moving at 4 m/sec in the same direction. If the other car is 35 m ahead when the driver sees it, and it takes him 0.3 sec to react and hit his brakes, what value of acceleration is required to avoid a collision?

3. A man standing on a cliff 30 m above the ground throws a stone vertically upward with an initial velocity v_0. If the stone hits the ground 3.5 sec after it is thrown, find v_0.

4. A man standing inside a building, by a 6-ft window, sees a ball go past outside which was dropped from the top of the building. If the ball passed the window in 0.2 sec, how far above is the top of the building?

2.6 ANSWERS

True or False?

1. False - in appropriate circumstances, an object of any size may be considered a particle. If all the information you care about can be specified by the position of one point, it's a particle.

2. True - in principle, the laws of particle motion are applied to each particle of the system.

3. False - it can be positive or negative, depending on which way the particle has moved.

4. False - all this says is that its position is the same at the beginning and end of the interval, regardless of what it's done in between.

5. False - distance per unit time.

6. True.

7. True.

8. False - its velocity is $\frac{dx}{dt} = 2Ct$, which increases with time.

9. False - its velocity is the same initially and finally, but may have changed in between.

10. True - instantaneous acceleration is the rate at which velocity is changing.

11. True.

12. False - $a = 2C$ in this case.

13. False - this is true if and only if the acceleration is constant.

14. False - for instance, if it is moving in the -x direction, but losing speed, its acceleration would be positive, but its velocity negative.

15. False - but this is picky; its equation of motion is $x = x_0 + v_0 t$, where $x = x_0$ is its position at time t = 0.

16. False - the antiderivative of a function is that other function whose derivative it is.

17. False - it is to find the equation of motion, given the acceleration.

18. True.

19. False - this does not give any simple kinematic quantity.

20. True - the acceleration is g = 32 ft/sec^2 or 9.8 m/sec^2.

Questions

1. (a) B to C. (b) 0 to A and B to C. Zero is a constant! (c) C to D.

2. (a) 0 to A and B to C. Your answer had better be the same as it was to 1(a)!
    (b) C to D. At the beginning of the interval, the acceleration is negative; at the end, plainly it is greater than zero.

3. Yes, its acceleration is constant. You should recognize the form of the expression; but if not, take the derivatives: you get $v(t) = b + 2ct$ and $a(t) = 2c = $ constant.

4. (a) Certainly. Consider something which has been thrown up in the air, at the instant it is at the very top of its flight. Its velocity - instantaneously - is zero, but its acceleration still is -g.
    (b) No. If the acceleration is zero, the velocity is constant, and speed is just the magnitude of the velocity.

5. If the elevator's speed in cases (a) and (b) is the same, the bolt hits the bottom at the same speed in these two cases, and with a lower speed in case (c). Stare at the expression $v^2 = v_0^2 + 2ax$ for a moment; the sign of v_0 doesn't matter.

6. If acceleration is constant, then average velocity over an interval is just the average of the initial and final speeds; here $v_{av} = \frac{1}{2}(15 + 11) = $ 13 ft/sec, so the car moves 13 ft in the 1-sec interval. If the particle's acceleration is not constant, however, we can't calculate v_{av} without knowing in detail how the velocity changed over the interval.

Examples

Partial Solutions (1)

1. Remember that all quantities must be in consistent units; don't bollix up feet with miles/hour. What is the definition of average velocity?

2. We can restate the problem - what is the (constant) acceleration required to slow from 12 m/sec to 4 m/sec while covering no more than the distance available. But what is the distance available? Remember 0.3 sec passes before the driver begins braking. By how much do the two cars close in this time?

3. Another constant acceleration problem. Note there are a lot of things you could find that you don't need to; nobody asked you how far up the stone went, or how fast it was going when it hit the ground. Don't get sidetracked! Keep track of the sign of everything. If up is plus, then it must be plus for all quantities.

4. This problem is a little hard to get ahold of because you aren't told any one instant at which the position or velocity of the ball is known. If you can find some such point, the rest is easy. The ball's average velocity while passing the window is -6 ft/0.2 sec = -30 ft/sec. At what point is this the ball's instantaneous velocity?

Partial Solutions (2)

1. Average velocity is just the total distance gone, divided by the time it took. So plainly you need to figure out the total distance the car went and the time. 30 mi/h is 44 ft/sec, and 1 mi is 5280 ft, so the first leg took

$$\frac{(2)(5280 \text{ ft})}{44 \text{ ft/sec}} = 240 \text{ sec}$$

Figure out how long the rest of the trip took.

2. In the 0.3 sec before he can begin braking, our hero goes (12 m/sec) x (0.3 sec) = 3.6 m, while the clown in front of him goes (4 m/sec) x (0.3 sec) = 1.2 m. They thus get 2.4 m closer together, so the distance available for braking is 35 - 2.4 = 32.6 m. If the velocity of a particle with constant acceleration changes from v_0 to v while it moves distance Δx, then

$$v^2 = v_0^2 + 2a(\Delta x)$$

Here we know Δx and want to solve for the acceleration a.

3. We are given the position at a given point in time, the acceleration is known, and we want to solve for the initial velocity. Don't be subtle, just plug into

$$x = x_0 + v_0 t + \tfrac{1}{2}at^2$$

What is x_0 in this case?

4. If the acceleration is constant, the average velocity over any time interval is the same as the instantaneous velocity at the midpoint of the interval. But this <u>isn't</u> the same as the velocity at the middle of the spatial interval - here, at the middle of the window. So what do we know? 0.1 sec after passing the top of the window, the ball's velocity is -30 ft/sec. But the acceleration is -32 ft/sec^2, so how fast was the ball moving at the top of the window? From this point it should be relatively easy to find how far it had fallen to that point.

Partial Solutions (3)

1. The second thing he did was to stop for 60 sec, and the last leg of the trip took

$$\frac{(3)(5280 \text{ ft})}{132 \text{ ft/sec}} = 120 \text{ sec}$$

Since the whole trip took 240 + 60 + 120 = 420 sec and covered 5 mi (= 26,400 ft), the average velocity was just

$$\bar{v} = \frac{\Delta x}{\Delta t} = \frac{26,400 \text{ ft}}{420 \text{ sec}} = \underline{62.9 \text{ ft/sec} = 42.9 \text{ mi/h}}$$

2. Solving for a with $\Delta x = 32.6$ m, $v_0 = 12$ m/sec, and v = 4 m/sec gives

$$a = \frac{v^2 - v_0^2}{2\Delta x} = \frac{16 \text{ m}^2/\text{sec}^2 - 144 \text{ m}^2/\text{sec}^2}{(2)(32.6 \text{ m})} = -1.96 \text{ m/sec}^2$$

just about 0.2 g. The acceleration is negative because the car is slowing down.

3. You can set things up however you like, as long as you're consistent. Call x = 0 the ground below the cliff; then $x_0 = 30$ m and we have

$$0 = 30 \text{ m} + (v_0)(3.5 \text{ sec}) + \tfrac{1}{2}(-9.8 \text{ m/sec}^2)(3.5 \text{ sec})^2$$

so

$$v_0 = \frac{60.0 \text{ m} - 30 \text{ m}}{3.5 \text{ sec}} = \underline{8.58 \text{ m/sec}}$$

4. In 0.1 sec the ball's speed increased by (32 ft/sec^2)(0.1 sec) = 3.2 ft/sec, so at the top of the window it was 30 ft/sec - 3.2 ft/sec =

26.8 ft/sec.   But now we are just asking how far (Δx) a ball has dropped if it has picked up a speed of 26.8 ft/sec.   Use

$$v^2 - v_0^2 = 2a(\Delta x)$$

$$(26.8 \text{ ft/sec})^2 - 0 = (2)(-32 \text{ ft/sec}^2)(\Delta x)$$

which gives $\underline{\Delta x = -11.2 \text{ ft}}$

All the minus sign means is that the ball has moved downward; thus the ball was dropped from 11.2 ft above the top of the window.

DIGRESSION
Vector Quantities

Many physical quantities must be specified with a direction in space as well as a magnitude. The obvious instance is a displacement: "5 miles north" is physically a different thing from "5 miles southeast." Such quantities are called <u>vectors</u>; we will here develop a few rules for specifying them and for performing arithmetical operations on them.

We denote a vector quantity with an arrow over the symbol: for $\vec{A}$ read "the vector A." I can specify what $\vec{A}$ is as I did above, by giving a magnitude and direction, as "5 miles southeast." Another way is to give <u>components</u> of $\vec{A}$, that is, projections of $\vec{A}$ along agreed-upon coordinate directions; instead of "5 miles southeast," I might say "3.54 miles south <u>and</u> 3.54 miles east," and specify the same displacement. In the sketch below, the vector $\vec{A}$ can be defined either by magnitude A and direction θ or by components A_x and A_y. The two specifications are entirely equivalent, and either one can be transformed into the other by simple trigonometry:

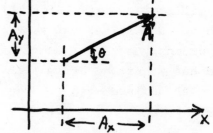

$$A_x = A \cos \theta$$
$$A_y = A \sin \theta$$
and
$$A = \sqrt{A_x^2 + A_y^2}$$
$$\tan \theta = A_y/A_x$$

I've done this in two dimensions for simplicity's sake; there are analogous relationships in three dimensions.

We can conveniently formalize specification by components by introducing the idea of <u>unit vectors</u>. A unit vector is a dimensionless vector quantity with magnitude 1; in other words, it simply specifies a direction. Let, for instance, $\hat{i}$, $\hat{j}$, and $\hat{k}$ be unit vectors in the x, y, and z coordinate directions, respectively, and let A_x, A_y, and A_z be the corresponding components of a vector $\vec{A}$. Then $\vec{A}$ can be written as

$$\vec{A} = A_x\hat{i} + A_y\hat{j} + A_z\hat{k}$$

The rule defining addition of vector quantities we may base on a displacement in space, again, as a prototype. If $\vec{A}$ is the vector displacement from point 1 to point 2, and $\vec{B}$ the displacement from point 2 to point 3, by $\vec{A} + \vec{B}$ we must mean the overall displacement from 1 to 3. Then the meaning of $\vec{C} = \vec{A} + \vec{B}$ is defined by the triangle sketched:

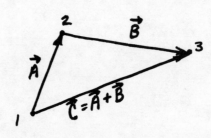

It can easily be seen that this rule of vector addition is equivalent to just adding corresponding components:

$$\vec{C} = \vec{A} + \vec{B} \qquad \text{means} \qquad \begin{array}{l} C_x = A_x + B_x \\ C_y = A_y + B_y \\ C_z = A_z + B_z \end{array}$$

(Equality of two vectors, rather obviously, just means that the two have both the same magnitude <u>and</u> the same direction.)

We define the negative $-\vec{A}$ of a vector $\vec{A}$ to be the vector with the same magnitude and <u>opposite</u> direction, so that $\vec{A} + (-\vec{A}) = 0$, as it must. Then the subtraction of vectors may be defined by

$$\vec{A} - \vec{B} \equiv \vec{A} + (-\vec{B}) \qquad \text{so that} \qquad \begin{array}{l} (A - B)_x = A_x - B_x \\ (A - B)_y = A_y - B_y \\ (A - B)_z = A_z - B_z \end{array}$$

in terms of components. The geometric construction for subtraction is then

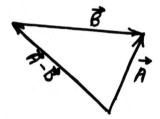

We will defer until later introducing rules for the multiplication of vector quantities; but note that multiplying a vector by a scalar quantity - an ordinary number - simply multiplies the magnitude: $q\vec{A}$ is parallel to $\vec{A}$ and has magnitude q times the magnitude of $\vec{A}$.

As defined, vector addition is associative and commutative. That is,

$$(\vec{A} + \vec{B}) + \vec{C} = \vec{A} + (\vec{B} + \vec{C}) \qquad \text{and} \qquad \vec{A} + \vec{B} = \vec{B} + \vec{A}$$

We introduce the properties of vector quantities using a displacement in space as a prototype. However, many physical quantities are vectors: velocity, force, electric field, torque, magnetic induction, and many others. A quantity which has a direction in space and which combines according to the law of vector addition we have introduced is a vector. The magnitude of the vector will have corresponding physical units.

CHAPTER 3
Motion in Two and Three Dimensions

3.1 CHAPTER SUMMARY

We may now extend our description of motion to two or three dimensions by
using the ideas of vector quantities. The position of a particle relative
to some axis system can be specified by a vector $\vec{R}$ drawn from the origin
to the particle. The displacement of the particle between times t_1 and t_2
is $\vec{R}_2 - \vec{R}_1$. Then call

$$\vec{v}_{av} \equiv \frac{\vec{R}_2 - \vec{R}_1}{t_2 - t_1} = \frac{\Delta\vec{R}}{\Delta t}$$

the particle's average velocity over this time interval. Note $\Delta\vec{R}$ is not
necessarily the length of path traversed by the particle, although it
approaches the path length as the time interval Δt is made very short. We
define the instantaneous velocity as the average velocity over a vanishingly small time interval:

$$\vec{v} \equiv \lim_{\Delta t \to 0} [\vec{v}_{av}] = \lim_{\Delta t \to 0} \left(\frac{\Delta\vec{R}}{\Delta t}\right) = \frac{d\vec{R}}{dt}$$

that is, as the time derivative of the position vector. $\vec{R}$ may change in
magnitude, in direction, or both; if it changes in magnitude only, the
particle is moving in a straight line and we have the one-dimensional
situation of the last chapter.

The velocity of the particle may likewise change in the course of
its motion. We define the average acceleration as the rate at which $\vec{v}$
changes over an interval:

$$\vec{a}_{av} \equiv \frac{\Delta\vec{v}}{\Delta t}$$

and the instantaneous acceleration by making the time interval very short:

$$\vec{a} \equiv \lim_{\Delta t \to 0} \left(\frac{\Delta\vec{v}}{\Delta t}\right) = \frac{d\vec{v}}{dt}$$

The velocity vector may change in magnitude, or direction, or both - either
is an equally real acceleration. In particular a particle may move with
constant speed and yet have nonzero acceleration, if its direction of
motion is changing.

A projectile is a particle falling freely under gravity which has
also some lateral motion; $a_x = 0$ and $a_y = -g$ if we call the y axis vertical.
The motions in the x and y directions are simultaneous but independent
constant-acceleration problems, which we solve as in the last chapter:

$$x = x_0 + v_{0x}t$$
$$y = y_0 + v_{0y}t - \frac{1}{2}gt^2$$

By eliminating t we get an equation for the trajectory of the particle,
can solve for the range, and so forth. The independence of the vertical
and lateral motions - the vertical free fall is independent of motion in

the horizontal plane - is a key point, which is made obvious by treating them as components of a single vector.

A highly important case of motion in two dimensions is circular motion; many physical situations involve motion which is at least nearly circular. If a particle moves in a circle with constant speed, its acceleration (the direction of $\vec{v}$ is changing!) is directed toward the center of the circle and has magnitude

$$a_c = v^2/R$$

If the speed of the circular motion varies, there is also a component of the acceleration <u>along</u> the circular path, of magnitude

$$a_t = \frac{dv}{dt}$$

The components of the acceleration may be directly inferred by doing the problem in terms of radial and tangential unit vectors (note these unit vectors themselves are time-dependent!) and simply differentiating $\vec{R} = R\hat{r}$ directly.

3.2 CHECK LIST

vector

projectile motion

circular motion

spherical coordinates

displacement

vector addition law

scalar

component of a vector

unit vector

$g = 9.80 \text{ m/sec}^2 = 32.2 \text{ ft/sec}^2$

velocity

acceleration

position vector

acceleration of gravity

range of a projectile

centripetal acceleration

satellite

tangential acceleration

radial and tangential unit vectors

3.3 TRUE OR FALSE?

_____1. Three dimensions are needed to describe the most general possible motion of a particle.

_____2. Spherical coordinates may be used to specify the position of a particle only if it moves on a spherical surface.

_____3. The displacement of a particle in some time interval is the change in its position.

_____4. A vector is a quantity possessing both magnitude and direction that obeys the rule of addition exemplified by displacements in space.

_____5. Both velocity and time must be described as vector quantities.

_____6. The magnitude of a vector quantity is a dimensionless pure number.

_____7. Vectors may be added by simply adding corresponding components.

_____8. The magnitude of a unit vector is a dimensionless pure number.

_____9. A vector quantity can be represented in terms of unit vectors only along rectangular-coordinate axes.

_____10. In the sketch at right,
$$\vec{A} + \vec{C} = \vec{B} + \vec{D} + \vec{E}$$

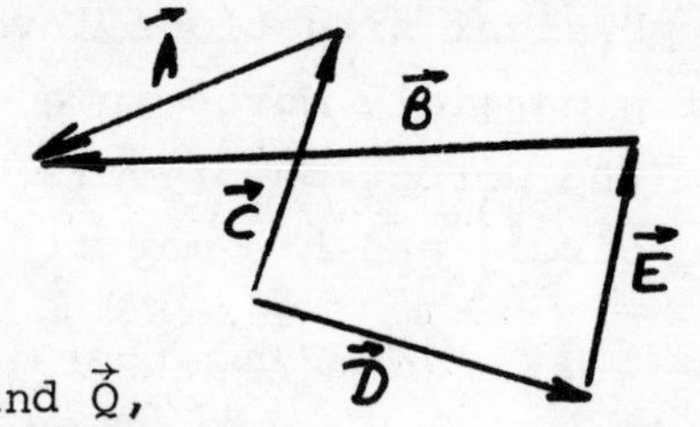

_____11. In the sketch at right,
$$\vec{A} + \vec{B} + \vec{C} = \vec{D} - \vec{E}$$

_____12. For any two vector quantities $\vec{P}$ and $\vec{Q}$, $\vec{P} - \vec{Q}$ is a vector having the same magnitude and opposite direction as $\vec{P} + \vec{Q}$.

_____13. The position vector of a particle is its displacement from the origin of coordinates.

_____14. The difference between two position vectors is the displacement vector from one of the two positions to the other.

_____15. The direction of the velocity vector in a uniform circular motion is radially inward.

_____16. The direction of the acceleration vector in a uniform circular motion is radially inward.

_____17. If a particle moves in a straight line, its position and velocity vectors are parallel.

_____18. If a particle's speed is constant, so is its velocity.

_____19. The acceleration is a vector whose magnitude is equal to the rate at which the magnitude of the velocity changes.

_____20. A projectile is a body in motion that cannot be treated as a particle.

_____21. The horizontal distance which a projectile has traversed when it returns to its initial height is called its range.

_____22. The velocity of a particle whose acceleration is constant may be changing in direction but not in magnitude.

_____23. The centripetal acceleration in a circular motion has magnitude v^2/r only if the motion is with constant speed.

_____24. A particle moves uniformly in a circle centered at the origin; its position vector then is parallel to its acceleration.

_____25. In a uniform circular motion there is no tangential component of acceleration.

_____26. A satellite in orbit around the earth is constantly falling toward the center of the earth, with the usual gravitational acceleration.

_____27. In some cases it may be useful to describe the motion of a particle in terms of unit vectors which themselves change with time.

3.4 QUESTIONS

1. Over a certain time interval the total distance which a particle moves along its path is 10 m. Is it possible that the displacement over this time interval is of magnitude (a) 15 m, (b) 7 m?

2. A ball is (a) thrown vertically upward at 7 m/sec, (b) thrown horizontally at 7 m/sec, (c) dropped. In which case does it hit the ground in the shortest time?

3. A car travels 13 mi due north, 11 mi southeast, then 17 mi west. How far has it gone altogether?

4. In projectile motion in the absence of air resistance, is it ever necessary to consider motion in three (rather than two) dimensions?

5. A bead slides at constant speed along the flat spiral wire sketched at the right. Describe the variation in its acceleration vector.

6. Of the following vectors, which are (a) of equal magnitude, (b) parallel?

$$\vec{A} = (6 \text{ ft})\hat{i} + (8 \text{ ft})\hat{j}$$
$$\vec{B} = (210 \text{ ft})\hat{i} + (280 \text{ ft})\hat{k}$$
$$\vec{C} = 5.1\hat{i} + 6.8\hat{j}$$
$$\vec{D} = (5.1 \text{ m/sec})\hat{i} + (6.8 \text{ m/sec})\hat{k}$$
$$\vec{E} = (3.6 \text{ ft})\hat{i} + (8 \text{ ft})\hat{j} + (4.8 \text{ ft})\hat{k}$$

7. A ball thrown through the air follows a parabolic trajectory in the absence of air resistance. Does its velocity vector change in magnitude, in direction, or both? How about its acceleration vector?

3.5 EXAMPLES

1. At a certain moment a particle is moving at 9 m/sec, straight up; 2.5 sec later it is moving at 12 m/sec, due east. What is its average acceleration during this interval? Is it equal to the (average) rate of change of the magnitude of its velocity?

2. A ball rolls off a tabletop 3 ft off the floor and lands on the floor 6 ft away from the edge of the table. At what speed did it roll off?

3. A football player tries to kick a field goal from the 35-yd line (45 yd from the goal posts). If he gives the ball an initial velocity of 70 ft/sec, directed 35° above the horizontal, does it clear the 10-ft crossbar? Neglect air resistance.

4. An earth satellite is in a circular orbit 1700 mi above the earth's surface (take the radius of the earth as 3950 mi). One complete circuit of the earth takes it 145 min. What is the acceleration of gravity at its altitude?

3.6 ANSWERS

True or False?

1. True.

2. False - they are as fully general a representation as rectangular

17

coordinates.

3. True.

4. True.

5. False - time has no direction in space.

6. False - it has dimensions appropriate to whatever physical quantity it measures.

7. True.

8. True - it is 1, by definition.

9. False - for instance, the polar-coordinate directions can be assigned appropriate unit vectors.

10. True.

11. False.

12. False - $\vec{P} + \vec{Q}$ and $\vec{P} - \vec{Q}$ are not simply related in magnitude or direction.

13. True.

14. True.

15. False - the velocity vector is in the direction in which the particle is moving.

16. True - hence "centripetal" acceleration.

17. False - this is picky, but as stated it is true only if the origin of coordinates is on the line of motion.

18. False - this isn't true for something moving with constant speed on a curved path.

19. False - consider the case of the previous question, for instance.

20. False - our analysis of the motion of a projectile treats it as a particle.

21. True.

22. False - in this case the direction of the acceleration changes also.

23. False - this is the radial component of acceleration in a circular motion regardless of whether or not the speed is constant.

24. True - or at least they are in the same line; the position and acceleration vectors are in opposite radial directions.

25. True.

26. True.

27. True - for instance, analyzing circular motion in terms of radial and tangential unit vectors.

Questions

1. (a) is not possible, but (b) is; the point-to-point displacement is the length of a straight line, which may well be shorter than the path the particle followed.

2. In cases (b) and (c) the ball has no initial <u>vertical</u> velocity component; in these two cases, in the absence of other forces, it hits the ground at the same time. In (a) there is an initial upward velocity component, and it takes longer to reach the ground.

3. Consider the motion in an axis system in which the x direction is east and the y direction north. Then the sum of the three vectors, in components, is $13\hat{j} + (7.8\hat{i} - 7.8\hat{j}) + (-17\hat{i}) = (-9.2\hat{i} + 5.2\hat{j})$ mi. The magnitude of its overall displacement is thus $(9.2^2 + 5.2^2)^{\frac{1}{2}} = \underline{10.6\ mi}$ (directed somewhat west of northwest).

4. No, at least to the degree that the acceleration of a freely falling body is really constant and downward. (There are quibbles which come in because of the earth's rotation, but ignore them.) Consider the plane defined by the vertical and the direction of the particle's initial velocity. Since neither initial velocity nor acceleration has a component perpendicular to this plane, the motion must remain in it.

5. At any instant, the particle's path is nearly circular and it moves with constant speed; but the radius of its "orbit" constantly decreases. Its acceleration vector thus points always toward the center, but steadily increases in magnitude.

6. (a) $\vec{A}$ and $\vec{E}$ both have magnitude 10 ft; (b) $\vec{A}$ and $\vec{C}$ are parallel and so are $\vec{B}$ and $\vec{D}$. For instance, both $\vec{B}$ and $\vec{D}$ are multiples of $3\hat{i} + 4\hat{k}$.

7. Initially the trajectory is upward, afterwards downward, and at the top of its arc the projectile's vertical velocity component vanishes. Thus the projectile's velocity changes in both magnitude and direction. Its acceleration, of course, is a constant (g) downwards.

Examples

Partial Solutions (1)

1. Put things in a coordinate system: say, x is east and y is up. Then what we are given is $\vec{v}_1 = (9\ m/sec)\hat{j}$, $\vec{v}_2 = (12\ m/sec)\hat{i}$, $t_2 - t_1 = 2.5$ sec. What is the definition of the average acceleration over a time interval?

2. A projectile's motion in the vertical and lateral directions are independent of one another. How long does something take to fall 3 ft?

3. There are a number of ways you could do this, all about equally messy. Try attacking it this way: at the point in time when the ball is 10 ft off the ground, how far downfield has it gone? More direct would be to use the trajectory equation directly and not bother with the time explicitly. The route I suggested again is using the independence of the two component motions.

4. What is the acceleration - regardless of whether or not it is caused by the earth's gravity - in <u>any</u> circular motion?

Partial Solutions (2)

1. The average acceleration is the change in velocity divided by the time interval.

   Here $\qquad \Delta\vec{v} = \vec{v}_2 - \vec{v}_1 = (12\ m/sec)\hat{j} - (9\ m/sec)\hat{i}$

   So $\qquad \vec{a}_{av} = \dfrac{\Delta\vec{v}}{\Delta t} = (4.8\ m/sec^2)\hat{j} - (3.6\ m/sec^2)\hat{i}$

2. To fall 3 ft takes a time given by
$$3\ ft = \tfrac{1}{2}(32\ ft/sec^2)t^2$$

$$t = \left(\frac{3 \text{ ft}}{16 \text{ ft/sec}^2}\right)^{\frac{1}{2}} = 0.433 \text{ sec}$$

so at what speed did it roll off the table?

3. The initial velocity in the y direction, v_{0y}, is (70 ft/sec) x (sin 35°) = 40.1 ft/sec, so the equation of motion in the y direction is

$$y = (40.1 \text{ ft/sec})t - \tfrac{1}{2}(32 \text{ ft/sec}^2)t^2$$

In this case what we want is the time at which it is 10 ft high; setting y (above) equal to 10 ft yields a quadratic which we can solve for t. The solutions of the quadratic are t = 0.280 sec and t = 2.23 sec. What do the two solutions mean?

4. The acceleration is v^2/R. The radius of the orbit here is R = 3950 + 1700 = 5650 mi = 2.98×10^7 ft. Given that it goes once around in 145 min, what is the speed?

Partial Solutions (3)

1. The magnitude of the average acceleration is
$$|\vec{a}_{av}| = [(4.8)^2 + (3.6)^2]^{\frac{1}{2}} = \underline{6.0 \text{ m/sec}^2}$$
directed east and 37° up. The rate at which $|\vec{v}|$ changes, however, is
$$\frac{\Delta|\vec{v}|}{\Delta t} = \frac{12 \text{ m/sec} - 9 \text{ m/sec}}{2.5 \text{ sec}} = \underline{1.2 \text{ m/sec}^2}$$
which is not at all the same thing.

2. It took 0.433 sec to fall, and in this time went 6 ft across the floor. Since its lateral motion is unaccelerated, its speed on rolling off the table was
$$v_0 = \frac{6 \text{ ft}}{0.433 \text{ sec}} = \underline{13.8 \text{ ft/sec}}$$

3. There are two instants at which the football is 10 ft high: once on the way up and again on the way down. The second one is what concerns us. The velocity in the x direction is v_{0x} = (70 ft/sec) x (cos 35°) = 57.3 ft/sec, so 2.23 sec after it was kicked, when it falls below 10 ft, the distance it has gone downfield is
$$x = (57.3 \text{ ft/sec})(2.23 \text{ sec}) = \underline{128 \text{ ft}}$$
But to clear the crossbar it would have to go 45 yd or 135 ft before falling below 10-ft height. Thus it does not clear.

4. The speed is
$$v = \frac{2\pi R}{T} = \frac{(2\pi)(2.98 \times 10^7 \text{ ft})}{(60)(145) \text{ sec}} = 2.15 \times 10^4 \text{ ft/sec}$$
and the centripetal acceleration is thus
$$a = \frac{v^2}{R} = \frac{(2.15 \times 10^4 \text{ ft/sec})^2}{2.98 \times 10^7 \text{ ft}} = \underline{15.6 \text{ ft/sec}^2}$$

CHAPTER 4
Newton's Laws

4.1 CHAPTER SUMMARY

The fundamental relationship of the motions of particles to the forces
that cause them is expressed by Newton's laws of motion:

1. A body on which no external force acts remains at rest or moves
   with a constant velocity.

2. The rate at which the momentum of a body changes in time is equal
   to the resultant external force applied to it:
   $$\vec{F} = d\vec{p}/dt = m\vec{a}$$

3. The forces which two bodies exert on one another are equal in
   magnitude and in opposite directions.

4. If more than one force acts on a body, they combine as vectors.

Newton's laws involve the concepts of force and mass, of which we have
some understanding from everyday usage. We must first develop precise
operational definitions for these terms.

The first law may be taken as asserting that uniform velocity defines
the condition of no net force on an object. If there is a net force
acting, the object accelerates; we make the notion of force quantitative
by measuring the acceleration of some standard object caused by a given
force, such as a stretched spring. The "fourth law" asserts that forces
add as vectors, so we may measure other forces by balancing them against
the force exerted by the spring. Masses, conversely, may be compared by
measuring the accelerations of different objects caused by the same
force; the second law asserts that to every object we can attach a number
m, measuring an intrinsic property of the object, which is inversely
proportional to the acceleration caused by a given force. The mass of
an object measures its inertia. We take 1 kg as the mass of the standard
object; the unit of force, the newton (N), is defined as the force which
causes an acceleration of 1 m/sec^2 when applied to a 1-kg object. Various
other units of mass and force are also used.

The momentum of a moving body is defined as $\vec{p} \equiv m\vec{v}$. As the mass of a
particle is constant,

$$\frac{d\vec{p}}{dt} = m\frac{d\vec{v}}{dt} = m\vec{a}$$

(At speeds approaching that of light, the special theory of relativity
requires some modification of these definitions; the mass of a particle
can then be considered to increase with speed.) Newton's third law
states that the forces which interacting bodies exert on one another are
always equal and opposite. (Note that the third-law forces never balance
each other - they always act on different objects.) Another way to state
this is that two particles interact always in such a way that their total
momentum is constant; this can in fact be generalized to an arbitrary

21

system of particles. A conceptual problem arises with forces, such as gravity, which act between distant objects; to cope with this we introduce the idea of a field: one mass, for instance, sets up a gravitational field, and the field exerts a force on the other mass. Because the fields do not propagate instantaneously, the third law is only approximately true in such cases, although conservation of momentum holds generally if appropriate momentum is assigned to the field itself.

Newton's laws relate motions to the forces that cause them. Their usefulness is that in many cases we can find regular empirical laws which describe the forces that act in nature. The most familiar force in our everyday experience is probably the pull of the earth's gravity on objects near it, which we call weight. If g is the acceleration of gravity, the weight of an object of mass m is $W = mg$. (The value of g is the same for all objects in a given location, but varies with the object's position relative to the earth.) In fact what we are aware of is usually other forces that balance our weight. The astronaut in orbit is falling freely under the earth's gravitational pull, but is weightless in the sense that this apparent weight is absent - there is no balancing force holding him up.

Velocity and acceleration are always implicitly referred to some frame of reference; Newton's first law is true in inertial frames of reference - this may be taken as the definition of an inertial frame. All frames of reference moving at uniform velocity relative to an inertial frame are themselves inertial. Although the position and velocity of a particle, expressed relative to different reference frames, will be different, the acceleration is the same in all inertial frames. The principle of relativity states that there is no physical distinction between different inertial frames of reference. (Einstein's special theory of relativity is essentially the reconciliation of the principle of relativity with Maxwell's theory of electromagnetism.) In noninertial frames, Newton's laws do not hold exactly: apparent extra forces arise in accelerated reference frames. Although it is rotating, and therefore noninertial, a frame of reference attached to the earth can be taken as inertial for many practical purposes.

4.2 CHECK LIST

kilogram	newton
gram	dyne
slug	pound
Newton's laws of motion	special theory of relativity
force	apparent weight
inertial frame of reference	centripetal acceleration
momentum	action and reaction
mass	action at a distance

frictional force

inertia

model

weight

law of inertia

field

noninertial frame of reference

principle of relativity

Michelson-Morley experiment

4.3 TRUE OR FALSE?

_____1. A body on which no forces act remains at rest.

_____2. The rate at which the momentum of a body changes is equal to the resultant external force on it.

_____3. Momentum is a vector quantity.

_____4. Force is a vector quantity.

_____5. The inertia which a body has depends on the total force acting on it.

_____6. If a particle is moving with a constant velocity, there are no forces acting on it.

_____7. A particle on which no net force acts moves at a constant velocity, unless there is friction.

_____8. If a body which moves in a circular path does so at constant speed, there is no net force acting on it.

_____9. The mass of an object may be defined in terms of the acceleration produced by a known standard force.

_____10. The following units all measure the same physical quantity: newton, pound, kilogram, dyne.

_____11. Newton's second law of motion can in all circumstances be written $\vec{F} = m\vec{a}$.

_____12. The weight of a body is a measure of its mass.

_____13. The weight of a body is the force that gravity exerts on it.

_____14. To say that an astronaut in an orbiting satellite is "weightless" means that his apparent weight is zero.

_____15. The two forces of which Newton's third law speaks never act on the same object.

_____16. Newton's third law can be restated as: the momentum of a particle remains constant in time.

_____17. Conservation of momentum is a theorem which can be applied only to collisions.

_____18. Because of the conceptual problem of "action at a distance," Newton considered that his laws of motion applied only to contact forces.

_____19. The concept of a "field" - the gravitational field, for instance - is introduced to cope with the problem of action at a distance.

_____20. Newton's third law applies only approximately to the interaction of two widely separated bodies.

21. The nature of Newton's laws of motion is to relate forces - without regard to their nature or origin - to the motions which result from them.

22. An inertial frame of reference is one that is fixed relative to the surface of the earth.

23. The principle of relativity states that the mass of an object increases at high speeds.

24. The principle of relativity states that there is no physical distinction between different inertial reference frames.

25. In practice Newton's laws, as they stand, are essentially useless because the earth's surface is not an inertial frame of reference.

26. Newton's laws of motion, as they stand, do not apply in a noninertial frame.

27. The acceleration of a particle is the same in all inertial frames of reference.

28. The Michelson-Morley experiment showed that the earth's surface is not an inertial frame of reference.

29. Inertial and gravitational mass are thought to be always exactly equal.

4.4 QUESTIONS

1. The maximum tension that a certain rope can stand without breaking is 200 lb. How can it be used to lower a 300-lb object?

2. An ox is urged to pull a cart but refuses, arguing that by Newton's third law the wagon will always pull back on the ox just as hard as he pulls on it, so he can never move it. How do you answer him?

3. A graph of v vs. t for the motion of some object is sketched at the right. Over what portions of the interval shown is there plainly a nonzero resultant force on the object? In what direction (the motion is one-dimensional) does the force act?

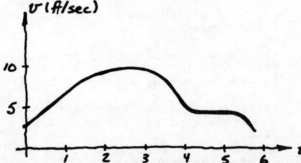

4. A car is being driven up a hill at a constant speed. Describe the various forces that act on it.

5. One way to define the magnitude of a force is the extension it causes on a standard spring. Suppose a force F stretches the spring Δx and a force F' stretches it 2Δx. Can you think of how to check whether F' is in fact 2F - that is, whether or not your spring's extension is in fact linear?

6. In a tug of war three men pull on each end of a rope and three others pull with an equal and opposite force on the other end. A 5-lb weight is hung from the middle of the rope. Can the men ever get the rope precisely straight?

7. A man rows a boat across a river. The speed at which he can row through the water is fixed, and the current in the river flows at a constant speed. In what direction should he row to get across in the shortest time? Is this the same as the direction in which the distance he goes (relative to the banks) is shortest?

4.5   EXAMPLES

1. A car whose mass is 1700 kg is moving at 15 m/sec. If it is braked uniformly to a stop in 5.5 sec, what force is required? What exerts the force?

2. Assume that by some magic the rotation rate of the earth is suddenly increased by enough that the apparent weight of objects at the equator is decreased by 3%. What then would be the length of the day?

3. In the sketch at right, the pull of the string is accelerating the 5-kg block at 0.8 m/sec². If the frictional force of one block on the other is 1.1 N, what is the tension in the string? (The tabletop is frictionless.) What is the acceleration of the 2-kg block?

4. A bullet of mass 18 gm traveling at 750 m/sec strikes and imbeds itself in a wood block (mass 2.5 kg). At what speed does the block recoil?

4.6   ANSWERS

True or False?

1. False - it may move at any constant velocity; this is Newton's first law.

2. True - this is Newton's second law.

3. True.

4. True.

5. False - its inertia is an intrinsic property measured by its mass.

6. False - all this says is that the forces on it add up (vectorially) to zero.

7. False - it moves at a constant velocity regardless; friction is a force.

8. False - the direction of its velocity vector is changing.

9. True.

10. False - kilogram is a unit of mass, the others are units of force.

11. False - at least not without gross redefinition of the quantities involved; at very high speeds $m\vec{v}$ is not an adequate definition of momentum.

12. False - in the most general circumstances; it's true in a constant gravitational field, such as near the surface of the earth.

13. True.

14. True.

15. True - the force of A on B is equal and opposite to the force of B on A.

16. False.

17. False - it is quite general.

18. False - he regarded them as general even though troubled by the action-at-a-distance difficulty.

19. True.

20. True - it is not strictly true at every instant because changes in the "field" take a finite time to propagate.

21. True.

22. False - such a frame is not inertial, because the earth rotates.

23. False - mass can be defined in such a way that this is true, but the connection with the principle of relativity is quite indirect.

24. True.

25. False - the noninertial effects of the earth's rotation exist but are for many practical purposes negligibly small.

26. True - in fact, this may be taken as the definition of an inertial frame.

27. True.

28. False - it isn't, but this wasn't the point of that experiment.

29. True.

Questions

1. By not trying to lower it at a constant velocity. See the sketch at right. If the object is allowed to accelerate downward at a rate a, then by Newton's third law the tension T in the string is given by mg - T = ma, and if the downward acceleration a is at least g/3, T will be less than 200 pounds. Of course, you can't get it back up again...

2. Tell him to go bone up on his physics. The two forces related to Newton's second law NEVER act on the same object; but what matters in moving the cart is the total force on it. All the ox has to do is pull forward on the cart harder than the ground pulls back on the cart.

3. Whenever the velocity is changing there is a nonzero net force on the thing. Up to t = 2.6 sec the force is in the +x direction, since the velocity is positive and increasing; the force is zero momentarily at t = 2.6 sec, thereafter in the -x direction, except for the interval from t = 4.3 to 5.2 sec, when there is zero net force and v remains constant.

4. The friction of the ground exerts an uphill force on it (the wheels are pushing back on the ground). The ground also exerts a force N which holds it up, and the earth's gravity pulls directly downward with a force mg. Since the car moves with constant velocity, these forces must add up to zero.

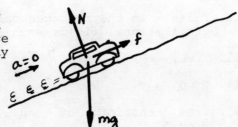

5. Recalling Newton's laws, you can check to see whether F' produces twice the acceleration that F produces on the same mass. Acceleration can be measured directly, but

26

a definition of force and mass must rest on Newton's laws.

6.   No. There must always be some vertical component of the tension in
     the rope to balance the downward pull of gravity on the 5-lb weight.

7.   If his velocity relative to the water
     (u_0) is fixed, plainly the quickest way
     is to row in a direction such that,
     relative to the water, he goes straight
     across. Relative to the riverbank,
     however, he is not going straight across
     but drifting downstream. (In the sketch,
     $\vec{v}_0$ is the velocity of the current.)

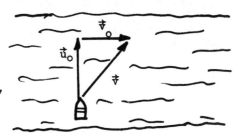

Examples

Partial Solutions (1)

1.   This is a very direct application of Newton's second law. Since the
     acceleration is in the horizontal direction, so is the force. Find
     the acceleration.

2.   A particle at the earth's equator is really moving
     in a circle whose radius is that of the earth. Thus
     when we apply Newton's second law, the acceleration
     is not zero, but v^2/R. How fast is the circular
     motion?

3.

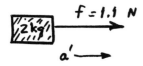

     Apply Newton's second law to each block
     directly. In the horizontal direction,
     the frictional force due to the 5-kg
     block is the only force acting on the
     2-kg one. What forces act on the 5-kg
     block?

4.   If the only force here - and it's the only one I told you about - is
     the one the bullet and block exert on each other, we can apply con-
     servation of momentum (Newton's third law) directly. The total
     momentum of the two stays constant.

Partial Solutions (2)

1.   The car brakes from 15 m/sec to rest in 5.5 sec with constant acceler-
     ation. Its acceleration is therefore
$$a = \frac{-15 \text{ m/sec}}{5.5 \text{ sec}} = -2.73 \text{ m/sec}^2$$
     The sign just means the acceleration is in the direction opposite the
     velocity.

2.   The earth's rotation carries the object once around in 24 h = 8.64 x
     10^4 sec. (At present.) The circumference of the earth is (2π) x
     (3950 mi) = 1.31 x 10^8 ft, so the velocity is now
$$v = \frac{1.31 \times 10^8 \text{ ft}}{8.64 \times 10^4 \text{ sec}} = 1.52 \times 10^3 \text{ ft/sec}$$
     From Newton's second law we get
$$mg - F = mv^2/R$$
     since the acceleration is v^2/R radially inward. Thus the object's
     apparent weight - the force the earth exerts to hold it up - is
$$F = m(g - v^2/R)$$

3.   Since only f acts on the top block,
$$f = 1.1 \text{ N} = (2 \text{ kg})a'$$

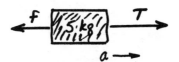

$$a' = \frac{1.1 \text{ N}}{2 \text{ kg}} = \underline{0.55 \text{ m/sec}^2}$$

The pull of the string to the right and the frictional force of the top block to the left are the forces that act on the lower block (we assumed the tabletop frictionless).

4. Before the bullet hits, the block is at rest; the total momentum of the two is thus that of the bullet:

$$p = mv = (0.018 \text{ kg})(750 \text{ m/sec}) = 13.5 \text{ kg-m/sec}$$

Partial Solutions (3)

1. Now we know the mass of the car and its acceleration, so the net force on it is

$$F = (1700 \text{ kg})(-2.73 \text{ m/sec}^2) = \underline{-4640 \text{ N}}$$

The road exerts the force on the car - the tires shove forward against the road, so the road drags backward on the tires.

2. The present value of v^2/R is

$$\frac{(1.52 \times 10^3 \text{ ft/sec})^2}{2.09 \times 10^7 \text{ ft}} = 0.110 \text{ ft/sec}^2$$

If the new rotation speed is v', then what we require is

$$g - v'^2/R = (0.97)(g - v^2/R)$$

To reduce apparent weight by 3%. Solving this (take $g = 32.0$ ft/sec^2) gives

$$v'^2/R = 1.067 \text{ ft/sec}^2 = 9.67 \, v^2/R$$

or

$$\underline{v' = 3.11v}$$

The length of the day is thus a factor 3.11 less, or $\underline{7.72 \text{ h}}$.

3. Applying Newton's second law to the lower block gives

$$T - f = (5 \text{ kg})(0.8 \text{ m/sec}^2) = 4.0 \text{ N}$$

so

$$T = 4.0 + 1.1 = \underline{5.1 \text{ N}}$$

4. After the bullet imbeds in the block, the total momentum is <u>still</u> 1.35 kg-m/sec - that's conservation of momentum. But the two moving together have a mass of 2 kg + 18 gm = 2.018 kg, so

$$v = \frac{p}{m} = \frac{1.35 \text{ kg-m/sec}}{2.018 \text{ kg}} = \underline{6.69 \text{ m/sec}}$$

CHAPTER 5
Applications of Newton's Laws

5.1   CHAPTER SUMMARY

Newton's laws may be used to determine the net resultant force on a body, given its motion, or conversely, given the forces which act, to determine its acceleration. Many features of such problems may be illustrated most simply in problems involving only linear motion under constant forces, and several such problems are analyzed in detail in this chapter. The following plan of attack is broadly useful:

1. For each body, or particle, in the system, draw a separate free-body diagram illustrating every external force that acts on that body.
2. Choose convenient coordinate axes and apply $\Sigma\vec{F} = m\vec{a}$ in component form.
3. Using whatever additional information is available (for instance, that a block is constrained to slide down an incline; or that the tension in a light string is the same throughout its length), solve the resulting equations for the unknowns.
4. Use extreme situations or other special cases to check your results against reasonable expectations.

Notice that Newton's laws may be directly applied only in an inertial frame of reference; the apparent weight of a mass m in an elevator that is accelerating upward is different from mg, because the elevator is a noninertial frame.

If an object moves in a circle, we know the components of its acceleration:

$$a_c = v^2/R \qquad\qquad a_t = dv/dt$$

and so we know what the resultant force on the rotating particle must be. For instance, in a conical pendulum (mass swung in a horizontal circle on the end of a string), the tension in the string and the downward pull of gravity must add to a resultant force which is mv^2/r directed horizontally, toward the center.

An object submerged in a fluid experiences an upward buoyant force. If the object is sufficiently light, the buoyant force can balance its weight and it floats. The origin of buoyancy is the increase of pressure with depth in the fluid; the upward pressure on the bottom of a submerged object is always larger than the downward pressure on the top. The pressure variation with depth (h) in an incompressible fluid is given by

$$P = P_0 + \rho gh$$

where P_0 is the pressure at the top and ρ the density of the fluid. Archimedes' principle states that the buoyant force upward on any object is equal to the weight of fluid which it displaces; if by this we mean the apparent weight of the displaced fluid, the principle is true in noninertial frames as well.

An object moving through a fluid experiences a viscous force that opposes the motion; in many situations the viscous force is well approximated by $\vec{F} = -b\vec{v}$, where the constant b depends on the fluid and on the shape of the object. An example is the air resistance on a body falling freely under gravity. The falling object accelerates - initially, when $v \simeq 0$, at a rate which is $\simeq g$, until it approaches a speed at which the drag force $-b\vec{v}$ balances its weight; thereafter it continues to fall at this terminal velocity:

$$v_t = mg/b$$

(A parachute is a device for reducing your terminal velocity by manipulating the value of b.)

5.2 CHECK LIST

resultant force	apparent weight
contact force	centripetal acceleration
action at a distance	tangential acceleration
weight	buoyant force
free-body diagram	Archimedes' principle
frictional force	pressure
constraint	density
action and reaction	viscous force
tension	terminal velocity

5.3 TRUE OR FALSE?

_____1. Given all the forces that act on an object, Newton's laws provide a complete description of its motion.

_____2. The forces exerted on one another by objects some distance apart, by means of strings, springs, etc., which connect them, are referred to as "action at a distance."

_____3. A free-body diagram can be used to analyze a given problem only if the forces acting on the body are all contact forces.

_____4. An object rests on a tabletop; the force exerted on it by the table is always normal to the surface of contact.

_____5. A block rests on a tabletop; Newton's third law says that the upward force of the table on it, and the downward force of gravity, are equal.

_____6. The tension in a light string connecting two points is, in all cases, the same throughout.

_____7. In the absence of friction, the acceleration of a block sliding down an incline is g.

_____8. A man of mass m stands in an elevator which is moving upward with an acceleration a; his apparent weight is then ma.

_____9. If an object moves at constant speed v in a circle of radius R, its tangential acceleration is v^2/R.

_____10. If an object moves in a circle with varying speed, its tangential acceleration is dv/dt.

_____11. If a particle moves in a circle with varying speed, the force on it has both radial and tangential components.

_____12. Archimedes' principle describes the variation of pressure with depth in a fluid.

_____13. An object submerged in a fluid experiences a buoyant force because the fluid pushes up harder on the bottom than it pushes down on the top.

_____14. Each team in a tug-of-war exerts a force of 600 N on a rope; the tension in the rope is, therefore, 1200 N.

_____15. The buoyant force on a body submerged in a fluid depends on the density of the fluid and the volume - but not the shape or composition - of the body.

_____16. The pressure in a fluid is the force per unit area on any small element of a surface.

_____17. A body floats in a fluid at a depth such that it displaces an amount of the fluid equal to its own weight.

_____18. In many cases, the viscous retarding force on an object moving through a fluid is approximately proportional to the velocity.

_____19. Archimedes' principle holds only in an inertial reference frame.

_____20. An object falling, under gravity, through a viscous fluid reaches a limiting value of velocity and thereafter falls at constant velocity.

5.4 QUESTIONS

1. In the sketch, one block is pulled by a string connecting it to another which is in turn pulled with a force F. It seems obvious that the acceleration of the system is F divided by the total mass of the two. Under what assumptions or conditions is this valid?

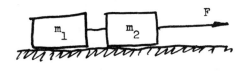

2. An object of mass m is being "weighed" in an elevator which is moving upward with an acceleration a. What is the result if the weighing is done in (a) a spring balance, (b) a pan balance?

3. Something is moving in a circle in a vertical plane, say, being swung on the end of a string. At some point which is neither the exact top nor bottom of its circular path, draw a diagram indicating the forces that act on the object and the direction of its resultant acceleration.

4. An ice cube is floating in a glass of water. As the ice melts, what happens to the water level? Explain.

5. The viscous force on an object moving through a fluid is approximately proportional to v; but according to Newton's second law, force is proportional to the acceleration. Is there a contradiction here?

6. Explain why curves - in a road, railbed, or whatever - are banked.

5.5 EXAMPLES

1. In the sketch at right, the incline is
    frictionless and is at an angle of 25º from
    the horizontal. Find the acceleration of
    the blocks.

2. A 1-kg mass and a 4-kg mass are hung by a
    light string from a frictionless pulley of
    negligible mass. Initially both are 1.2 m
    off the floor. If they are released find
    the maximum height reached by the smaller
    mass.

3. A coin of mass 25 gm rests on a phonograph turntable rotating at
    78 rpm. The coin is 13 cm from the turntable axis. If the coin does
    not slip, what must be the frictional force between the turntable and
    the coin?

4. An object is projected at initial speed 8 ft/sec up a 17º frictionless
    incline. How far up does it go?

5. Under ordinary conditions the density of air is about 1.2×10^{-3} gm/cm^3;
    that of helium, 1.7×10^{-4} gm/cm^3. How big must a spherical helium-
    filled balloon be in order to lift a load of 780 lb?

5.6 ANSWERS

True or False?

1. True.

2. False - "action at a distance" refers to forces without some mechani-
    cal agency such as a string.

3. False - the diagram must include all forces that act on the object.

4. True - at least if the tabletop is level; then there is no frictional
    force on the object if it is not moving.

5. False - the force of table on block is equal and opposite to the
    force of block on table.

6. True - provided that between the two points no force acts longitudin-
    ally on the string.

7. False - it is g sin θ, if θ is the angle the incline makes with the
    horizontal.

8. False - think what this says if the elevator's acceleration is zero.

9. False - this is the centripetal acceleration, directed radially inward.

10. True.

11. True.

12. False - it gives the buoyant force on an object immersed in a fluid.

13. True - this is essentially what is happening.

14. False - the tension is 600 N, and this is the force it exerts on what-
    ever it connects to at each end.

15. True - it is equal to the weight of the displaced fluid.

16. True.

17. True - so that the buoyant force on the object balances its weight.

18. True.

19. False - at least, if we read it as <u>apparent</u> weight of the displaced fluid, it holds in noninertial frames also.

20. True - this is the "terminal velocity."

Questions

1. Essentially it assumes that the two blocks have the same acceleration - thus, for instance, that the string doesn't stretch and that the tension of the string is the same throughout - that is, that it has no mass of its own.

2. A spring balance measures apparent weight, by counteracting it with the force of a stretched spring; its reading will increase with upward acceleration. A pan balance compares the weights of two masses; the apparent weights of both will increase with upward acceleration, but the comparison is unaffected.

3. See the sketch at right. T is the tension in the string, mg the weight of the object.

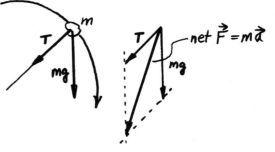

4. That part of the ice which is under the surface displaces a weight of water that is equal to the whole of the ice. But when the ice melts, it <u>is</u> water; it just fills the space displaced by the ice and the water level doesn't change.

5. Newton's second law says that the acceleration of a body is proportional to the net resultant force on it, regardless of what causes the force or what its detailed behavior is. A force proportional to the velocity of a particle is no more unreasonable than one proportional to its displacement.

6. The bank provides an inward force to accelerate the car radially inward. The result is that friction (between tires and road, or whatever) is not required to produce all the centripetal force which turns the car.

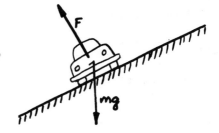

Examples

Partial Solutions (1)

1. Since I didn't give you any more specific information, assume as usual a light string and a massless, frictionless pulley. Draw a free-body diagram for each of the two blocks.

2. The system of two blocks hung over a massless pulley is called an Atwood's machine. You work out the acceleration of the system, as usual, by applying Newton's laws to each weight; it's done in your text. When the heavier weight hits the floor, what happens to the other one?

3. The centripetal force on an object undergoing uniform circular motion is mv^2/R, regardless of what exerts the force. What exerts it here?

4. This involves the problem of resolution of forces on an incline, of course; but except for that it's really just a kinematics problem. What is the acceleration of an object sliding without friction on an incline?

5. According to Archimedes, the buoyant force is equal to the weight of the surrounding fluid displaced. What fluid is the balloon displacing? Watch out for units here - they aren't stated consistently.

Partial Solutions (2)

1. The free-body diagram for each of the masses is shown below.

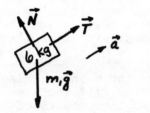 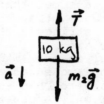

Under the usual assumptions, the two have the same acceleration (magnitude). From the diagram for m_1,

$$T - m_1 g \sin \theta = m_1 a$$

and for m_2,

$$m_2 g - T = m_2 a$$

Solve for a.

2. The acceleration is

$$a = \frac{m_2 - m_1}{m_2 + m_1} g = \frac{4 - 1}{4 + 1} g = 0.6 g = 5.88 \ \text{m/sec}^2$$

When the 4-kg mass hits the ground, it has fallen 1.2 m with this acceleration; thus its speed is

$$v = \sqrt{2ay} = \sqrt{(2)(5.88 \ \text{m/sec}^2)(1.2 \ \text{m})} = 3.76 \ \text{m/sec}$$

at this instant the smaller mass is moving upward, with this same speed, and has already risen 1.2 m above its initial position. How high does it go?

3. There is nothing to exert the centripetal force except the frictional force of the turntable on the coin - which is what we're looking for. The coin is 13 cm from the center and rotates 78 times in 60 sec. The speed is thus

$$v = \frac{(2\pi)(13 \ \text{cm})(78)}{60 \ \text{sec}} = 106 \ \text{cm/sec} = 1.06 \ \text{m/sec}$$

4. The acceleration is

$$a = g \sin \theta = (32 \ \text{ft/sec}^2)(0.2924) = 9.36 \ \text{ft/sec}^2$$

directed down the plane. You are given v_0 and now know a. How far up does it go?

5. In the free-body diagram, B is the buoyant force and m the mass of the balloon. If it is to lift a load of 780 lb = 3.46×10^3 N, then B - mg $\geq$ 3460 N, but

$$B = \rho_{air} g V$$

is the weight of the displaced air, and the mass of the helium is $\rho_{He} V$ (V is the volume). So

$$(\rho_{air} - \rho_{He}) g V \geq 3460 \ \text{N}$$

Partial Solutions (3)

1. Solving the two equations by eliminating T gives

$$a = \frac{m_2 - m_1 \sin \theta}{m_2 + m_1} g = \frac{10 \text{ kg} - 6 \text{ kg}(\sin 25^\circ)}{16 \text{ kg}} g$$

$$= \frac{10 - 2.54}{16}(9.80 \text{ m/sec}^2) = \underline{4.57 \text{ m/sec}^2}$$

2. The rest is just kinematics. We have $v_0 = 3.76$ m/sec and $a = -g$ in free fall; the added height h to which it rises is given by

$$v^2 - v_0^2 = -2gh$$

$$h = \frac{v_0^2}{2g} = \frac{(3.76 \text{ m/sec})^2}{(2)(9.80 \text{ m/sec}^2)} = 0.72 \text{ m}$$

so altogether it rises 1.2 + 0.72 = $\underline{1.92 \text{ m}}$ above its initial position.

3. The centripetal force - which is the frictional force - is therefore

$$f = \frac{mv^2}{R} = \frac{0.25 \text{ kg}(1.06 \text{ m/sec})^2}{0.13 \text{ m}} = \underline{2.17 \text{ N}}$$

4. Again use

$$v^2 - v_0^2 = 2ax$$

$$-(8 \text{ ft/sec})^2 = (2)(-9.36 \text{ ft/sec}^2)(x)$$

$$x = \frac{(8 \text{ ft/sec})^2}{18.72 \text{ ft/sec}^2} = \underline{3.42 \text{ ft}}$$

5. The densities are given; so we have

$$\left[(1.2 \times 10^{-3} - 1.7 \times 10^{-4}) \text{ gm/cm}^3\right](980 \text{ cm/sec}^2)(V) \geq 3.46 \times 10^8 \text{ dynes}$$

note we have had to put everything in consistent units. This gives the required volume

$$V \geq \frac{3.46 \times 10^8 \text{ dynes}}{1.009 \times 10^0 \text{ dynes/cm}^3} = 3.44 \times 10^8 \text{ cm}^3$$

If the balloon is spherical its volume is $\frac{4}{3}\pi R^3$; the corresponding radius is $\underline{R \geq 4.35 \text{ m}}$.

CHAPTER 6
Forces in Nature

All the forces of nature can be understood as manifestations of four basic
interactions: the gravitational force, the electromagnetic force, and the
weak and strong nuclear forces. Most familiar forces between everyday
objects are electromagnetic in origin.

Newton's law of gravitation gives for the force on a mass m_2 due to
another mass m_1

$$\vec{F} = - \frac{Gm_1 m_2}{r_{12}^2} \hat{r}_{12}$$

The force is always attractive: if $\hat{r}_{12}$ is the unit vector from 1 to 2,
$\vec{F}$ is in the direction $-\hat{r}_{12}$. G is very small, and the gravitational force
between ordinary objects is usually negligibly small. The force of the
earth's gravity on objects near its surface is substantial only because
the mass of the earth is large. The $1/r^2$ form of the force law was inferred by Newton from empirical laws of planetary motion; as a check, he
was able to reconcile the acceleration of bodies at the earth's surface
with that of the moon's orbit around the earth. (Newton was able to
show that the force of a large spherical mass, such as the earth, is the
same as if all its mass were at the center; hence the acceleration of
gravity at the earth's surface is

$$g = \frac{GM_e}{R_e^2}$$

decreasing slowly with increasing height above the earth.)

Electromagnetic forces arise between bodies with an electric charge.
(Charge is a fundamental property of elementary particles; it is conserved and exists only in multiples of the elementary charge e.) The
basic law of electrostatic force is Coulomb's law,

$$\vec{F} = \frac{K_e q_1 q_2}{r_{12}^2} \hat{r}_{12}$$

where q_1 and q_2 are the values of the charges and K_e is a constant. The
form is like that of the gravitational force, but there are important
differences. Charge can be positive or negative in amount, so that the
force may be either attractive or repulsive; furthermore, there are
magnetic forces between charges in motion which obey a wholly different
force law.

The ordinary structure of atoms is a balance of positive and negative
charge, so that atoms - and consequently matter in general - are ordinarily electrically neutral. Objects become charged when, by one means
or another, some atomic electrons are lost or some excess ones acquired.
Some materials contain electrons that are bound to individual atoms only

very loosely and move fairly freely through the body of the material; these conduct electricity. Insulators are materials without such "free" electrons.

Even in neutral objects, positive and negative charges are not in exactly the same place, so that when macroscopic objects are brought very close together there are large contact forces between them. The forces binding atoms together into molecules, and molecules into solids, are electric in origin although very complicated in detail. Typically such binding forces are attractive at large distances between atoms, repulsive at short distances; so that there is an equilibrium separation of each pair of atoms, as if they were joined by springs.

Electrostatic forces are enormously stronger than gravitational; the ratio for a pair of protons (independent of separation) is of the order 10^{36}. Still stronger is the nuclear force that binds protons and neutrons together in atomic nuclei. The nuclear force, however, acts only over very short range ($\sim 10^{-14}$ m), thus is not observed between macroscopic objects; it can be investigated only by scattering experiments with nuclear-scale particles, and no universal force-law is known. It is apparently charge-independent. There is also a second, distinct, very much weaker "nuclear" force which is responsible for the stability or instability of various nuclear species.

If a macroscopic solid, such as a spring, is extended or compressed, the force tending to restore it to its natural length is typically proportional to the deformation:

$$F = -k \, \Delta x$$

This is Hooke's law. Such a force causes a mass on the end of a spring, for instance, to oscillate back and forth around its equilibrium position. A mass at rest on a tabletop compresses it very slightly; the restoring force of the compressed tabletop is the "normal force" which holds the mass up.

In the last case, if the mass is shoved laterally across the tabletop, some minimum force f_s is required to start it moving; once moving, some (generally lesser) force f_k must be applied to keep it moving at constant speed. These forces of (respectively, static and kinetic) friction are usually well represented by

$$f_s = \mu_s N \qquad \text{and} \qquad f_k = \mu_k N$$

where N is the normal force and the frictional coefficients μ_s and μ_k are constants characteristic of the two materials in contact.

Newton's laws are valid in inertial frames of reference. In noninertial frames, fictitious forces arise due to the acceleration of the frame of reference; the apparent force on a mass m is $-m\vec{a}_{fr}$. From the viewpoint of an observer in a noninertial frame, these pseudo forces are just as real as any other force. In a rotating frame of reference, such as one attached to the surface of the earth, the pseudo forces which arise are the centrifugal force and the Coriolis force. It is the

Coriolis force which is responsible for the anticlockwise circulation of cyclones in the Northern hemisphere.

6.2 CHECK LIST

coulomb

$G = 6.67 \times 10^{-11}$ N-m^2/kg^2

$K_e = 8.99 \times 10^9$ N-m^2/C^2

gravitational force

electromagnetic force

strong nuclear force

weak nuclear force

universal gravitational constant

electrostatic force

insulator

oscillation

nucleon

charge independence

saturation

ionic bond

covalent bond

Hooke's law

force constant

magnetic force

quantization of charge

conservation of charge

Coulomb's law

ion

conductor

polarization

normal force

coefficient of static friction

coefficient of kinetic friction

pseudo force

fictitious force

inertial and noninertial frames of reference

centrifugal force

Coriolis force

contact force

6.3 TRUE OR FALSE?

_____ 1. All natural interactions can be understood in terms of four fundamental forces.

_____ 2. Most forces we encounter in everyday phenomena are manifestations of the electromagnetic force.

_____ 3. The gravitational constant G would be different if measured on some other planet.

_____ 4. The gravitational force is the weakest of the four basic forces.

_____ 5. Newton deduced the inverse-square nature of the gravitational-force law from Kepler's empirical rules of planetary motion.

_____ 6. Newton deduced the inverse-square nature of the gravitational-force law from the trajectories of apples near the surface of the earth.

_____ 7. The gravitational attraction due to an extended mass distribution is the same as if all the mass were concentrated at its center.

_____ 8. Newton confirmed his gravitational-force law by the fact that the centripetal acceleration of the moon in its orbit works out to the same as g.

_____ 9. Cavendish's experiment provided an independent determination of the mass of the earth, from which a value of the gravitational constant G could be inferred.

_____ 10. The gravitational-force law for two point masses, and the electro-

38

static force law between two point charges, have the same form.

_____11. The magnetic force is that part of the force between charges which arises from their motion.

_____12. Electrostatic forces are always attractive, magnetic forces always repulsive.

_____13. The constitution of matter is ordinarily a balance of positive and negative charge, overall electrically neutral.

_____14. Macroscopic objects become electrically charged when by some means or other they either lose some of their atomic electrons or gain an excess.

_____15. Electric charge is quantized.

_____16. The forces which bind atoms together into molecules are electric in origin.

_____17. Contact forces between ordinary macroscopic objects are electric in origin.

_____18. The electromagnetic force is the strongest of the four basic forces.

_____19. Nuclear forces arise from strong electric attractions between the protons in atomic nuclei.

_____20. Nuclear forces are effective only over very short distances.

_____21. Nuclear forces are essentially charge-independent.

_____22. Exchange of atomic electrons, resulting in positive and negative ions which are then bound together electrostatically, is spoken of as "covalent" bonding.

_____23. Hooke's law says that the restoring force of a deformed elastic solid - such as a stretched spring - is simply proportional to the deformation.

_____24. If an elastic solid is deformed and released, in the absence of other forces it will oscillate about its equilibrium size or position.

_____25. The force of static friction is the force which must be exerted to start two surfaces sliding against each other.

_____26. The force of static friction between two surfaces depends only on the nature of the surfaces and the normal force of each on the other.

_____27. For given surfaces, the coefficient of kinetic friction is typically larger than that of static friction.

_____28. Pseudo forces are fictitious or apparent forces that arise in noninertial reference frames.

_____29. The centripetal force mv^2/r on an object moving in a circle is an example of a pseudo force.

_____30. The Coriolis force is another name for the weak nuclear interaction.

1. There are only two forces that we know about in ordinary large-scale phenomena: gravitation and electromagnetism. What are the properties which say that the force which binds together atomic nuclei can be neither of these?

2. Two bodies a distance d apart have mass and charge such that the electrostatic repulsion exactly balances the gravitational attraction between them. The two are not necessarily identical. If the bodies are moved to a distance 1.5 d apart, is the net force between them (a) attractive, (b) repulsive, (c) zero, (d) more than one possibility, depending on details?

3. A crate sits on the floor of a truck; the coefficient of friction is 0.22. At what rate must the truck accelerate to cause the crate to slip? What force is making the crate slip?

4. Beyond some point, further polishing of two surfaces may <u>increase</u> the coefficient of friction. How come?

5. There are only two forces that we know about in ordinary large-scale phenomena: gravitation and electromagnetism. If I hit you with a brick it plainly isn't gravity that crushes your skull, so it must be electromagnetic force. How can we understand this as an electric interaction?

6. Gravitational and electrostatic forces have the same form – both obey an inverse-square force law. Discuss some of the substantial differences.

6.5   EXAMPLES

1. Find the location of the point between earth and moon at which their gravitational attractions balance and cancel; $M_e = 5.98 \times 10^{24}$ kg, $M_m = 7.35 \times 10^{22}$ kg, and the earth-moon distance is R = 3.84×10^{8} m.

2. In the sketch at right, the coefficient of sliding friction between the 3.5-lb block and the tabletop is 0.4, that between it and the 1.5-lb block is 0.2; friction in the pulley and the mass of pulley and string may be neglected. What force F is necessary to cause the lower block to move at constant speed?

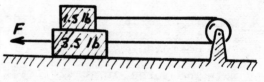

3. A favorite science-fiction trick is to create artificial "gravity" at the outer wall of a space station, say, by spinning it. Imagine that a cylindrical space station of 200-ft diameter is spun at a rate sufficient to cause an apparent gravity at the outer wall equal to that on the earth. An occupant standing on the outer wall throws some object "upward" - that is, toward the rotation axis - at 25 ft/sec. Find the magnitude and direction of the Coriolis force on it.

4. A block weighing 5.5 lb is connected to the top of an incline by a spring with k = 4.4 lb/ft. The incline makes an angle of 36.9° with the horizontal; the coefficient of static friction between block and incline is 0.15. What is the <u>range</u> of positions in which the block can sit at rest?

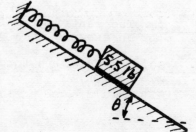

6.6 ANSWERS

True or False?

1. True - as far as we know.

2. True.

3. False - it is believed to be a universal constant.

4. True.

5. True.

6. False - come on, now.

7. False - this is true outside a spherically symmetric distribution, but for an arbitrary system the gravitational attraction of each bit of mass must be added up.

8. False - it is much smaller than g, but in the proper ratio of the square of the distances.

9. False - the other way around.

10. True - each depends on the product of masses or charges, divided by the square of the distance between them.

11. True.

12. False - either force can be attractive or repulsive.

13. True.

14. True.

15. True - it exists only in multiples of the elementary charge e.

16. True.

17. True.

18. False - the nuclear force is stronger.

19. False - the nuclear force is a phenomenon wholly separate from electromagnetism.

20. True - on the order of 10^{-15} m.

21. True - the force between two nucleons is apparently independent of whether they are neutrons or protons.

22. False - this is a description of ionic bonding.

23. True.

24. True - a spring, for instance.

25. True.

26. True - at least, to a good approximation for most surfaces.

27. False - it's the other way around.

28. True - the centrifugal and Coriolis forces are examples.

29. False - this is real, the object is really accelerated. Don't confuse centrifugal and centripetal forces!

30. False.

Questions

1. The electromagnetic force between nucleons would be repulsive, the gravitational force far too weak, and nuclear forces have properties that don't fit - they are short-range and charge-independent.

2. The forces still balance - the net force is zero. For given mass and charge the ratio of gravitational and electrostatic forces is independent of the separation, since both go as $1/r^2$.

3. The maximum force of static friction is $\mu_s N = \mu_s mg = (0.22)m(32 \text{ ft/sec}^2) = (3.52 \text{ ft/sec}^2)m$ - if the acceleration of the truck is larger than this, static friction is insufficient to accelerate the block and it slips. Thus the acceleration of the truck must be at least 3.52 ft/sec^2. In a frame of reference moving with the truck, the pseudo force $-m\vec{a}$ overcomes static friction and causes the block to slip back.

4. As irregularities in the surfaces are made very small, molecules of the two objects are close enough together for intermolecular forces to begin to bind them together.

5. If I attempt to bring the electrons and positively charged nuclei of the brick too closely in contact with those of your head, strong electrostatic forces of repulsion occur.

6. Electrostatic forces can be either attractive or repulsive; gravitational forces occur between every two particles in the universe, electric forces only between charged particles; a separate and different electric force (magnetism) arises between charged particles in motion for which no gravitational analogue is known.

Examples

Partial Solutions (1)

1. The point must clearly be on the line between earth and moon; if not:

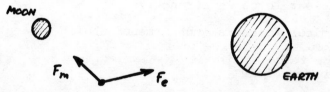

the net force on a particle always has a nonzero lateral component. For an arbitrary point on the line, write out the net gravitational force on a particle of mass m.

2. Draw a free-body diagram for each block. For the one on top, it looks like this:

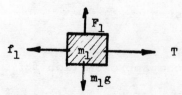

F_1 is the upward force of the block underneath, f_1 the frictional force exerted by it on the upper one. What is the value of the frictional force f_1?

3. The value of the Coriolis acceleration is $2\omega v$. From the information given here, what is the value of ω?

4. The way to attack this is to <u>assume</u> the block is at rest and solve for the frictional force required, as a function of its position. The frictional force - in either direction - cannot be larger than $\mu_s N$. For an object resting on an incline, what is the value of the normal force N?

Partial Solutions (2)

1. The magnitudes of the forces are (at a distance r from the moon)

$$F_e = \frac{GM_e m}{(R - r)^2} \qquad\qquad F_m = \frac{GM_m m}{r^2}$$

and the problem is just to find r such that they are equal, since on the line between earth and moon they are necessarily opposite.

2. The frictional force f_1 is $\mu_k F_1 = \mu_k m_1 g = (0.2)(1.5\ lb) = 0.3\ lb$. A free-body diagram for the lower block looks like this:

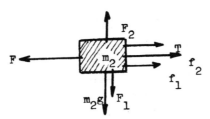

where F_2 is the upward force of the table on the lower block and F is the pull of the string, which is what we're looking for. Remember that the problem specified that the blocks are moving at a constant speed.

3. The station rotates at a rate such that $v^2/r = \omega^2 r$ (the centrifugal acceleration) is equal to g. Thus

$$\omega = \sqrt{\frac{g}{r}} = \sqrt{\frac{32\ ft/sec^2}{200\ ft}} = 0.566\ sec^{-1}$$

is the angular speed of rotation.

4. In the sketch at right, the spring is stretched a distance x from its equilibrium length. Depending on whether the force of the spring or the downslope force of gravity is larger, we must have either

$$f + kx - mg \sin\theta = 0$$

or

$$f - kx + mg \sin\theta = 0$$

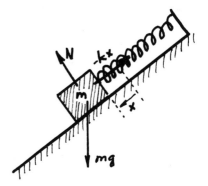

for the block to be at rest. But f cannot be larger than $\mu_s N$, where $N = mg \cos\theta$.

Partial Solutions (3)

1. For the forces to be equal we have

$$\frac{M_e}{(R - r)^2} = \frac{M_m}{r^2} \qquad\qquad \text{or} \qquad\qquad \left(\frac{R - r}{r}\right)^2 = \frac{M_e}{M_m}$$

Solving for r gives

$$r = \frac{1}{1 + \sqrt{M_e/M_m}}R = \frac{1}{1 + \sqrt{81.30}}(3.84 \times 10^8 \text{ m}) = \underline{3.83 \times 10^7 \text{ m}}$$

about a tenth of the way from moon to earth.

2. The acceleration of each block is zero. Thus from the diagrams

$F_1 = m_1 g = 1.5$ lb $\qquad\qquad F_2 = F_1 + m_2 g = 1.5 + 3.5 = 5.0$ lb

$T - f_1 = 0$ so $T = f_1 = 0.3$ lb $\qquad f_2 = \mu_2 F_2 = (0.4)(5 \text{ lb}) = 2.0$ lb

and $F - f_1 - f_2 - T = 0$

so $F = f_1 + f_2 + T = 0.3 + 2.0 + 0.3 = \underline{2.6 \text{ lb}}$

3. The Coriolis force is

$$F_C = ma_C = m(2\omega v) = (m)(2)(0.566 \text{ sec}^{-1})(25 \text{ ft/sec})$$
$$= \underline{(m)(28.3 \text{ ft/sec}^2)} = \underline{0.884 \text{ mg}}$$

It is directed "horizontally"; looking along the axis such that the rotation of the station is anticlockwise, the Coriolis force is to the right.

4. Plugging in the normal force gives for the range of x

$$(mg/k)(\sin \theta) - \mu_s \cos \theta \le x \le (mg/k)(\sin \theta) + \mu_s \cos \theta$$

here $mg = 5.5$ lb, $k = 4.4$ lb/ft, $\mu_s = 0.15$, $\theta = 36.9°$. With these values we get $\underline{0.48 \text{ ft} \le x \le 0.72 \text{ ft}}$ for the block to be in equilibrium.

DIGRESSION
The Scalar Product

When earlier we introduced vector quantities, we left open the question
of the multiplication of vectors. In fact, there is more than one useful
multiplication rule; the first one we will have need of is a multiplication of two vectors to yield a scalar result.

For any two vector quantities, $\vec{A}$ and $\vec{B}$, we define the scalar (or
"dot") product as

$$\vec{A} \cdot \vec{B} \equiv |\vec{A}| \, |\vec{B}| \cos \theta$$

where θ is the angle between the directions of $\vec{A}$ and $\vec{B}$. $\vec{A} \cdot \vec{B}$ is a scalar
quantity, it has no direction. $\vec{A} \cdot \vec{B}$ is the magnitude of either vector
multiplied by the component along it of the other vector.

It follows that the scalar product of two vectors which are parallel
to one another is the product of their magnitudes; the scalar product of
two vectors which are perpendicular to one another is zero. Plainly

$$\vec{A} \cdot \vec{A} = A^2$$

In terms of the rectangular components of the vectors A and B, the
scalar product is easily shown to be

$$\vec{A} \cdot \vec{B} = A_x B_x + A_y B_y + A_z B_z$$

and it follows that the scalar product is both a commutative and an
associative rule of multiplication. From this also the derivative of
a scalar product of two vector quantities is given by

$$\frac{d}{dt} \vec{A} \cdot \vec{B} = \frac{d\vec{A}}{dt} \cdot \vec{B} + \vec{A} \cdot \frac{d\vec{B}}{dt}$$

analogous to the usual rule for differentiation of a product.

CHAPTER 7
Work and Energy

7.1 CHAPTER SUMMARY

Thus far, in applying Newton's laws of motion, we have usually been able to consider the forces acting on a body as constant. In many situations this is not the case. If the force is known explicitly as a function of time, Newton's second law can be integrated directly; it is more common, however, to know the force as a function of the <u>position</u> of a particle. For instance, the gravitational force on a body depends inversely on the square of its distance from the earth. We now develop methods for treating this type of problem.

Consider first a problem in one dimension, in which a particle moves from x_1 to x_2 under the action of a force F_x which depends on the particle's position. Define the <u>work</u> done by the force to be

$$W \equiv \int_1^2 F_x \, dx$$

Notice that it is possible for the work done to be negative if the displacement is opposite the direction of the force. If more than one force acts on the particle, the net work done, W_{net}, is the sum of the work done by each - or, equivalently, the work done by the net resultant force. If also we define the <u>kinetic energy</u> of a moving body as $\frac{1}{2}mv^2$, then from Newton's second law

$$W_{net} = \frac{1}{2}mv_2^2 - \frac{1}{2}mv_1^2 = \Delta E_k$$

The work done by the resultant force is equal to the change in kinetic energy. This is known as the <u>work-energy theorem</u>; it is quite general.

With a proper generalization of the idea of work, the theorem extends directly to problems in three dimensions. The point is that the component of a force <u>perpendicular</u> to the direction of motion does not act to change the particle's kinetic energy; consider, for instance, the centripetal force in uniform circular motion. Thus define

$$dW = F_{\parallel} \, ds = \vec{F} \cdot d\vec{s} \qquad \text{or} \qquad W \equiv \int_1^2 \vec{F} \cdot d\vec{s}$$

that is, the component of $\vec{F}$ <u>along</u> the instantaneous displacement $d\vec{s}$ is everywhere used. (This type of integral is known as a line integral.) With this definition of work, the work-energy theorem applies unchanged to problems in three dimensions.

If in a given situation we can calculate the net work done on an object, the work-energy theorem gives us its speed at any point. Notice that in a three-dimensional problem this is only a partial solution - the direction of the velocity is not given explicitly.

In many situations, the work that is done by a force applied to

46

something does not increase its kinetic energy, because some other force is doing negative work. For instance, suppose I pull a block at constant speed up a smooth incline. The work I do is cancelled by the (negative) work done by the earth's gravity; the net work done, and the change in E_k, is zero. But the work done in pulling it up, in a sense, has been "stored up" and is potentially available: if I let the block slide down again freely, the earth's gravity does work on it and increases its kinetic energy - by an amount equal to the work I did in dragging it up. We can say that the work I did pulling the block up the slope increased its potential energy, and that its potential energy was converted to kinetic energy when it was allowed to slide freely back down. This is an instance of the conservation of energy; in later chapters we will encounter many others.

The dimensions of work and of energy must of course be the same - the dimensions of force times distance. The rate at which a force does work on something is called power; thus if a force $\vec{F}$ acts on a particle whose velocity is $\vec{v}$, the power is

$$P = \vec{F} \cdot \vec{v}$$

7.2   CHECK LIST

joule	watt
foot-pound	horsepower
work	scalar product
kinetic energy	potential energy
Hooke's law	conservation of energy
work-energy theorem	power

7.3   TRUE OR FALSE?

_F_ 1.   Force is a form of energy.

_F_ 2.   If a force F acts on a particle of mass m which is moving at a speed v, we define the work done to be the change in the quantity $\frac{1}{2} mv^2$.

_F_ 3.   Work is necessarily a positive quantity.

_F_ 4.   The kinetic energy of an object is the same for all observers, regardless of their state of motion.

_F_ 5.   Twice the power is expended in applying a force to an object moving at speed v as in applying the same force to an object moving with speed 2v.

_T_ 6.   Work is required to accelerate a particle in a direction perpendicular to its instantaneous direction of motion.

_F_ 7.   The work-energy theorem is best suited to problems in which the force on a particle is known explicitly as a function of time.

_____ 8.   Newton's law of gravitation and Coulomb's law of electrostatic force both give the force on a particle as a function of its position.

9. The definition of work as force times distance moved is generally valid only for one-dimensional problems.

10. The dimensions of work are those of force times distance.

11. Joule, foot-pound, watt-second, and erg are all units of energy.

12. If several forces act on a particle, the total work done by all of them is the work done by the net resultant force.

13. The theorem stating that the work done on a particle is equal to its change of kinetic energy is generally valid only for one-dimensional problems.

14. If a particle's speed is doubled, its kinetic energy is increased by a factor of four.

15. In three dimensions, work is defined as the scalar product $\vec{F} \cdot \vec{v}$.

16. In the most general case, the work-energy theorem states that the net work done, over any interval, by the resultant force on a particle is equal to the change in the particle's kinetic energy.

17. An object, starting from rest, slides down a frictionless hill; its speed at the bottom depends only on the height, and not the shape, of the hill.

18. The kinetic energy acquired by a block sliding down a frictionless incline is the same as if it had simply fallen freely through the same height.

19. The work done on an object by frictional forces is always negative.

20. A heavy crate is dragged across a rough floor from point A to point B; the work done on it is independent of the path taken from A to B.

21. In the case described in the last question, the work done by the normal force of the floor on the crate is independent of the path taken from A to B.

22. I lift a 50-lb box, slowly and steadily, 4 ft off the floor. The work I have done is 200 ft-lb.

23. In the previous question, I have increased the box's kinetic energy by 200 ft-lb.

24. In the previous question, I have increased the box's potential energy by 200 ft-lb.

25. In the previous question, the work done on the box by gravity is -200 ft-lb.

26. A block slides down an incline; conservation of energy says that the work done on the block by the incline is equal to the work done on the incline by the block.

27. The following units all measure the same physical quantity: foot-pound/second, horsepower, watt, joule/hour.

28. The "scalar" or "dot" product is a rule for multiplying a scalar and a vector.

29. The scalar product of two perpendicular vectors always vanishes.

48

____30. The time derivative of the product $\vec{A} \cdot \vec{B}$ is $\vec{A} \cdot \frac{d\vec{B}}{dt}$.

7.4 QUESTIONS

1. The graph shows the force acting on
    a particle as a function of its posi-
    tion in some one-dimensional problem.
    (a) Estimate the work done on the
        particle between x = 0 and
        x = 2 ft.
    (b) Identify the 2-ft displacement
        in which the work done on the
        particle is maximum.
    (c) Identify a 1-ft displacement
        during which the work done is
        zero.

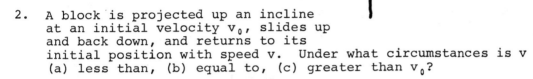

2. A block is projected up an incline
    at an initial velocity v_0, slides up
    and back down, and returns to its
    initial position with speed v. Under what circumstances is v
    (a) less than, (b) equal to, (c) greater than v_0?

3. The moon's motion around the earth is essentially a uniform circular
    motion. Its kinetic energy thus doesn't change. Yet there is
    certainly a force on it - the gravitational attraction of the earth.
    Is there a contradiction here?

4. The nonzero resultant force on a particle does zero work over some
    interval. Is it possible that the particle has moved in a straight
    line?

5. An object slides down a frictionless incline, hits a spring at the
    bottom, compresses it, and is projected back up the incline to its
    starting position. Follow the changes of energy and the work done
    through this sequence of events.

6. A particle undergoes a displacement given by $(2.42\hat{i} - 6.6\hat{j})$ m.
    What work is done on it by a force given by (a) $(30\hat{i} - 11\hat{j})$ N,
    (b) $(30\hat{i} + 11\hat{j})$ N?

7.5 EXAMPLES

1. A 90-lb sled slides 28 ft down a straight hill inclined 20° above
    the horizontal. The coefficient of friction between hillside and
    sled is 0.18. What is (a) the work done by gravity, (b) the work
    done by friction, (c) the work done by the resultant force, (d) the
    change in the sled's kinetic energy.

2. A boy shoves his 20-lb sled back up the
    hill of example 1 (the boy himself was
    the other 70 lb). He shoves it at
    constant speed with a force $\vec{F}$ directed
    as sketched. What is the magnitude of
    this force, and how much work must the
    boy do?

3. If the maximum power the boy of the previous example can put out is
    0.08 horsepower, how long does it take him to shove the sled back
    up the hill?

4. A block is projected along the curved track shown in the sketch. If

the track is frictionless, what initial
velocity must it be given to make it
"over the top" without falling off the
track?

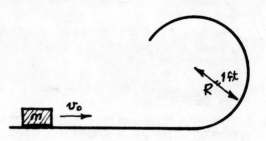

5. An 18-gm bullet traveling at 600 m/sec
strikes and imbeds itself in a 1.2-kg
wooden block. Neglect external forces
on the two objects. Find the total
kinetic energy of the two objects before and after impact. Comment on
changes of kinetic energy and on what
does work on what. What work was done
on the bullet? On the block?

7.6 ANSWERS

True or False?

1. False - force and energy are distinct dynamical quantities.

2. False - this is not the definition of work.

3. False -consider the work done by friction, which always opposes the
   motion of an object.

4. False - since it depends on the magnitude of the object's velocity.

5. False - half the power; $P = fv$.

6. False - no work is done if force and displacement are perpendicular.

7. False - best suited to those in which force is known as a function
   of position.

8. True - both have an inverse-square distance dependence.

9. True - if the force and displacement are not in the same line, only
   the component of the force along the direction of the displacement
   matters.

10. True.

11. True - a watt is a joule/second.

12. True.

13. False - it is general.

14. True - kinetic energy is proportional to v^2.

15. False - this expression is the power being expended by the force.

16. True.

17. True - the work done by gravity, hence the change in kinetic energy,
    depends only on the vertical distance traversed.

18. True - this is a special case of the previous question.

19. True - friction always acts to oppose the motion.

20. False - the longer the path, usually, the more work done.

21. True - in fact the work it does is zero.

22. True.

23. False - if I lift at a steady speed, the kinetic energy isn't changing.

24. True - in effect, the work I have done against gravity is "stored" as potential energy.

25. True.

26. False.

27. True - all are units of energy per unit time, or power.

28. False - it is a rule of multiplication of two vectors which yields a scalar result.

29. True.

30. False - it is $\vec{A} \cdot \frac{d\vec{B}}{dt} + \frac{d\vec{A}}{dt} \cdot \vec{B}$ - just like the usual rule for differentiation of a product.

Questions

1. (a) Between x = 0 and x = 2 ft the force increases <u>uniformly</u> from 1.2 to 4.0 lb; the average force during this interval is thus 2.6 lb, and the work done is (2.6 lb)(2.0 ft) = 5.2 ft-lb.

   (b) This would be the part of the graph in which the force is maximum, roughly between <u>x = 1.6 ft and x = 3.6 ft</u>.

   (c) This would be a 1-ft displacement during which as much area lies below the x axis, roughly <u>from x = 3.7 to 4.7 ft</u>.

2. It will be less on a rough incline, equal on a frictionless one; it cannot be greater unless the block is rocket-powered.

3. There is a force, but it is directed radially inward, toward the center of the earth. Force and displacement in every small time interval are perpendicular, thus the force does no work and so does not change the moon's kinetic energy.

4. Yes, it is possible, although not if the force is anything like steady. The force would have to be along the particle's direction of motion and would have to reverse its direction during the given interval. In this case the total work could be zero.

5. As the object slides down it is trading in gravitational potential energy for kinetic energy; the force of the incline doesn't enter because it is normal to the object's line of motion, does no work. At the bottom it compresses the spring, yielding its kinetic energy to potential energy stored in the compressed spring. On the way back up, the sequence is reversed; since the whole mess is conservative, it comes back to its starting point.

6. (a) W = (30i - 11j)(2.42i - 6.6j) J = (72.6 + 72.6) J = <u>145.2 J</u>.

   (b) W = (30i + 11j)(2.42i + 6.6j) J = (72.6 - 72.6) J = <u>0</u>.

Examples

Partial Solutions (1)

1. The forces that act on the sled are gravity, friction, and the normal force of the hill. The latter does no work on the sled. (Why not?) (a) The work done by gravity is simply the sled's weight times the vertical distance it moves:

$$W_{gr} = (-90\ lb)(-28\ \sin 20^{\circ}\ ft) = (90)(9.58) = \underline{+862\ ft\text{-}lb}$$

the minus signs come in only because I choose to call up positive.

2. We have to do a little resolution of forces on this one. A free-body diagram is shown at right. Writing components <u>along</u> the plane gives

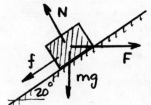

$$F(\cos 20^{\circ}) - f - (90\ lb)(\sin 20^{\circ}) = 0$$

Write out components perpendicular to the plane and solve for the unknown forces.

3. Put this one off until you have example 2 more or less worked out - you'll need the answer to that one.

4. Finding the speed at the level of the top of the loop is simple; but what speed is needed there? What does the condition, that it goes over the top without slipping, require? <u>Hint</u>: Draw a free-body diagram for the instant it's at the top.

5. For two isolated bodies Newton's third law says the total momentum is constant. Thus, since after impact the two move together, $mv_0 = (m + M)v$.

Partial Solutions (2)

1. (b) Since the frictional force always opposes the motion, the work done by friction is

$$W_{fr} = -f(28\ ft)$$

where f is the frictional force. What is the value of f?

2. Perpendicular to the incline we get

$$N - F(\sin 20^{\circ}) - (90\ lb)(\cos 20^{\circ}) = 0$$

so

$$N = F(\sin 20^{\circ}) + (90\ lb)(\cos 20^{\circ})$$

and the frictional force $f = \mu_k N = \mu_k F(\sin 20^{\circ}) + \mu_k(90\ lb)(\cos 20^{\circ})$

All you have left is to solve for F. It's worth noting that the normal force on an incline isn't <u>always</u> mg sin θ.

3. The power he expends is the work he does per unit time; a horsepower is 550 ft-lb/sec. Remember he is taking himself up the hill, as well as the sled! How much work does this take?

4. A free-body diagram is sketched at right. Since the track is given frictionless, the force it exerts on the sliding block must be normal. Thus

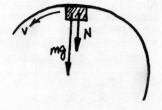

$$F = N + mg = mv^2/R$$

Since the particle is moving in a circle, this has to be the value of the net force. Are there any limits on the value of N?

5. With the data given, the speed of bullet and block together after impact is

$$v = \frac{10.8\ kg\text{-}m/sec}{1.218\ kg} = \underline{8.87\ ft/sec}$$

The kinetic energies are

	Before	After
Bullet	6480 J	0.7 J
Block	-	47.2 J
Total	6480 J	47.9 J

Partial Solutions (3)

1. (b) $f = \mu_k (90 \text{ lb}) (\cos 20^\circ) = (0.18)(90)(0.940) = 15.2$ lb, so the work it does is

$$W_{fr} = (-15.2 \text{ lb})(28 \text{ ft}) = \underline{-426 \text{ ft-lb}}$$

(c) The total work done is the sum of the work of each force:

$$W = W_{gr} + W_{fr} + 0 = 862 - 426 = \underline{436 \text{ ft-lb}}$$

(d) And 436 ft-lb must be the change in kinetic energy, by the work-energy theorem. Remember that the total work done is the same as the work done by the net resultant force.

2. From the horizontal components we have

$$F(\cos 20^\circ) = f + (20 \text{ lb})(\sin 20^\circ) = f + 6.84 \text{ lb}$$

but

$$f = \mu_k F(\sin 20^\circ) + \mu_k (20 \text{ lb})(\cos 20^\circ) = 0.0616F + 3.38 \text{ lb}$$

thus

$$0.9397F = 0.0616F + 10.24 \text{ lb}$$

yielding $\underline{F = 11.7 \text{ lb}}$

The component of this force up the plane is $(11.7)(\cos 20^\circ) = 10.96$ lb, so the work the boy does on the sled is

$$W = (10.96 \text{ lb})(28 \text{ ft}) = \underline{307 \text{ ft-lb}}$$

3. The vertical height of the hill is $(28 \text{ ft})(\sin 20^\circ) = 9.58$ ft, so the total work the boy does on himself and the sled is

$$W = (70 \text{ lb})(9.58 \text{ ft}) + 306 \text{ ft-lb} = 977 \text{ ft-lb}$$

But his maximum power output is 0.08 horsepower = $(0.08)(550) = 44$ ft-lb/sec so it takes him at least

$$\frac{977 \text{ ft-lb}}{44 \text{ ft-lb/sec}} = \underline{22.2 \text{ sec}}$$

to get up.

4. The value of N cannot be negative - the track has no way of pulling the block onto itself. Thus on the assumption we've made - that the block stays on the track, thus moves in a circle - the velocity at the top must be at least

$$v = \sqrt{gR}$$

Now we can get something out of the work-energy theorem. To move up a distance 2R, the work done on the particle by gravity (regardless of path!) is $-2mgR$; so

$$\Delta K = \tfrac{1}{2}mv^2 - \tfrac{1}{2}mv_0^2 = W = -2mgR$$

so

$$v_0^2 = 5gR, \quad v_0 = \sqrt{(5.0)(32 \text{ ft/sec}^2)(1 \text{ ft})} = \underline{12.6 \text{ ft/sec}}$$

5. The bullet lost kinetic energy 6479 J, so the block did work $\underline{-6479 \text{ J}}$ on it; the block gained $\underline{47.2 \text{ J}}$, so this is the work the bullet did on it. There is a temptation to think that these two numbers should be equal, maybe because of Newton's third law. But although the forces are of equal magnitude, bullet and block don't move through the same distance during the interaction, and the total kinetic energy of the two does not remain the same.

CHAPTER 8
Potential Energy and Conservative Forces

8.1 CHAPTER SUMMARY

In many situations, we can speak of work as being "stored" in the form of potential energy. A force which can be described in this way is called a conservative force; examples include gravitational, elastic, and electrostatic forces. If only conservative forces act on a body, its total mechanical energy remains constant, although kinetic and potential energy may each transform into the other.

The basic criterion for a conservative force is that it do zero net work on a particle which moves around any <u>closed</u> path. The net work by gravity, for example, on an object which moves up an incline and then slides back down to its starting point is zero; if gravity is the only force acting, the object returns to its starting point with its initial kinetic energy. Sliding friction, on the other hand, is a nonconservative force; as the frictional force always opposes the motion, the net work done by it on <u>any</u> path is negative. Another way to state the same criterion is that the work done by a conservative force on a particle which moves from point 1 to point 2 is independent of the path taken; it depends only on where 1 and 2 are. If this is the case, we can plainly define the potential energy, U, by

$$W(1 \to 2) = \int_1^2 \vec{F} \cdot d\vec{s} \equiv U_1 - U_2 = -\Delta U$$

Notice that only <u>changes</u> in potential energy are defined; the point at which $U = 0$ is always arbitrary. The sign of U is defined so that positive work corresponds to a decrease in potential energy; since the work done increases the kinetic energy by the same amount, the sum of the two remains constant, for a conservative force.

In one dimension, a necessary and sufficient condition for a force to be conservative is that it depend only on the position of the particle; then a potential-energy function can always be defined by $\Delta U \equiv -\int F\,dx$. This gives, for instance, $U = mgy$ for the force of gravity near the earth, or $U = \frac{1}{2}kx^2$ for the force of a stretched spring. (Notice that by our definition the force is in the direction of <u>decreasing</u> potential energy.) If a force depends on variables other than position, a potential-energy function cannot be defined in this way.

In three dimensions, it is a necessary but <u>not</u> a sufficient condition that the force depend on position only. A uniform force - one everywhere the same in magnitude and direction - is plainly conservative. Another important case is that of a <u>central</u> force. A central force is one directed toward or away from some origin and dependent only on distance from the origin:

$$\vec{F} = f(r)\hat{r} \qquad \text{then} \qquad \Delta U = -\int_{r_1}^{r_2} f(r)\, dr$$

Both electrostatic and gravitational forces are central, with $f(r) \propto r^{-2}$ in each case. (In electrostatic problems we often speak in terms of the electrostatic potential, defined as the potential energy on a unit charge.)

In the case of a uniform or a central force, where the potential-energy function depends on only one variable, the force may be found from the potential energy just by differentiating:

$$F_x = -\frac{dU}{dx} \qquad \text{or} \qquad f(r) = -\frac{dU}{dr}$$

In general, if a potential-energy function exists, the force may be found as the slope of the potential energy, taken in the direction of maximum change (the "gradient" of the potential-energy function). It follows that, at a point where U has an extreme value - a maximum or minimum - the force on the particle vanishes. At such a point the particle is in equilibrium. Since the force is in the direction of decreasing U, the equilibrium at a potential-energy minimum is stable; at a maximum, unstable.

We have been speaking of the potential energy of a particle due to a force on it from some external agency. More generally, for a system of interacting particles, the potential energy is a property of the configuration of the whole system and not of individual particles. For a pair of interacting particles, for instance, the potential energy is the work done on either by the other in the process of placing them in the given configuration.

We noted already that not all forces depending only on position are conservative. A general test for a conservative force in three dimensions is that

$$\frac{\partial F_x}{\partial y} = \frac{\partial F_y}{\partial x} \qquad \frac{\partial F_z}{\partial x} = \frac{\partial F_x}{\partial z} \qquad \frac{\partial F_y}{\partial z} = \frac{\partial F_z}{\partial y}$$

for $\vec{F}$ to be a conservative force.

8.2 CHECK LIST

joule

volt

electron volt

potential energy

conservative and nonconservative forces

total mechanical energy

line integral

central force

$e = 1.60 \times 10^{-19}$ C

partial derivative

electrostatic potential

gradient

stable and unstable equilibrium

55

8.3 TRUE OR FALSE?

_____1. Potential energy can be regarded as work that is "stored" by being done against some force.

_____2. If I lift a 50-lb box 4 ft in the air, I have increased its potential energy by 200 ft-lb.

_____3. Potential energy and work have the same dimensions.

_____4. Potential energy can be unambiguously associated only with a conservative force.

_____5. We so define potential energy that, if a body is acted upon only by conservative forces, the sum of its potential and kinetic energy is constant.

_____6. A conservative force is one such that the work it does on a particle in moving it along any path is zero.

_____7. Friction is a nonconservative force.

_____8. If a particle is acted upon only by conservative forces, then whenever it returns to its initial position, it has its initial velocity.

_____9. In one dimension, any force which depends only on the position of the particle is conservative.

_____10. The work done by a conservative force on a particle is equal to the increase of the corresponding potential energy of the particle.

_____11. The potential energy of a constant force acting in the x direction can be written simply Fx.

_____12. The absolute value of potential energy is indeterminate.

_____13. The potential energy of a spring compressed a distance x is proportional to x^2.

_____14. The force is in the direction of increasing potential energy.

_____15. A force is nonconservative if the work done by it in moving a particle between two given points depends on the path taken.

_____16. In general, that a force depend only on position is a necessary but insufficient condition for it to be conservative.

_____17. A force depending on position is the form $\vec{F} = f(r)\hat{r}$ is conservative.

_____18. Any force whose magnitude depends only on $r = |\vec{r}|$ is conservative.

_____19. The force of gravity is conservative only sufficiently near the surface of the earth so that it may be considered a uniform force.

_____20. The electrostatic force given by Coulomb's law is conservative.

_____21. Electrostatic potential is defined as the electrostatic force per unit charge on a charged particle.

_____22. The force on a particle is zero at a point where its potential energy has a maximum value.

_____23. The electron volt is defined as the work done on an electron charge in moving through a potential difference of one volt.

_____24. Most generally, given a potential-energy function, we can define the force as the derivative of the potential energy taken in the direction of the force.

_____25. A minimum in the potential-energy function is a point of stable equilibrium.

_____26. In general, the potential energy of a system of particles is simply the sum of the potential energies of each particle.

_____27. The general condition for a force to be conservative is that its partial derivatives with respect to the position coordinates vanish.

8.4   QUESTIONS

1. A particle moves in the xy plane under the action of a force given by

$$\vec{F} = (6xy^3 + 2)\hat{i} + (9x^2y^2)\hat{j} \text{ N}$$

Is this force conservative?

2. I pick up a 50-lb crate and set it on a shelf 4 ft off the floor. Is the total mechanical energy of the crate conserved?

3. A certain spring does not obey Hooke's law precisely; the restoring force it exerts when stretched an amount x is $F = -kx + bx^3$. Is this still a conservative force? If not, why not? If so, what would be the corresponding potential-energy function?

4. A particle acted on by a single conservative force is moving in such a way that its potential energy is decreasing. What can you say about its motion?

5. The graph at right represents some force in one dimension. Sketch what you think the corresponding potential-energy function would look like.

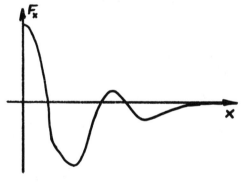

6. A parachutist is descending toward the earth at a constant (terminal) velocity. Comment on what is happening to energy of various kinds, in this situation.

8.5   EXAMPLES

1. A mass of 3.5 kg hangs vertically from a spring whose force constant is 140 N/m. (a) Find the potential-energy function U(x), where x is the displacement of the spring from its equilibrium unstretched length. (b) Where is the potential energy a minimum? (c) If the mass is pulled 6 cm down from this point, what work must be done on it?

2. The potential energy of an object in the gravitational field of the earth is

$$U(r) = -GM_e m/r$$

where M_e is the earth's mass, r the distance from its center. Find the potential-energy difference between a point on the earth's surface and another point at a height h above the surface, and show that for small h it reduces to U = mgh.

3. A particle moves in the xy plane under the action of a force given by

$$\vec{F} = (1.7 \, y)\hat{i} + (3.6)\hat{j} \text{ N}$$

Show explicitly that this is not a conservative force by calculating the work done by it in moving around some closed path in space.

4. The potential energy, due to the nuclear force, of a nucleon near a heavy nucleus is often approximated by a potential energy of the form

$$U(r) = \frac{-U_0}{1 + e^{(r - r_0)/a}}$$

where r is the distance from the origin and r_0, a, and U_0 are constants. This is called a "Woods-Saxon potential." (a) Using $U_0 = 35$ MeV, $r_0 = 6 \times 10^{-15}$ m, and $a = 1.5 \times 10^{-15}$ m, sketch U(r). (b) Find the force $\vec{F}(r)$. (c) What is the effect of different values of the parameter a on this nuclear-force model?

8.6 ANSWERS

True or False?

1. True.

2. True.

3. True.

4. True.

5. True.

6. False - this wouldn't leave much point to defining work!

7. True - it cannot be written as a function of the position of a particle, since its direction depends on the direction of the particle's motion.

8. False - I'm being picky, but it returns with its initial _speed_; the kinetic energy is independent of the direction of the _velocity_ vector.

9. True.

10. False - the decrease of potential energy. Gravity does positive work on a particle moving downward - its gravitational potential energy is decreasing.

11. True.

12. True - we really define only _differences_ of potential energy.

13. True - if the force constant of the spring is k, $U(x) = \frac{1}{2}kx^2$.

14. False - decreasing potential energy; see answer 10.

15. True.

16. True - it is a sufficient condition only in one dimension.

17. True - this is a central force.

18. False - it must be radially directed as well.

19. False - it is conservative in general.

20. True.

21. False - this defines the electric field.

22. True.

23. True.

24. True - it sounds a little like a circular definition but this essentially is what the gradient of a function is.

25. True.

26. False - the potential energy of a system is a property of the system. The statement is true, however, if there are no internal forces.

27. False - this would define a uniform force.

Questions

1. The condition for - conservativity? - is

    $$\frac{\partial F_x}{\partial y} = \frac{\partial F_y}{\partial x}$$

    For the force given here

    $$\frac{\partial F_x}{\partial y} = 18xy^2 \qquad \frac{\partial F_y}{\partial x} = 18xy^2$$

    so $\vec{F}$ is conservative.

2. No. It started and finished at rest, so its kinetic energy didn't change; but its gravitational potential energy increased by 200 ft-lb. The force I exerted on it to raise it is not conservative.

3. Certainly. In one dimension, <u>any</u> force that depends only on position is conservative. The potential energy would be

    $$U(x) = -\int_0^x (-kx + bx^3)\ dx = \frac{1}{2}kx^2 - \frac{1}{4}bx^4$$

4. Its speed is increasing, and that is all you can say.

5. Something like the sketch at the right.

6. His kinetic energy is constant if he is falling at constant speed. His gravitational potential energy is decreasing, but work is being done on him by a nonconservative force - the viscous drag of the air - which is dissipating this potential energy.

Examples

Partial Solutions (1)

1. The potential energy has two parts: that due to the force of gravity and that due to the spring. Call potential energy zero at the point where the mass would be with the spring <u>unstretched</u>, and let the y direction be up. Then

    $$U_{sp} = \frac{1}{2}ky^2$$

    What is U_{gr}?

2. To be explicit I talked of a potential-energy difference; all we are doing is writing the potential energy of the earth's gravity, measured from $U(R_e) = 0$. In the usual formulation, obviously

    $$U(R_e) = -\frac{GM_e m}{R_e}$$

3. The trick is to choose an easy path. A relatively easy one is shown in the sketch, the square circuit: $(x,y) = (0,0) \to (1\text{ m, }0) \to (1\text{ m, }1\text{ m}) \to (0,1\text{ m}) \to (0,0)$. (To be a little bit sneaky, an even easier path would be a comparable square circuit in the <u>xz</u> plane. Would this work?)

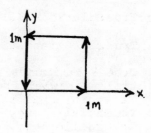

4. A graph of $U(r)$ vs. r for the parameters given is shown at the right. It is a "potential well" of depth $\sim U_0$ and radius $\sim r_0$. The given U depends only on

$$r = |\vec{r}|$$

What does this tell you about the corresponding force?

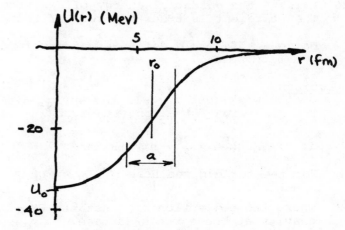

Partial Solutions (2)

Partial Solutions (2)

1. U_{gr} can plainly be written

$$U_{gr} = mgy$$

So that the potential-energy function for the particle is

(a) $\underline{U = mgy + \frac{1}{2}ky^2 = (34.3\text{ N})(y) + (70\text{ N/m})(y^2)}$

To find the point where the potential is minimum, set its derivative equal to zero.

2. At a height h above the earth's surface, $r = R_e + h$ and

$$U(R_e + h) = -\frac{GM_e m}{R_e + h}$$

so

$$U(R_e + h) = U(R_e) = \Delta U = GM_e m \left[\frac{1}{R_e} - \frac{1}{R_e + h}\right] = \frac{GM_e mh}{R_e(R_e + h)}$$

For values of h very much less than R_e, what does this reduce to?

3. Now calculating the work done along each leg of the path is easy because each is a constant-force problem:

for $y = 0$, $F_x = 0$ and $F_y = 3.6$ N

for $y = 1$, $F_x = 1.7$ N and $F_y = 3.6$ N

The xz plane is a nice idea, beacuse the force varies only with y; but in the xz plane the work <u>does</u> turn out to be zero. Oh well.

4. Because U depends only on the magnitude of $\vec{r}$, we know that the force is everywhere radial:

$$\vec{F}(r) = f(r)\,\hat{r} \quad \text{with} \quad f(r) = -dU/dr$$

To make the differentiation look less messy, put $\xi = \frac{r - r_0}{a}$ and take

$$f(r) = -\frac{dU}{dr} = -\frac{d\xi}{dr}\frac{dU}{d\xi} = -\frac{1}{a}\frac{dU}{d\xi}$$

where

$$U = \frac{-U_0}{1 + e^{\xi}}$$

This is just the "chain rule" for differentiation.

Partial Solutions (3)

1. For the potential-energy function we are dealing with

$$\frac{dU}{dy} = 34.3 \text{ N} + (140 \text{ N/m})y$$

Set this equal to zero to get $y_0 = -34.3/140 = \underline{-0.245 \text{ m}}$ for the potential-energy minimum. This is the point at which the mass is in equilibrium.

(c) The potential energy at minimum is

$$U_0 = (34.3)(-0.245) + (70)(-0.245)^2 = -4.20 \text{ J}$$

and 6 cm below,

$$U' = (34.3)(-0.305) + (70)(-0.305)^2 = -3.95 \text{ J}$$

So the work done to pull the spring 6 cm below equilibrium is

$$\Delta U = -3.95 + 4.20 = \underline{0.25 \text{ J}}$$

2. If $h \gg R_e$ then $(R_e + h) \simeq R_e$ and

$$U(h) = \frac{GM_emh}{R_e^2} \qquad m\frac{GM_e}{R_e^2}h = mgh$$

where the collection of constants GM_e/R_e^2 defines the acceleration of gravity at the earth's surface.

3. Starting from the origin, the work done on the four legs of the path sketched is

$$W = (0)(1 \text{ m}) + (3.6 \text{ N})(1 \text{ m}) + (1.7 \text{ N})(-1 \text{ m}) = (3.6 \text{ N})(-1 \text{ m})$$

$$= 0 + 3.6 \text{ J} - 1.7 \text{ J} - 3.6 \text{ J} = -1.7 \text{ J} \neq 0$$

Thus the force given is not conservative: to be conservative, the work must be zero around every closed path.

4. We have

$$f(r) = +\frac{U_0}{a}\frac{d}{d\xi}(1 + e^\xi)^{-1} \qquad \text{with } \xi = \frac{r - r_0}{a}$$

$$= -\frac{U_0}{a}e^\xi(1 + e^\xi)^{-2}$$

so

$$f(r) = -\frac{U_0}{a}\frac{e^{(r - r_0)/a}}{(1 + e^{(r - r_0)/a})^2}$$

The force is radially inward, with a maximum value near $r = r_0$; it vanishes both at the origin and far away from the nucleus.

Increasing the parameter a broadens and depresses the maximum in the attractive force from this potential. In the usual application of this potential model, a is an index of the "softness" or "fuzziness" of the nuclear potential well, and so is somehow connected to the range of nuclear forces.

CHAPTER 9
Conservation of Energy

9.1 CHAPTER SUMMARY

We have defined potential and kinetic energy in such a way that the sum
of the two remains constant, for a body acted on by conservative forces.
This principle of <u>conservation of energy</u> is one of the most important in
all physics, even though in any real macroscopic situation nonconservative forces are always present. The dissipation of macroscopic mechanical
energy in such a case is accompanied by an increase of internal energy -
of kinetic and potential energy on a microscopic scale. An increase in
the energy of a given system can always be associated with a corresponding
input of energy in some form from the surroundings. In short, the idea
of conservation of energy can be made quite general.

We limit ourselves for the present to cases of conservation of macroscopic mechanical energy, $E = E_k + U$. If nonconservative forces act,
it is useful to rewrite the work-energy theorem in the form

$$\Delta E = W_{nc} = \int \vec{F}_{nc} \cdot d\vec{s}$$

as the conservative forces are accounted for in the potential-energy
function. If in a given case no work is done by nonconservative forces,
then $\Delta E = 0$; the total mechanical energy is constant. Notice that since
this principle is derived from Newton's laws, there is no information in
it that cannot be had by directly applying Newton's laws. In most cases
where it can be applied at all, however, conservation of energy is a
much more convenient approach.

For instance, the total mechanical energy is written explicitly in
terms of the speed and position of a particle:

$$E = E_k + U = \frac{1}{2}mv^2 + U(x)$$

Hence, in a given case, conservation of energy yields the speed as a
function of position directly. (Notice also from this expression that by
differentiating the expression E = constant we get Newton's second law
$F = ma$.) A variety of examples are worked through in the text.

In many situations a great deal of information about the motion of a
particle can be inferred directly from the behavior of the potential-
energy function. Consider the potential-energy diagram sketched below.
$U(x)$ is minimum at $x = x_0$; hence at this position the particle is in
stable equilibrium. Suppose the total energy of the particle is E.
(E is indicated by a horizontal line in the sketch, since it is constant.)
As kinetic energy can only be positive, we always have $E > U$. Thus it
is only possible for the particle to be in the region between x_1 and x_2;

in fact, it must oscillate back and forth between these two turning points. If the particle is given a larger total energy E', it oscillates between the wider limits indicated.

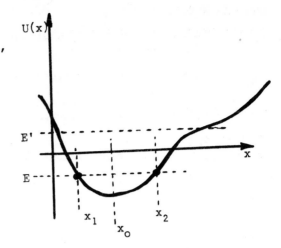

This is a bound system, as is, for instance, a mass on the end of a spring: the particle oscillates with an amplitude which increases with increasing energy. Certain systems become unbound for sufficiently large total energy - that is, one or both turning points become infinitely distant. For instance, a particle at the surface of the earth is unbound if its speed is greater than the escape velocity $v_e = \sqrt{2gR_e}$; at lower speeds, it is bound and will eventually fall back to earth. On a microscopic scale, ionization of an atom or dissociation of a molecule are analogous situations; if given sufficient extra energy - the "binding energy" - above the equilibrium value, the system becomes unbound.

If we apply conservation of energy to the nonviscous flow of an incompressible fluid, we find the expression

$$P + \rho gy + \frac{1}{2}\rho v^2 = \text{constant}$$

throughout the fluid. ρ is the density, and y the vertical height; thus the second and third terms are identifiable as gravitational potential energy and kinetic energy, respectively, per unit volume, and the expression can be read as relating the change in mechanical energy of the fluid to the force arising from differences in the pressure P. This is Bernoulli's equation; for a fluid at rest (v = 0) it reduces to Archimedes' principle.

9.2 CHECK LIST

potential energy
kinetic energy
total mechanical energy
conservation of energy
conservative and nonconservative forces
internal energy
simple pendulum
Atwood's machine
potential-energy diagram
bound and unbound systems

turning points
equilibrium point
oscillation
escape velocity
binding energy
ionization
dissociation
Bernoulli's equation
incompressible fluid
Archimedes' principle

9.3   TRUE OR FALSE?

_____1. The different forms of energy are conserved independently in all physical processes.

_____2. The total mechanical energy of a bound system is negative.

_____3. A body of mass 2m requires only half as much speed to escape the earth as does a body of mass m.

_____4. A body of mass 2m requires twice the momentum to escape the earth as does a body of mass m.

_____5. If a body is acted on only by conservative forces, its total mechanical energy is constant.

_____6. In most real phenomena, total mechanical energy is not conserved.

_____7. A change in the total mechanical energy of a system can always be accounted for by the appearance or disappearance of energy somewhere else or in some other form.

_____8. The work-energy theorem can be restated in the form: the work done on a system by nonconservative forces is equal to the change in its total mechanical energy.

_____9. The mechanical energy of a simple pendulum contains potential-energy terms representing the force of gravity and the force of the supporting spring.

_____10. If total mechanical energy were conserved exactly, a pendulum would swing forever.

_____11. Conservation of mechanical energy allows the solution of many problems which cannot be treated at all using Newton's laws of motion.

_____12. Newton's second law of motion, for a one-dimensional problem, can be derived from conservation of energy.

_____13. "Turning points" are points at which the potential energy is a maximum or minimum.

_____14. A mass oscillating on the end of a spring is an example of an unbound system.

_____15. The earth and the moon, taken together, are an example of a bound system.

_____16. The escape velocity from the earth is that velocity which gives a particle at the surface of the earth a zero total energy.

_____17. For a satellite orbiting the earth the kinetic energy is twice the magnitude of the potential energy.

_____18. The dissociation of a molecule into its component atoms is called ionization.

_____19. A maximum in the potential energy of a particle is a point of stable equilibrium.

_____20. The binding energy of a bound system is that energy which must be supplied by an external agency in order to cause the system to become unbound.

_____21. Bernoulli's theorem is simply conservation of energy applied to the motion of a nonviscous incompressible fluid.

_____22. Bernoulli's principle breaks down for a viscous fluid.

_____23. For a fluid at rest, Bernoulli's theorem reduces to Archimedes' principle.

_____24. If an incompressible fluid flows through a level pipe with a constriction in it, the pressure in the fluid is greater in the constricted section.

9.4   QUESTIONS

1.   A bicyclist is pedaling downhill; because he is moving into a strong headwind, he moves at constant speed. Discuss briefly what is happening to energy of various forms in this situation.

2.   The diagram at right represents the potential energy of a particle in some one-dimensional motion. If the total energy of the particle is 19 J, describe its motion.

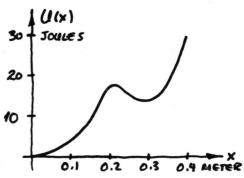

3.   A spring with a force constant of 400 N/m is compressed 5 cm. (a) What potential energy is stored in the spring? (b) If the ends of the compressed spring are tied together and it is dissolved in a vat of acid, what happens to the stored potential energy?

4.   A disk rolls, without slipping, down an incline; it will take longer to reach the bottom than will an object sliding, without friction, down an incline of the same slope. How come?

5.   In a potential-energy diagram, how would one represent a perfectly rigid wall?

6.   A certain planet has the same density - assumed uniform - but half again the diameter of the earth. What is its escape velocity?

7.   An object slides down a rough incline, hits a spring, and bounces back up the slope to half the height from which it started. What has happened to the lost potential energy?

8.   In a real pipe the fluid pressure drops downstream, even if the pipe is straight and level and the fluid incompressible. Why?

9.5   EXAMPLES

1.   A certain ball loses 20% of its kinetic energy when it bounces from the floor. At what speed must it be thrown down from a height of 6 ft to bounce back to the same height?

2.   A block of mass 0.2 kg is dropped, from a height of 0.6 m, onto a vertically mounted spring. The spring's force constant is 380 N/m. What is the maximum distance by which the spring is compressed?

3.   An object is projected somehow from the moon directly toward the earth. What is the minimum possible speed with which it can strike the earth? The radius of the earth R_e = 6.38 x 10^6 m, its mass M_e = 5.98 x 10^{24} kg. The gravitational constant G = 6.67 x 10^{-11} N-m^2/kg^2. The mass of the moon is 0.0123 M_e, and its distance (center-to-center) from the earth is 60.2 R_e.

4. A boy slides on a sled down a hill 3.6 m high and 18 m long. The mass of boy and sled together is 40 kg. Assume that friction exerts a constant force on him as he slides. If he reaches the bottom of the hill with a speed of 6.3 m/sec, what was the magnitude of the frictional force?

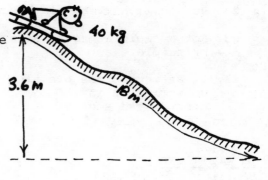

5. A small hole, 1 m above the ground, is punched in the wall of a large water tank. Water squirts out horizontally from the hole and strikes the ground a distance 2.5 m away from the wall of the tank. How deep is the water in the tank?

9.6 ANSWERS

True or False?

1. False - the total is what is conserved.

2. True - in the usual way of defining the potential energy, which is to call it zero at infinite separation; strictly speaking, it is arbitrary.

3. False - the escape speed is independent of the mass.

4. True - twice as much mass and the same escape velocity.

5. True - this is the basic form of the law of conservation of mechanical energy.

6. True - in macroscopic phenomena, at least, there are always nonconservative forces present to some degree.

7. True - so far as we know, the conservation of energy in all its forms is completely general.

8. True - the change of kinetic energy due to conservative forces is accounted for by the potential-energy change.

9. False - the supporting string does no work, need not be included.

10. True - in reality its mechanical energy is dissipated by nonconservative forces.

11. False - conservation of mechanical energy is a method of applying Newton's laws and is derived from them.

12. True.

13. False - they are points at which the kinetic energy vanishes.

14. False - its motion is bounded, for any finite value of its total energy.

15. True - the moon has not enough kinetic energy to escape the earth's gravity.

16. True - since in the usual way of formulating potential energy it is zero at infinite separation.

17. False - the other way around.

18. False - ionization is the gain or loss of electrons by an atom.

19. False - it is a point of equilibrium, but unstable.

20. True.

21. True.

22. True - viscosity is internal friction in the fluid.

23. True.

24. False - it is smaller in the constricted section, because it is moving faster there.

Questions

1. He has a constant speed, therefore a constant kinetic energy. He is doing work, putting mechanical energy into the system, by pedaling, and as he moves downhill his gravitational potential energy is decreasing. Both his work input and his potential energy are being dissipated by friction in the bicycle mechanism and the viscous drag of the air through which he moves.

2. Include the value of the total energy in the potential-energy diagram as sketched. Suppose the particle is at $x = 0$ moving in the $+x$ direction. As it does so it decelerates; its kinetic energy $E - U$ is decreasing. Its speed reaches a minimum at $x = 0.21$ m; in fact, with slightly less energy, there would be a turning point near this value. Thereafter it is accelerated to a maximum speed near 0.30 m, then decelerated until brought to rest at $x = 0.35$ m. It then recoils back in the other direction.

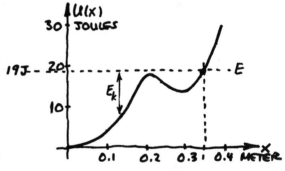

3. (a) Its potential energy $\frac{1}{2}kx^2 = \frac{1}{2}(400 \text{ N/m})(0.05 \text{ m})^2 = 0.5$ J.
(b) The vat of acid-and-dissolved-spring would end up at a slightly higher temperature than if the same spring had been dissolved uncompressed. The stored potential energy is an extra contribution to the internal energy of the final system.

4. The same amount of potential energy is transformed into the same amount of kinetic energy. However, in the case of the rolling disk, some of the kinetic energy is involved in the disk's rotation about its axis, leaving less for translation down the plane. This point is discussed more thoroughly in Chapter 10.

5. At the appropriate position, by a straight vertical curve of infinite height. Any slope of the potential curve would represent yielding of the wall.

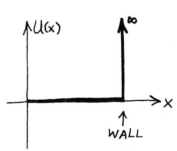

6. The escape velocity is

$$v_e = \sqrt{2gR_e} = \sqrt{2GM_e/R_e}$$

but if the density is ρ,

$$M_e = \rho V = \rho \frac{4\pi}{3} R_e^3$$

if the density is uniform; so

$$v_e = \sqrt{8\pi G\rho R_e^3/3R_e} = \sqrt{8\pi G\rho/3}\ R_e$$

For given density, v_e is proportional to the radius of the planet; in this case it would be 50% bigger than that of the earth.

7. It has been dissipated by work done by nonconservative forces; in this case, the friction of the incline.

8. Because energy is dissipated - a real pipe with a real fluid in it is not a frictionless system. A pressure differential is needed to drive the fluid through at constant speed.

Examples

Partial Solutions (1)

1. This problem is a simple application of conservation of energy. Do it in two stages - because you need to know the kinetic energy at the moment it bounces to evaluate the energy loss. Except for the moment it bounces, everything is conservative.

2. The forces that act on the thing are the restoring force of the spring (when it is compressed) and gravity. Both are conservative forces, so we can apply conservation of energy directly. Don't overlook the fact that there are two contributions to the potential energy of the block.

3. The only force that acts on the object is gravity - which is conservative - but the gravity of both earth and moon. Its potential energy is therefore

$$U = -\frac{GM_e m}{r} - \frac{GM_m m}{R - r} = -GM_e m\left(\frac{1}{r} + \frac{0.0123}{R - r}\right)$$

on the line between earth and moon, at a distance r from the earth. What does this potential-energy function look like? In particular, why should the object's speed on reaching the earth have a minimum possible value?

4. There is a nonconservative force - friction - acting on the sled; so mechanical energy isn't conserved. We can, though, use the work-energy theorem in the form

$$\Delta E = W_{nc}$$

5. Apply Bernoulli's theorem to the top surface of the water and to the hole in the wall. What is the pressure at these two points?

Partial Solutions (2)

1. Write conservation of energy between (1) the moment the block is thrown, and (2) the moment it strikes the ground. If it is thrown at speed v_0,

$$U_1 + E_{k1} = mgh + \frac{1}{2}mv_0^2 = U_2 + E_{k2} = \frac{1}{2}mv^2$$

if it strikes the ground with speed v. What is its energy on the way back up?

2. Write conservation of energy between (1) the initial position, and (2) the moment at which the spring, at maximum compression, stops the block. The point is that at both these moments the block is (instantaneously) at rest. Since at these two points $E_k = 0$ and total mechanical energy is conserved, the potential energy of the block must be the same at (1) and (2).

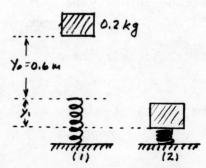

3. The potential energy is maximum at some
    intermediate position $r = r_0$, as in the
    sketch. If it moves from the moon to
    the earth, it must pass this point, but
    that is not possible unless its total
    energy is at least equal to U_0 since
    E_k cannot be negative. But this means
    the object's speed v on reaching the
    earth cannot be less than that given by

    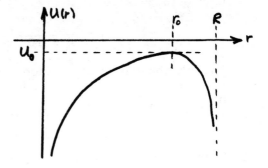

$$E = U(R_e) + \tfrac{1}{2}mv^2 = U_0$$

To find r_0 and U_0, solve for the value
of r at which dU/dr is equal to zero.

4. Since the frictional force is assumed constant and always opposes the
    motion, the work done by it is

$$W_{nc} = -f(18 \text{ m})$$

so this must be the amount by which the total energy has decreased
as the sled moves from the top to the bottom of the hill.

5. Let (1) refer to the top surface of the water, (2) to the hole in the
    wall. As both points are in contact with the atmosphere, $P_1 = P_2 =
    P_{atm}$. We can infer v_2 from the trajectory of the water that squirts
    out. On the assumptions of the problem, what can we say about v_1?

Partial Solutions (3)

1. At the moment after it bounces, we know that its kinetic energy is
    20% less than the moment before:

$$E_k' = (0.8)(\tfrac{1}{2}mv^2) = (0.8)(mgh + \tfrac{1}{2}mv_0^2)$$

It rises back to the point where all this kinetic energy is transformed
to potential energy (that is, until it stops). If this happens at
the height from which it was thrown,

$$(0.8)(mgh + \tfrac{1}{2}mv_0^2) = mgh$$

or

$$v_0^2 = \tfrac{1}{2}gh \qquad v_0 = \sqrt{(0.5)(32 \text{ ft/sec}^2)\ (6 \text{ ft})} = \underline{9.80 \text{ ft/sec}}$$

2. At point (2), the spring is compressed; this must be included in the
    potential energy. Thus we get (taking $U = 0$ at the top of the spring)

$$U_1 = mgy_0 = U_2 = mg(-y_1) + \tfrac{1}{2}ky_1^2$$

$$(0.2 \text{ kg})(9.8 \text{ m/sec}^2)(0.6 \text{ m}) = (0.2 \text{ kg})(9.8 \text{ m/sec}^2)(-y_1) = \tfrac{1}{2}(380 \text{ N/m})(y_1^2)$$

or

$$y_1^2 - (0.0103 \text{ m})y_1 - (0.0619 \text{ m}^2) = 0$$

This quadratic has two solutions; we want the one with $y_1 > 0$, so
$\underline{y_1 = 0.084 \text{ m}}$.

3. We find for the point of maximum potential energy

$$r_0 = \frac{R}{1 + \sqrt{M_m/M_e}} = 0.900R = 54.2R_e = 3.50 \times 10^8 \text{ m}$$

and plug this in to find the maximum value of U:

69

$U_0 = -(6.67 \times 10^{-11} \text{ N-m}^2/\text{kg}^2)(5.98 \times 10^{24} \text{ kg})(m)$

$$\left[\frac{1}{3.50 \times 10^8 \text{ m}} + \frac{0.0123}{0.39 \times 10^8 \text{ m}}\right] = -(1.27 \times 10^6 \text{ J/kg})(m)$$

But at the earth's surface $(r = R_e = 6.38 \times 10^6 \text{ m})$

$U(R_e) = -(6.67 \times 10^{-11} \text{ N-m}^2/\text{kg}^2)(5.98 \times 10^{24} \text{ kg})(m)$

$$x\left(\frac{1}{6.38 \times 10^6 \text{ m}} + \frac{0.0123}{3.82 \times 10^8 \text{ m}}\right) = -(6.25 \times 10^7 \text{ J/kg})(m)$$

Thus, from energy conservation, the minimum speed at the earth is given by

$$-(6.25 \times 10^7 \text{ J/kg})(m) + \frac{1}{2}mv_e^2 = -(1.27 \times 10^6 \text{ J/kg})(m)$$

which yields $v_e = 1.11 \times 10^4$ m/sec.

4. At the top, initially, $v = 0$ and $E = U = mgh = (40 \text{ kg})(9.8 \text{ m/sec}^2) \times (3.6 \text{ m}) = 1411$ J. At the bottom we call $U = 0$ so $E = E_k = \frac{1}{2}mv^2 = \frac{1}{2}(40 \text{ kg})(6.3 \text{ m/sec})^2 = 794$ J, so

$$\Delta E = 794 - 1411 = -617 \text{ J} = W_{nc} = -f(18 \text{ m})$$

which gives

$$f = \frac{617 \text{ J}}{18 \text{ m}} = 34.3 \text{ N}$$

5. Since the hole in the wall is small, continuity gives $v_2 \gg v_1$. Neglecting v_1 leaves us with

$$\rho g(y_1 - y_2) = \frac{1}{2}\rho v_2^2$$

The water squirting out travels 2.5 m in the time it takes it to fall 1 m under gravity. Thus

$$t = \sqrt{2y_2/g} = 0.452 \text{ sec} = \frac{2.5 \text{ m}}{v_2}$$

so $v_2 = 5.53$ m/sec. From the above, then,

$$y_1 - y_2 = \frac{(5.53 \text{ m/sec})^2}{(2)(9.80 \text{ m/sec}^2)} = 1.56 \text{ m}$$

or, finally, the water depth is $y_1 = 2.56$ m.

CHAPTER 10
Many-Particle Systems

10.1 CHAPTER SUMMARY

Up to this point, everything we have said deals with the mechanics of particles, or of objects small enough to be approximated as particles. We will now begin developing some tools for treating the collective behavior of an arbitrary system of particles. Notice that an extended continuous body may also be treated as a system of particles, in this sense.

An essential point is the behavior of the center of mass of such a system. Call the mass of the "i^{th}" particle m_i, and its location relative to some coordiante system the position vector $\vec{r}_i$. Then we define the center of mass as the point located by

$$\vec{R}_{cm} \equiv \frac{1}{M}(m_1\vec{r}_1 + m_2\vec{r}_2 + \cdots + m_i\vec{r}_i + \cdots)$$

where $M = m_1 + m_2 + \cdots + m_i + \cdots$ is the total mass of the system. The center of mass is a sort of average position of all the system's mass; notice that it is not necessarily located at the position of any particle of the system. If a given system has any plane or axis of symmetry, the center of mass will be located on it. If, instead of discrete particles, we consider a continuous body, the sum is evaluated as an integral:

$$\vec{R}_{cm} \equiv \frac{1}{M} \int \vec{r} \; dm$$

where dm is the mass of an element of the body located at $\vec{r}$.

The reason for all this is that the motion of the system's center of mass is particularly easy to describe. Differentiating the expression for $\vec{R}_{cm}$ gives

$$M\vec{V}_{cm} = \vec{P}$$

The total momentum of the system is just that of a particle, having the total mass M, moving with the center of mass. Differentiating again gives

$$M\vec{A}_{cm} = \frac{d\vec{P}}{dt} = \vec{F}_{ext}$$

where $\vec{F}_{ext}$ is the (vector) total of all external forces on particles of the system. (By Newton's third law, the forces exerted by one particle of the system on another must all cancel out when we add up the total.) But this last is just the equation of motion - Newton's second law - as it would read for a single particle of mass M, acted on by the total external force $\vec{F}_{ext}$ on the system. Thus, whatever the messy details of the motion of various parts of the system, its center of mass simply moves as a point particle, acted on by the net external force on the system. (In fact, this has been our excuse for treating extended bodies as point particles up to now.)

A case of particular importance is that of a system on which the net external force is zero. Then plainly $d\vec{P}/dt$ vanishes, and so in this case

$$\vec{P} = M\vec{V}_{cm} = constant$$

This is the law of conservation of momentum. Notice that it is, in a way, more general than the law of conservation of mechanical energy; the total momentum of an isolated system is constant regardless of the nature of the internal forces.

Another way to say this is that the center of mass of an isolated system - one on which no net external force acts - moves at constant velocity. It is often convenient to look at such cases with respect to an (inertial) frame of reference that moves with the center of mass; in this "center-of-mass" reference frame, plainly the total momentum of the system is zero. If a particular problem is more naturally described in terms of some other frame of reference, we can transform results from the center-of-mass frame simply by adding $\vec{V}_{cm}$ to the velocity of everything.

The total kinetic energy of a system is not necessarily constant, even if P is; internal forces may act to change E_k. We can state a very useful theorem concerning the total kinetic energy:

$$E_k = \frac{1}{2}MV_{cm}^2 + E_{kr}$$

Here, E_{kr} is the total kinetic energy of the system relative to the center of mass - that is, as calculated in the center-of-mass reference frame. If the system is an isolated one, then $\vec{V}_{cm}$ is constant, and only the relative-motion part E_{kr} of the system's total kinetic energy can change in whatever motions it may undergo. We will make use of this theorem in many situations in the next chapters.

10.2 CHECK LIST

center of mass   center-of-mass reference frame
external force   zero-momentum reference frame
internal force   center-of-mass kinetic energy
momentum   relative kinetic energy
conservation of momentum

10.3 TRUE OR FALSE?

_____1. Newton's laws and the other theorems of mechanics that have been discussed thus far apply only to the motion of particles.

_____2. The general motion of a system of particles is that of a particle having the whole mass of the system, acted on by the total force on it.

_____3. The center of mass of a system of particles is located on the particle nearest the geometric center of the system.

____4. The center of mass of a system consisting of just two particles lies on the line joining them, midway between them.

____5. The total momentum of a system of particles is its total mass multiplied by the velocity of the center of mass.

____6. Internal forces in a system of particles are those exerted by one particle of the system on another.

____7. The action of internal forces does not change the total momentum of a system.

____8. The motion of the center of mass of a system of particles is that of a particle having the whole mass of the system, acted on by the total external force on it.

____9. The theorem of the previous question permits us to treat an extended object approximately as a particle; what we are really doing is treating the motion of its center of mass.

____10. The center of mass of a circular- or disk-shaped object is necessarily on its central axis.

____11. If a system possesses a plane or an axis of symmetry, the center of mass necessarily lies in that plane or axis.

____12. The total momentum of a system is conserved if and only if all the internal forces vanish.

____13. For a system consisting of two particles only, conservation of momentum is identical with Newton's third law of motion.

____14. The total momentum of a system is conserved if and only if all the internal forces are conservative.

____15. If the momentum of a given system of particles is conserved, its total mechanical energy must be also.

____16. Relative to the center-of-mass frame of reference, the total momentum of a system of particles always vanishes.

____17. To transform from the center of mass to the laboratory reference frame, one just adds the velocity of the center of mass to that of every particle.

____18. The center of mass of an isolated system moves at a constant velocity.

____19. The total mechanical energy of an isolated system cannot increase.

____20. The total kinetic energy of a system can be divided into (a) that of the total mass moving with the velocity of the center of mass, and (b) that of all the particles of the system, moving with respect to the center-of-mass frame.

____21. The "relative-motion" part of the kinetic energy of a system is the same as seen in all frames of reference.

____22. If a rigid body is pivoted at some point, free to swing about the pivot, the center of mass always hangs straight downward.

____23. If a system consists of three point particles in a line, the center of mass is located on the middle one.

____24. The center of mass of a system consisting of several extended objects can be found by treating each as a point particle located at its center of mass.

_____25. The center of mass of a continuous solid body must be in the body.

10.4   QUESTIONS

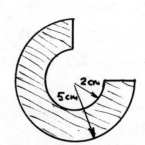

1. In the sketch at right, consider the pulley and the
    two blocks as a system.   What are the internal forces?
    The external forces?

2. In the sketch at right, can you tell in what direction
    the center of mass will accelerate?   Explain.

3. If only external forces can cause acceleration of a
    system as a whole - that is, of its center of mass -
    how can a rocket, isolated in space, move?

4. An object slips without friction down an incline, and a cylinder
    rolls without slipping down an identical incline.   Which reaches
    the bottom faster?   Why?

5. You are presented with a plane solid object of irregular shape.
    What experiments could you perform to locate its center of mass?

6. Can a system have zero kinetic energy and nonzero momentum?   Can it
    have nonzero kinetic energy and zero momentum?

7. A boy sits in one end of a closed railroad car which rolls without
    friction on a level track.   He amuses himself by tossing bowling
    balls to the other end of the car; the balls bounce off and roll
    around and do all sorts of erratic things.   What can you say about
    how far the boy can move the car along its track in this way?

10.5   EXAMPLES

1. An Atwood's machine consists of a 1.5-kg mass and a 2.5-kg mass hung
    by a light string over a frictionless pulley of negligible mass.
    Considering blocks and pulley as a system, show explicitly that the
    resultant external force on the system equals its total mass times
    the acceleration of the center of mass.

2. Two railway cars weighing 40 tons each are rolling along that same
    frictionless track.   The front one is moving at 2.5 ft/sec, the
    rear one overtaking it at 4.0 ft/sec.   The two collide and couple
    together, and continue rolling down the track together.   At what
    speed?   How much kinetic energy disappears in this process?

3. The sketch at right is of an annular disk with
    one quadrant missing.   Locate its center of
    mass by integration, if the disk is of uniform
    density.

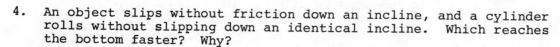

4. A sled of mass 15 kg is at rest on the ground.
    A boy whose mass is 40 kg runs up and jumps on
    the sled at a speed of 7 m/sec.   If the coeffi-
    cient of friction between sled and ground is
    0.23, how far does it slide before coming to rest?

10.6   ANSWERS

True or False?

1. True - strictly speaking; see answer 9 below.

74

2. False - the motion of an arbitrary system is plainly more complex than any motion of a single point particle.

3. False - it depends on the mass of each particle and need not be at the position of any particle of the system.

4. False - it is on the line between them, but where depends on the masses.

5. True - this can be taken as the definition of the center of mass.

6. True.

7. True - because of Newton's third law, the effects of internal forces cancel.

8. True.

9. True.

10. False - this is true if the thing is of uniform density; however, see answer 11.

11. True.

12. False - the internal forces cancel regardless.

13. True.

14. False - the nature of the forces is irrelevant.

15. False - the conservation of mechanical energy does depend on the nature of the forces, internal and external.

16. True - hence the center-of-mass frame is also called the "zero-momentum" frame.

17. True.

18. True - this is an expression of conservation of momentum.

19. False - consider a rocket.

20. True.

21. True - it really has nothing to do with a frame of reference, as it's the total kinetic energy as seen in the center-of-mass frame.

22. True.

23. False - again, it depends on the masses.

24. True.

25. False.

Questions

1. If the system consists of the pulley and the two blocks, the internal forces are those that one of these objects exerts on another - here, by means of the tension in the string by which the blocks hang from the pulley. The external forces are those exerted by outside agencies - here, the spring supporting the pulley and the earth's gravity pulling the whole thing down.

2. You can't tell. The net external force is either upward or downward, depending on how much the spring is stretched.

3. The whole rocket system - its center of mass - doesn't move. Some part of its mass is exhausted backwards at high speed, giving the rest of the rocket a forward momentum.

4. In both cases an identical amount of potential energy is available for conversion to kinetic energy. In the case of the rolling cylinder, however, some of this kinetic energy goes into rotation of the cylinder about its center of mass, leaving less for translation of the center of mass; thus it is slower to move down the incline.

5. Knowing that the center of mass will always hang down, you pivot it at various points:

Or - in principle - you could try balancing the figure horizontally on a pencil point; the point at which it balances is the center of mass.

6. No and yes. If there's momentum, something is moving and there must be kinetic energy. But the total momentum will be zero so long as the center of mass is at rest.

7. Regardless of the details, he can't move it as much as its own length. As the question is stated, the center of mass, which remains at rest, must stay within the length of the railroad card.

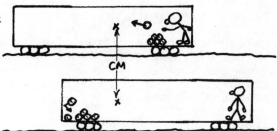

Examples

Partial Solutions (1)

1. The only tricky part about this one is that the force holding the pulley up is an external force on the system, so you need to know it. To find it, draw a free-body diagram for the <u>pulley</u>. The simple Atwood's machine is a problem we've already treated. You'll remember the acceleration is

$$a = \frac{m_1 - m_2}{m_1 + m_2} g$$

of each mass. What is the acceleration of the center of mass?

2. The final speed is found by applying conservation of momentum quite directly. As for how much kinetic energy disappears, how would you describe the <u>relative</u> motion of the two cars after they collide?

3. If you simply try to set this up as a single integration, it is awfully messy. So try to simplify it a little bit first. The figure is symmetric about the line y = x (if it is drawn centered at the origin). What does this tell you about the location of the center of mass?

4. Obviously you want to use conservation of momentum for this - the question is how. Can you apply momentum conservation to the whole process, that is, from before the boy jumps on until after he's stopped?

Partial Solutions (2)

1. The acceleration of each mass is

$$a = \frac{2.5 - 1.5}{2.5 + 1.5} (9.8 \text{ m/sec}^2) = 2.45 \text{ m/sec}^2$$

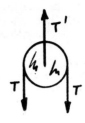

A free-body diagram for the pulley is sketched at the right. Plainly, since the pulley doesn't move, $T' = 2T$. And what is T?

2. The final speed is given by $(m)(2.5 \text{ ft/sec}) + (m)(4.0 \text{ ft/sec}) = (2m)(v)$ or $\underline{v = 3.25 \text{ ft/sec}}$. After the collision, there isn't any relative motion. So how much kinetic energy is lost?

3. Since the center of mass is on the line $x = y$, we know $y_{cm} = x_{cm}$. Now find x_{cm} of one quadrant by integration: the mass of the little slice shown is $dM = (\rho s y) dx$, where s is the thickness of the disk and ρ its density. For y we have, from the diagram,

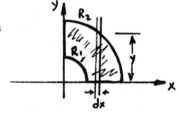

$$y = \sqrt{R_2^2 - x^2} \qquad \text{if } R_1 < x < R$$

or

$$y = \sqrt{R_2^2 - x^2} - \sqrt{R_1^2 - x^2} \qquad \text{if } 0 < x < R_1$$

Set up the integral to find x_{cm}. Now in the figure, there are three such identical quadrants, located as shown at right. What is the center of mass of the whole mess?

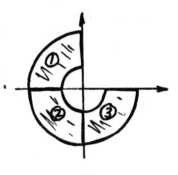

4. No. If the boy and the sled are considered to be "the system," then while they are sliding across the ground there is an external force - friction - on the system in the horizontal direction. You can use conservation of momentum to find his velocity just after jumping on.

Partial Solutions (3)

1. For the heavier mass, Newton's second law gives

$$m_1 a = m_1 g - T$$

so

$$T = m_1 (g - a) = (2.5)(9.80 - 2.45) = 18.38 \text{ N}$$

and $T' = 2T = 36.75 \text{ N}$. The resultant external force on the system is thus

$$F_{ext} = T' - m_1 g - m_2 g$$

$$= 36.75 \text{ N} - (2.5 + 1.5)(9.8) = \underline{-2.45 \text{ N}}$$

The acceleration of the center of mass is

$$a_{cm} = \frac{m_1 a + m_2 a}{m_1 + m_2} = \frac{(2.5)(-2.45) + (1.5)(+2.45)}{(2.5 + 1.5)} = -0.612 \text{ m/sec}^2$$

So $F_{ext} = m_{tot} a_{cm}$ is $-2.45 \text{ N} = (4.0 \text{ kg})(-0.612 \text{ m/sec}^2)$.

2. All the kinetic energy of relative motion is lost - that is, all the kinetic energy relative to the center-of-mass frame. Since each has speed 0.75 ft/sec relative to the center of mass, this is

$$K_r = 2(\tfrac{1}{2}m)(0.75 \text{ ft/sec})^2 = (80,000 \text{ lb/g})(0.75 \text{ ft/sec})^2 = \underline{1410 \text{ ft-lb}}$$

3. The integral is

$$x_{cm} = \frac{1}{M} \int x \; dM = \frac{1}{M} \int_0^{R_1} (x)(\rho s)(\sqrt{R_2^2 - x^2} - \sqrt{R_1^2 - x^2}) \; dx$$

$$+ \frac{1}{M} \int_{R_1}^{R_2} (x)(\rho s) \sqrt{R_2^2 - x^2} \; dx$$

$$= \frac{\rho s}{M} \left(\int_0^{R_2} x\sqrt{R_2^2 - x^2} \; dx - \int_0^{R_1} x\sqrt{R_1^2 - x^2} \; dx \right) = \frac{\rho s}{3M}(R_2^3 - R_1^3)$$

The whole mass of the quadrant is $(\rho)(\frac{1}{4})(\pi R_2^2 - \pi R_1^2)(s)$, so at last

$$x_{cm} = (4/3\pi) \; \frac{R_2^3 - R_1^3}{R_2^2 - R_1^2} = \underline{2.36 \; cm}$$

for $R_1 = 2$ cm and $R_2 = 5$ cm, as given. Now in the whole figure there are three identical quadrants; so for the whole thing

$$x_{cm} = \frac{-2.36 + -2.36 + 2.36}{3} \; cm$$

$$\underline{x_{cm} = y_{cm} = -0.787 \; cm}$$

4. Just after he jumps on we get

$$(40 \; kg)(7 \; m/sec) + (15 \; kg)(0) = (55 \; kg)(v)$$

$$v = \frac{280 \; kg\text{-}m/sec}{55 \; kg} = 5.09 \; m/sec$$

From the given coefficient of friction the force of friction on the sled is

$$f = \mu mg = (0.23)(55 \; kg)(9.8 \; m/sec^2) = 124 \; N$$

If he slides a distance s in coming to a stop, the work-energy theorem gives

$$fs = \frac{1}{2}mv^2$$

so

$$s = \frac{mv^2}{2f} = \frac{(55 \; kg)(5.09 \; m/sec)^2}{(2)(124 \; N)} = \underline{5.75 \; m}$$

CHAPTER 11
Collisions and Reactions

An important special case of the motion of a system of particles is that
of a collision between two bodies: an event in which the two come together and interact strongly over a short time interval. (If the nature
of the bodies is changed in the collision, we speak of it as a reaction.)
Typically the forces that act during the collision are very large.

   We define the impulse of a force, acting during a time Δt, as the
time integral

$$\vec{I} \equiv \int_{\Delta t} \vec{F} \, dt = \Delta \vec{p}$$

That I is equal to the momentum change Δp caused by the force during Δt
follows from Newton's second law. The average value of the force over
the interval Δt is

$$\vec{F}_{av} = \frac{\vec{I}}{\Delta t}$$

In a situation where many collisions occur in succession, the average
force exerted by them is the impulse of each times the rate at which
they occur. An extreme example of this case is the pressure of a gas
on the walls of a container; if there are N gas molecules in a container
of volume V, we find

$$PV = \frac{1}{3}N (mv^2)_{av}$$

This relates molecular properties to the macroscopic state of the gas;
at ordinary temperatures we infer values of several hundred meters per
second for molecular speeds.

   In collision processes the colliding bodies typically interact over
a very short time interval, yet exchange substantial momentum; it follows
that the average external forces on the bodies are negligible by comparison. If this is the case, we may to a good approximation apply conservation of momentum during the collision, even in the presence of external
forces. It is often possible, in fact, to assume that the collision
occurs instantaneously - that the interaction of the two bodies is over
before they have had time to move significantly. This is called the
"impulse approximation."

   Since momentum is conserved, the center of mass of the two bodies
moves at constant velocity through the collision. It follows that only
the relative-motion part of their total kinetic energy can be altered by
their interaction. We distinguish elastic collisions, in which E_{kr} is
unchanged, from inelastic collisions, in which some or all of the relative
kinetic energy is lost.

   Collision problems are most simply discussed in the center-of-mass

reference frame. Consider, for instance, an elastic collision in one
dimension. In the center-of-mass frame, all that happens is that each
body is turned around and goes off with its initial velocity reversed.
In practice we would more likely view the collision in a frame of
reference in which one body is initially at rest and is struck by the
other. The center-of-mass result is transformed to such a frame by
simply adding the appropriate $\vec{V}_{cm}$ to the final velocities in the center-
of-mass frame. Now the collision looks less simple, as some of the
kinetic energy of the incoming body is transferred to the target - all
of it, if the masses of the two are equal - but it is still true that
the <u>relative</u> velocity of the two is simply reversed in a one-dimensional
elastic collision.

The opposite extreme is a perfectly <u>in</u>elastic collision - one in
which <u>all</u> the relative kinetic energy is lost. Here, both bodies are
at rest in the center-of-mass frame after the collision; in another frame
of reference, they stick and move off together with velocity $\vec{V}_{cm}$. Intermediate cases, in which part of E_{kr} disappears in the collision process,
we speak of in terms of a "coefficient of restitution," ε. ε is the
fraction of the initial relative velocity - ε^2 the fraction of the
initial E_{kr} - which remains after the collision. Thus $\varepsilon = 1$ is a
perfectly elastic, $\varepsilon = 0$ a perfectly inelastic, collision.

A collision process in which the motion is not confined to one
dimension is more complicated to analyze because the bodies may come
off in various directions after the collision, depending on the details
of how they collide. It is still simplest to treat the problem in the
center-of-mass frame of reference and then transform the results to a
more natural frame.

A "reaction" is a collision in which the physical or chemical
nature of the colliding bodies is changed. The change may absorb
energy from the system or add energy to it. If the energy release,
Q, is negative, energy must be supplied - part of the initial kinetic
energy of the system - to make the reaction possible; it cannot take
place unless the initial kinetic energy exceeds some "threshold" value.
The threshold condition is

$$E_{kr} \geq |Q|$$

since the center-of-mass motion cannot change during the collision.

11.2 CHECK LIST

collision	perfectly elastic collision
reaction	perfectly inelastic collision
impulse	center-of-mass frame of reference
impulse approximation	laboratory frame of reference
average force	collision time
pressure	moderator

impact parameter   exothermic reaction

ballistic pendulum   endothermic reaction

reaction threshold   impulse of deformation

coefficient of restriction   impulse of restoration

11.3 TRUE OR FALSE?

_____1. A strong interaction between two bodies that form an isolated
         system is called a collision.

_____2. A collision in which the nature of the colliding bodies is
         changed is called a reaction.

_____3. The impulse of a force is a measure of its maximum value during
         a collision.

_____4. The impulse of a force measures the change of momentum which it
         causes.

_____5. Impulse is a vector quantity whose direction is that of the
         resultant momentum change.

_____6. Typically, in a collision process, a force of moderate size acting
         over a very short time interval produces a very large impulse.

_____7. The impulse of a force over an interval Δt can be considered as
         the average value of the force multiplied by Δt.

_____8. The pressure exerted by a given number of gas molecules on the
         walls of their container depends only on the average kinetic
         energy of the molecules.

_____9. The pressure of a gas arises from occasional gas molecules
         bouncing off the walls of the container.

_____10. The average speed of molecules of a gas, under ordinary conditions,
         is found to be of the order of the speed of sound in the gas.

_____11. The "impulse approximation" consists of ignoring collision
         forces because they act over a very short time interval.

_____12. Typically, in the impulse approximation, conservation of momentum
         can be applied to collision processes despite the presence of
         external forces.

_____13. In a collision, the part of the total kinetic energy associated
         with the center-of-mass motion does not change.

_____14. A collision in which the collision forces are conservative is
         perfectly elastic.

_____15. In a perfectly inelastic collision, all the kinetic energy of
         the colliding particles is lost.

_____16. The zero-momentum reference frame is that in which the incoming
         particle is at rest.

_____17. In a perfectly elastic collision in one dimension, all that
         happens is that the relative velocity of the two particles is
         reversed.

_____18. After a perfectly inelastic collision, both particles are at
         rest in the laboratory frame of reference.

_____19. The coefficient of restitution ε is the fraction of the kinetic energy of relative motion which survives a partially inelastic collision.

_____20. In a perfectly elastic one-dimensional collision, the kinetic energy transferred to the target particle is greatest if its mass is much less than that of the incident particle.

_____21. Moderation of neutrons occurs by their losing mechanical energy in repeated partially inelastic collisions.

_____22. In general, in a perfectly elastic collision, considered in the center-of-mass frame, all that happens is that the initial velocities are reversed.

_____23. A collision in which the two colliding objects stick and, after the collision, move off together is perfectly inelastic.

_____24. In a perfectly elastic collision in three dimensions, in which one of the colliding bodies is initially at rest, the final velocities are at right angles to one another.

_____25. A reaction is a collision between microscopic bodies such as atoms.

_____26. A reaction in which an incoming particle ionizes a target atom is an example of an exothermic reaction.

_____27. The threshold energy for an endothermic reaction, in the laboratory frame, is equal to the magnitude of the Q value.

_____28. If the impulse of deformation equals the impulse of restitution, the collision is elastic.

11.4 QUESTIONS

1. Consider a perfectly elastic collision in one dimension, in the extreme case in which the incident particle is very much more massive. In this extreme what happens is that the incident particle continues with its speed virtually unaltered while the target rebounds forward with twice this speed. Doesn't this violate conservation of (kinetic) energy?

2. You are dribbling a basketball up and down repeatedly on the floor. In terms of conservation of momentum, what is happening? Does the earth recoil?

3. In terms of the kinetic model of a gas, explain briefly why the pressure in a gas increases if the volume of its container is decreased.

4. A bowling ball hits a pin which is initially at rest. The collision is partially inelastic. Is it possible that after the collision both ball and pin are at rest?

5. Consider the nuclear reaction $p + H^3 \rightleftarrows H^2 + H^2$. If protons are incident on H^3 as a target, the kinetic energy required to make this reaction take place is 5.37 MeV; however, if H^3 is incident on protons (ordinary hydrogen) as a target, the threshold energy is 16.1 MeV. Explain the difference.

6. A bat strikes a baseball (mass 0.2 kg) with a force of 900 N which lasts only 4 msec. With what velocity does the ball leave the bat?

11.5 EXAMPLES

1. A machine gun fires 12-gm bullets at a rate of 150 per minute, with
   a speed of 550 m/sec. The bullets strike a sheet of armor plate
   and rebound elastically. What is the (average) force exerted on the
   sheet?

2. A meteoroid of mass 1.6×10^8 kg passes the earth at a speed of
   1.09×10^7 m/sec (the mass of the earth is 5.98×10^{24} kg). Its
   initial direction is along a line whose closest approach to the
   earth's surface is 10^6 m. Assume, as an approximation, that the
   interaction does not change the direction of the meteoroid and that
   it happens so fast that the earth does not move by an appreciable
   amount during the encounter. What momentum is transferred to the
   earth by the encounter?

3. In the sketch, masses m_1 and m_2 collide on
   a frictionless tabletop. After the collision, m_2 - which was initially at rest -
   collides elastically with a wall and bounds
   back. Under what conditions will m_1 and m_2
   collide again?

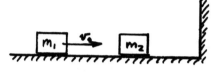

4. A heavy ball (weight 12 lb) hits a 160-lb man in the chest and bounds
   directly back at a speed of 2 ft/sec. If its initial speed was
   20 ft/sec, find (a) the speed imparted to the man, (b) the coefficient
   of restitution of the collision.

5. Two objects move without friction in a horizontal plane - an idealized
   billiard table, for instance. One is initially at rest when the
   other collides with it. After the collision their directions of
   motion are at right angles to one another. Find the ratio of their
   masses.

11.6 ANSWERS

True or False?

1. False - we need to specify that it happens in a short time interval;
   the interaction of the earth and moon wouldn't be called a collision,
   for instance.

2. True.

3. False - it is the time integral of the force over the collision
   interval.

4. True.

5. True.

6. False - typically very large forces act in collision processes.

7. True - see answer 3.

8. False - it depends on the volume of the container also.

9. True.

10. True.

11. False - it consists of assuming the interaction happens in a very
    short time interval.

12. True.

13. True.

14. True.

15. False - all of the realtive-motion part of the kinetic energy is lost.

16. False - it is another name for the center-of-mass frame.

17. True.

18. False - both are at rest in the center-of-mass frame, but in the laboratory continue to move with the velocity of the center of mass.

19. False - but close; this is ε^2, ε measures the fraction of the relative velocity that remains.

20. False - maximum kinetic energy is transferred if they are of equal mass.

21. False - by transferring some energy in repeated elastic collisions.

22. False - in general; in three dimensions this is generally not what happens.

23. True.

24. False - not necessarily, it depends on the masses; see example 5.

25. False - see answer 2.

26. False - this would require an energy input, hence is endothermic.

27. False - this is true in the center-of-mass frame.

28. True.

Questions

1. No; the incoming particle doesn't continue with precisely its incoming velocity, but the kinetic energy transferred to the very much less massive target particle has a very small effect.

2. The simple way to think of this is to consider that you are attached to the earth. In fact, the sequence of events by which upward momentum imparted to you is transferred to the earth is messy, because you're not a rigid object. But then all that is happening is that the ball is bouncing up and down off of different parts of the earth, and the downward momentum that it imparts to the earth is canceled by the upward momentum it transfers to you. The center of mass of the whole mess - you, ball, and earth - can't move.

3. For a given molecular speed, collisions with the walls will be more frequent if the dimensions of the container are reduced. Thus the rate at which momentum is transferred to the walls - the force of the gas on the walls - increases.

4. No, the velocity of their center of mass can't change in the collision.

5. Because only the relative-motion part of the initial kinetic energy is available to make the reaction go. Since the center of mass is more nearly tied to the heavier particle, a larger fraction of the initial kinetic energy is involved in center-of-mass motion when it is the heavier particle which is moving. (In both cases the kinetic energy of relative motion is 4.03 MeV.)

6. The impulse is F Δt = (900 N)(4 x 10^{-3} sec) = 3.6 N-sec = 3.6 kg-m/sec.

This must be equal to the momentum transferred to the ball; its speed is therefore (3.6 kg-m/sec)(0.2 kg) = 18 m/sec. It wasn't hit very hard.

Examples

Partial Solutions (1)

1. What momentum is transferred to the sheet of armor by each bullet? How is this different from the case in which the bullets are stopped by the target?

2. This is a rather messy problem, but it serves to illustrate the usefulness of the approximation that the interaction "happens all at once;" done exactly it is very much messier. In the diagram, what is the component of the gravitational force in the y direction? (What happens in the x direction doesn't matter; the negative impulse before the meteor passes and the positive impulse after, cancel out, just by symmetry.) What is the impulse of the force?

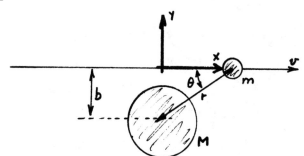

3. Mass m_2 is given some velocity v_2 in the first collision and has velocity v_2' after bouncing off the wall. Under what circumstances will they collide again?

4. Find the speed imparted to the man by conservation of momentum - this applies whether the collision is elastic or not. What is a coefficient of restitution, anyway?

5. There is a trick which will make this one a lot easier; since you know that the final velocities are at right angles, set them up along the coordinate axes. You can certainly use conservation of momentum. Is the total kinetic energy conserved?

Partial Solutions (2)

1. The momentum transferred by one bullet is, since it bounces back,

    $$\Delta p = (mv) - (-mv) = 2mv = (2)(0.012 \text{ kg})(550 \text{ m/sec})$$

    $$= 13.2 \text{ kg-m/sec}$$

    twice what it would be if the bullet was just stopped. What is the total rate at which momentum is transferred to the target?

2. The component of the force in the y direction is (see preceding diagram)

    $$F_y = -F \sin \theta = -\frac{GMm}{r^2}\frac{b}{r} = -\frac{GMmb}{r^3}$$

    and note that $r = \sqrt{x^2 + b^2}$. The impulse of the force, which will be equal to the momentum transfer, is

    $$\int F_y \, dt = \Delta p$$

    Set up and work out the integral and you're done.

3. After the first collision

    $$v_2 = \frac{2m_1}{m_1 + m_2} \qquad\qquad v = \frac{m_1 - m_2}{m_1 + m_2}$$

From the sketch at right, the two will collide again if $v_2' > -v_1$. What is v_2'?

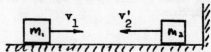

4. The man's speed of recoil is v, given by

$$(12 \text{ lb/g})(20 \text{ ft/sec}) = (12 \text{ lb/g})(-2 \text{ ft/sec}) + (160 \text{ lb/g})(v)$$

so

$$v = \frac{240 + 24}{165} = \underline{1.65 \text{ ft/sec}}$$

One way to define the coefficient of restitution is as the fraction of the initial relative speed which remains after the collision.

5. From the diagram at right, conservation of momentum gives (x and y components)

$$m_1 v_0 \cos \theta = m_1 v_1$$

$$m_1 v_0 \sin \theta = m_2 v_2$$

Since the collision is given to be elastic, the total kinetic energy is also the same before and after:

$$\frac{1}{2} m_1 v_0^2 = \frac{1}{2} m_1 v_1^2 + \frac{1}{2} m_2 v_2^2$$

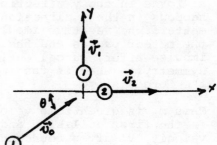

Partial Solutions (3)

1. 150 bullets per minute, or 2.5 per second, strike the sheet, so the interval between collisions is $\Delta t = 0.4$ sec, and

$$\frac{\Delta p}{\Delta t} = \frac{13.2 \text{ kg-m/sec}}{0.4 \text{ sec}} = \underline{3.3 \text{ N}}$$

2. The integral is

$$\Delta p = \int F_y \, dt = \int F_y \, (dx/v) = \frac{GMmb}{v} \int_{-\infty}^{\infty} \frac{dx}{(b^2 + x^2)^{3/2}}$$

The integral is a standard form - you do it by substitution or look it up in a table. We get for the momentum transfer

$$\Delta p = \frac{2GMm}{bv}$$

Which, with the numbers given, is

$$\Delta p = \frac{(2)(6.67 \times 10^{-11} \text{ N-m}^2/\text{kg}^2)(5.98 \times 10^{24} \text{ kg})(1.6 \times 10^8 \text{ kg})}{(7.56 \times 10^6 \text{ m})(1.09 \times 10^7 \text{ m/sec})}$$

$$= \underline{1.55 \times 10^9 \text{ kg-m/sec}}$$

This is very much smaller than the initial momentum of the meteor, which is more or less what justifies the approximations we've made.

3. Since we are given that m_2 bounces off the wall elastically, $v_2' = v_2$ and we get

$$\frac{2m_1}{m_1 + m_2} > -\frac{m_1 - m_2}{m_1 + m_2}$$

which is just $2m_1 > m_2 - m_1$ or $3m_1 > m_2$; that is, they will collide if m_1/m_2 is $\underline{\text{larger than } 1/3}$.

4. Before the collision, the relative speed of the two objects is 20 ft/sec. Afterward, it is (1.65 ft/sec) - (-2 ft/sec) = 3.65 ft/sec. Thus ε = 3.65/20 = $\underline{0.182}$.

5. Square the two conservation-of-momentum equations, add them, and divide out m_1 to get

$$v_0^2 = v_1^2 + (m_2/m_1)^2 v_2^2$$

and divide out m_1 from the kinetic-energy equation to get

$$v_0^2 = v_1^2 + (m_2/m_1) v_2^2$$

Subtracting these two equations gives $(m_2/m_1)^2 = (m_2/m_1)$ or $\underline{m_2 = m_1}$.

CHAPTER 12
Rotation of a Rigid Body about a Fixed Axis

12.1 CHAPTER SUMMARY

Another important special case of the motion of a system of particles is that of a rigid body. The most general motion of a rigid body can be considered as the motion of its center of mass - which depends only on the net external force on it - combined with an arbitrary rotation <u>about</u> the center of mass. Here we consider the simpler case of rotation about a <u>fixed</u> axis.

Although, in such a rotation, different parts of the body are in motion at different speeds and in different directions, every particle rotates through the same <u>angle</u> in a given time interval. We thus describe the motion of the rotating body in terms of an <u>angular</u> velocity

$$\omega \equiv \frac{d\theta}{dt}$$

and an angular acceleration

$$\alpha \equiv \frac{d\omega}{dt} = \frac{d^2\theta}{dt^2}$$

A particle at a distance r from the axis of rotation is moving with speed

$$v = \omega r$$

Its acceleration has components along its circular path and radially inward:

$$a_t = \alpha r \qquad\qquad a_r = -\frac{v^2}{r} = -\omega^2 r$$

The definitions are analogous to those of the linear velocity and acceleration of a particle moving in one dimension; so, for example, if a body rotates with a constant angular acceleration, the angle through which it has turned is given by

$$\theta = \theta_0 + \omega_0 t + \frac{1}{2}\alpha t^2$$

and so forth.

There is plainly a unique direction - that of the rotation axis - associated with these rotational quantities; can they be treated as <u>vectors</u>? They can be, only if combining two rotations is commutative; this is true for **differentially** small rotations $d\theta$, so ω and α can be treated as vector quantities. (For rotation about a <u>fixed</u> axis, their vector nature is not important.)

Calculating the kinetic energy of the rotating body gives

$$E_k = \frac{1}{2}I\omega^2 \qquad\qquad \text{where } I \equiv \Sigma(m_i r_i^2)$$

For a continuous body, the moment of inertia I is calculated as

$$I = \int \rho^2 \, dm$$

where ρ is the distance of the mass element dm from the axis or rotation. I is a measure of rotational inertia; it depends, plainly, on how the body's mass is distributed about the rotation axis. Often useful in calculating moments of inertia is the "parallel-axis theorem"

$$I = I_{cm} + Mh^2$$

where I_{cm} is the moment of inertia about a parallel axis through the center of mass.

The quantity of fundamental <u>dynamic</u> importance in rotation of a rigid body is not the net force on it - in fact, if the rotation is about a fixed axis through the center of mass, this must always vanish. Instead we define the <u>torque</u> of a force,

$$\tau \equiv Fd$$

where the "lever arm" d is the distance from the axis to the line of action of the force. In terms of the net resultant torque on the body,

$$\tau = I\alpha$$

Notice that, in general, torque will also be a vector quantity.

A special case of some importance is that of a body in static equilibrium - that is, at rest. If the body is at rest, both the net resultant torque and the net external force on it must be zero; from these conditions we can analyze the forces that act on a body in static equilibrium. In doing so we often wish to combine the effects of several forces into a single equivalent one. If the equivalent force is also to have the same torque about an axis, it must be applied at the right place. For instance, the effect of gravity on every bit of the body is the same as if its total weight acted at its center of mass. Forces that act in opposite directions cannot be replaced, in general, by a single equivalent force; but any combination of forces can be replaced by a combination of an equivalent force and an equivalent <u>couple</u>. A couple is a pair of equal and opposite forces acting at different points on the body; the torque it exerts is the same about any axis.

12.2 CHECK LIST

rigid body	moment of inertia
rotation	Steiner's theorem
axis of symmetry	parallel-axis theorem
angular velocity	radius of gyration
radian	torque
tangential acceleration	lever arm
radial acceleration	static equilibrium
angular acceleration	center of gravity
right-hand rule	couple

12.3 TRUE OR FALSE?

_____1. A system of particles in which the distance between every two particles of the system remains fixed is a rigid body.

_____2. The general motion of a rigid body can be considered as a translation of its center of mass combined with a rotation about its center of mass.

_____3. The acceleration of the center of mass of a rigid body is the resultant external force on it divided by its total mass, provided that the body does not rotate.

_____4. The moment of inertia is a quantity which plays a role in rotational motion analogous to that of the momentum in linear motion.

_____5. Angular velocity and acceleration can be defined only in terms of angles expressed in radian measure.

_____6. A disk of radius R rotates about its axis with an angular acceleration α; the acceleration of a point on its rim has magnitude αR.

_____7. Rotations in space may be treated as vector quantities, with the direction of the vector along the rotation axis.

_____8. The kinetic energy of a rigid body rotating about a fixed axis depends only on the mass and angular velocity of the body.

_____9. The second hand of a watch rotates with an angular velocity of about 0.1 radian per second.

_____10. The moment of inertia of a rigid body must be specified with respect to a particular axis of rotation.

_____11. The moment of inertia of a rigid body about an axis through its center of mass is smaller than that about any other parallel axis.

_____12. The radius of gyration of a rigid body is the distance from its center of mass to the axis of rotation.

_____13. If the net resultant force on a body is zero, there can be no torque about an axis through its center of mass.

_____14. If the net resultant torque about the center of mass of a body is zero, there can be no net force on it.

_____15. The net resultant force on a rigid body rotating about a fixed axis through its center of mass is always zero.

_____16. Two wheels have the same shape but different diameters; a given torque will always produce a larger angular acceleration on the smaller one.

_____17. The lever arm of a force is the distance from the axis of rotation to the point at which the force acts.

_____18. A solid sphere has a smaller moment of inertia about an axis through its center than does a disk of the same mass and diameter.

_____19. If a body is in static equilibrium, the resultant force on it is zero.

_____20. If the net resultant force on a body is zero, it is in static equilibrium.

_____21. Any two forces in a situation of static equilibrium are always equivalent to a single force acting at an appropriately chosen point.

90

_____22. Any number of forces acting on a body in static equilibrium which act along the same line can be replaced by a single force plus a couple.

_____23. For the purpose of calculating its moment of inertia, all the mass of a body may be considered as concentrated at the center of mass.

12.4 QUESTIONS

1. A phonograph turntable is rotating counter-clockwise as seen from above. In what direction is the angular velocity vector?

2. What other important mechanical quantity has the same dimensions as torque? Is it equivalent to torque?

3. A circular hoop rotates about its symmetry axis. It is made of some flexible material and, as it rotates, it is somehow squashed inward into a more elliptical shape - still in the same plane. Does its moment of inertia increase or decrease? You can answer this without doing any involved calculation at all.

4. Distinguish between center of mass and center of gravity of a rigid body. How big would an object have to be for the distinction to become important near the surface of the earth?

5. In the sketch, the hoop is big enough to pass over the solid cylinder. Both are rotated about their central axes. Without any calculation, explain how you know which has the larger moment of inertia.

6. Describe the vector angular velocity representing the earth's daily rotation.

7. In the sketch, a man is hanging from one side of a Ferris wheel. His weight is 160 lb. The wheel may be assumed frictionless, its radius is 9 ft and its moment of inertia 10^4 slug-ft^2. If the wheel is at rest in the sketch, with what angular acceleration does it begin to rotate? Could you use constant-acceleration formulas to find how long it takes for the man to swing to the bottom of the wheel?

12.5 EXAMPLES

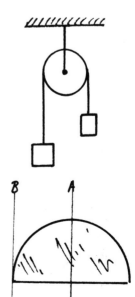

1. In the sketch at the right, the pulley is a disk of radius 6 cm and mass 0.4 kg and the blocks have masses of 0.8 and 1.6 kg. Assume there is no friction in the pulley axle but that the string does not stretch or slip, and find the acceleration of either block.

2. Calculate the moments of inertia about the axes shown for the uniform solid half-disk in the sketch.

3. A phonograph turntable of mass 1.8 kg and radius 15 cm, mounted horizontally, is being braked to a stop. After 30 sec it has lost 15% of its initial angular velocity. Assuming constant angular acceleration, (a) how long

does it take to come to a stop? (b) If the initial angular velocity
was 33 1/3 rev/min, how many revolutions did the turntable make
while coming to rest? (c) How much work did something have to do
to bring it to a stop?

4. A small mass sits on the turntable of the previous problem, 10 cm
    from the axis. The coefficient of friction between it and the
    turntable is 0.21. The turntable starts from rest with an angular
    acceleration of 1.2 sec^{-2}; how much time passes before the mass
    begins to slip?

5. In the sketch, an 18-ft plank is supported
    on two rocks, 6 ft and 2 ft from the
    opposite ends. The plank weighs 100 lb.
    How far out can a 150-lb man walk before
    the plank tips up and swats him?

12.6 ANSWERS

True or False?

1. True.

2. True - instantaneously; in general, the rotation axis may change in
    time.

3. False - this is the acceleration of the center of mass, regardless
    of whether the body rotates or not.

4. False - it is most nearly analogous to mass: it measures rotational
    inertia.

5. False - angular velocity is often expressed in revolutions per minute,
    but the formulas for converting to linear velocity and acceleration
    only work for radian measure.

6. False - this is its tangential component; there is also a radial
    component of the acceleration, the centripetal acceleration.

7. True - for vanishingly small angular displacements and for angular
    velocity; a finite angular displacement is not a vector quantity.

8. False - it also depends on the distribution of the mass; this affects
    the moment of inertia.

9. True - it moves through 2π radians every 60 sec.

10. True.

11. True - see the parallel-axis theorem.

12. False.

13. False - there may be torque even though forces balance; see answer 15.

14. False - an unbalanced force need not exert any torque.

15. True - if its center of mass isn't accelerating, the resultant
    force is zero.

16. False - it depends on the moments of inertia, therefore on mass as
    well as size.

17. False - it is the perpendicular distance from the axis of rotation
    to the <u>line along</u> which the force acts.

18. True - more of the sphere's mass is closer to the axis.

19. True.

20. False - static equilibrium requires that the net torque vanish also.

21. False - two forces acting along the same line cannot be replaced by a single equivalent force.

22. True.

23. False - the distribution of the body's mass is the whole point.

Questions

1. Up - use the right-hand rule.

2. Work and energy also have dimensions of force times distance, but are in no way equivalent. The role the distance plays in the definition of work is totally different from that in the definition of torque; the distance in the torque definition is not a displacement.

3. The moment of inertia of the hoop is MR^2. Consider what happens when it is squashed all the way flat - then we have a long rod of length $\ell = \pi R$ rotating about a perpendicular axis through its center. The moment of inertia for this is $ML^2/12 = (\pi^2/12)(MR^2)$. This is less than MR^2; so squashing the hoop decreased its moment of inertia.

4. The center of mass is the mass-weighted average of all the particles of a system; the center of gravity the effective point at which the pull of gravity on all particles of the system acts. In a uniform gravitational field they are the same. In the earth's gravitational field, g is 1% less at the top than at the bottom of an object 50 mi high, so something has to be pretty big for the distinction to matter.

5. Because all the mass of the hoop is farther from the rotation axis than is any of the mass of the cylinder.

6. Its magnitude is $2\pi/24$ h = $2\pi/8.64$ x 10^4 sec $\simeq 7.3$ x 10^{-5} sec^{-1}; it points in the direction of the earth's axis, pointing north.

7. The torque is (160 lb)(9 ft) = 1.44 x 10^3 lb-ft, so its angular acceleration is

$$\alpha = \frac{\tau}{I} = \frac{1.44 \times 10^3 \text{ lb-ft}}{1.0 \times 10^4 \text{ slug-ft}^2} = 0.144 \text{ sec}^{-2}$$

You could not carry this on with constant-acceleration formulas because the torque is not constant; as the man swings down, the torque he exerts on the wheel decreases.

Examples

Partial Solutions (1)

1. Do this by finding the resultant torque on the pulley and setting it equal to $I\alpha$ as a third equation (in addition to F = ma for the two masses). Note that the tension in the string isn't the same on both sides of the pulley in this case. How do you know this?

2. Since axis A passes through the center of mass, by symmetry, you can use the parallel-axis theorem to get I_B once you have I_A. If ρ is

the density of the figure and s its thickness, the mass of the slice in the sketch is

$$dM = \rho s \sqrt{R^2 - x^2} \, dx$$

Set up the integral for the moment of inertia about the y axis (A).

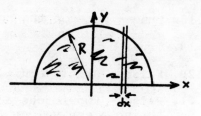

3. This is a kinematics problem - mostly - with the angular acceleration given as constant. Thus we can use the rotational analogues of the prescriptions we developed for linear motion with constant acceleration:

$$\omega = \omega_0 + \alpha t$$

$$\theta = \omega_0 t + \frac{1}{2} \alpha t^2$$

4. The force of static friction, which must supply the acceleration of the small mass, cannot be greater than $\mu_s mg$. What are the components of its acceleration?

5. This is a relatively simple problem in static equilibrium. Under what conditions will the board overbalance? Assume the board is at rest, with the man at some arbitrary position x, and find at what value of x the conditions are not met.

Partial Solutions (2)

1. From the diagram at right,

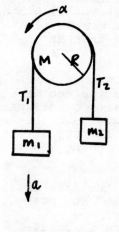

$$m_1 g - T_1 = m_1 a$$

$$T_2 - m_2 g = m_2 a$$

$$T_1 R - T_2 R = I \alpha$$

I is $\frac{1}{2} MR^2$ for a disk. What is α?

2. The integral is

$$I = \int x^2 \, dM = \rho s \int_{-R}^{R} x^2 \sqrt{R^2 - x^2} \, dx$$

This is a standard form which you can dig out of a table; or, if you want to crank it out, substitute $x = R \sin \theta$. You get

$$I = \frac{\pi}{8} \rho R^4 s$$

To put this in the usual form, what is the mass of the figure?

3. (a) We are given $\omega = 0.85\omega_0$ after $t = 30$ sec. When does it stop?

$$0.85\omega_0 = \omega_0 + \alpha(30 \text{ sec})$$

so

$$\alpha = -0.15\omega_0/30 \text{ sec} = -\omega_0/200 \text{ sec}$$

is the angular acceleration. Fairly obviously, therefore, it takes <u>200 sec</u> to come to a stop.

4. The radial component of its acceleration is

$$a_c = v^2/r = \omega^2 r$$

the tangential component

$$a_t = \alpha r$$

If the turntable starts from rest with constant angular acceleration, what relation is there between α and ω?

5. In the diagram, m is the mass of the plank, M that of the man. For simplicity, figure torques around point B. There is nothing at point A holding the plank down; thus F_A must be greater than zero. What does this have to do with where the man can stand?

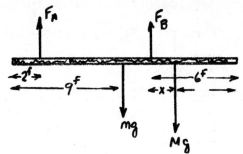

Partial Solutions (3)

1. Since we are given that the string doesn't slip on the pulley, we know that $a = \alpha R$. Thus we have

$$m_1 a = m_1 g - T_1 \qquad m_2 a = T_2 - m_2 g \qquad T_1 = T_2 = \tfrac{1}{2}Ma$$

Eliminating the T's from these three equations leaves

$$a = \frac{m_1 - m_2}{m_1 + m_2 + \tfrac{1}{2}M}\, g$$

With the numbers given, this is

$$a = \frac{1.6 \text{ kg} - 0.8 \text{ kg}}{1.6 \text{ kg} + 0.8 \text{ kg} + 0.2 \text{ kg}}(9.8 \text{ m/sec}^2) = \underline{3.02 \text{ m/sec}^2}$$

2. The mass of the disk is $M = (\rho)(\tfrac{1}{2})(\pi R^2)s$, so the moment of inertia is

$$I_A = \tfrac{1}{4}MR^2$$

(Note that this has the same form as for a whole disk about a diameter. Does this make sense?) By the parallel-axis theorem,

$$I_B = I_A + MR^2 = \tfrac{5}{4}MR^2$$

3. (b) Use the equation of motion

$$\theta = \omega_0 t + \tfrac{1}{2}\alpha t^2$$

with $\omega_0 = 33.3 \text{ rev/min} = 3.49 \text{ sec}^{-1}$ and $\alpha = -\omega_0/200 \text{ sec} = -0.0174 \text{ sec}^{-2}$
To find θ at $t = 200$ sec:

$$\theta = (3.49 \text{ sec}^{-1})(200 \text{ sec}) + \tfrac{1}{2}(-0.0174 \text{ sec}^{-2})(200 \text{ sec})^2$$

$$= \underline{349 \text{ radians}}$$

(c) The moment of inertia is $\tfrac{1}{2}(18 \text{ kg})(0.15 \text{ m})^2 = 0.202 \text{ kg-m}^2$, so the initial kinetic energy is

$$E_k = \tfrac{1}{2}I\omega^2 = \tfrac{1}{2}(0.202 \text{ kg-m}^2)(3.49 \text{ sec}^{-1})^2 = 1.23 \text{ J}$$

by the work-energy theorem, therefore, the work that had to be done to stop it was $\underline{-1.23 \text{ J}}$.

4. For constant acceleration we have $\omega = \alpha t$ and so $a_r = \alpha^2 t^2 r$. The magnitude of the acceleration is thus

$$a = \sqrt{a_t^2 + a_r^2} = \alpha r\sqrt{1 + (\alpha t^2)^2}$$

But the force of static friction cannot provide an acceleration larger than

$$a_{max} = \mu g = (0.21)(9.8 \text{ m/sec}^2) = 2.06 \text{ m/sec}^2$$

So put

$$a = (1.2 \text{ sec}^{-2})(0.1 \text{ m})\sqrt{1 + (\alpha t^2)^2} = 2.06 \text{ m/sec}^2$$

giving $\alpha t^2 = 17.1$ or $\underline{t = 3.78 \text{ sec}}$ for the time at which it starts to slip.

5. Forces: $F_A + F_B = mg + Mg$

Torques: $F_A(10 \text{ ft}) + Mg(x) = mg(3 \text{ ft})$

If the plank is static, then $F_A > 0$; therefore

$$Mg(x) > mg(3 \text{ ft})$$

so

$$x = \frac{m}{M}(3 \text{ ft}) = \frac{100}{150}(3 \text{ ft}) = \underline{2.0 \text{ ft}}$$

DIGRESSION
The Vector Product

On page 45 we defined a rule for multiplying two vectors - the "scalar product" - which yields a scalar (directionless) result. Another useful rule for multiplying vector quantities can be defined which yields a vector product. The first examples we shall encounter are the definitions of torque and angular momentum in the next chapter.

Consider any two vector quantities, $\vec{A}$ and $\vec{B}$. We define the vector product $\vec{A} \times \vec{B}$ as a vector whose <u>magnitude</u> is

$$|\vec{A} \times \vec{B}| \equiv |\vec{A}| \ |\vec{B}| \ \sin \theta$$

where θ is the angle between the directions of $\vec{A}$ and $\vec{B}$, <u>and</u> whose <u>direction</u> is that perpendicular to both $\vec{A}$ and $\vec{B}$ in a "right-handed" sense (see sketch).

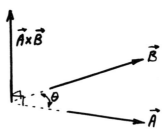

It follows that

$$\vec{A} \times \vec{B} = -\vec{B} \times \vec{A}$$

The <u>order</u> in which the two are multiplied matters; the vector product is a noncommutative one. Plainly it follows that

$$\vec{A} \times \vec{A} = 0$$

Hence the vector product of any two vectors which are parallel vanishes.

The magnitude of $\vec{A} \times \vec{B}$ can be considered as the magnitude of either vector, multiplied by the <u>component</u> of the other one <u>perpendicular</u> to the first. Or, geometrically, the magnitude of $\vec{A} \times \vec{B}$ is the area of the parallelogram defined by $\vec{A}$ and $\vec{B}$.

In terms of the rectangular components of $\vec{A}$ and $\vec{B}$, the vector product

$$\vec{A} \times \vec{B} = \hat{i}(A_y B_z - A_z B_y) + \hat{j}(A_z B_x - A_x B_z) + \hat{k}(A_x B_y - A_y B_x)$$

The rule for differentiating a vector product is

$$\frac{d}{dt}(\vec{A} \times \vec{B}) = \vec{A} \times \frac{d\vec{B}}{dt} + \frac{d\vec{A}}{dt} \times \vec{B}$$

Notice that the <u>order</u> of $\vec{A}$ and $\vec{B}$ must be preserved.

CHAPTER 13
Rotation in Space and Angular Momentum

13.1 CHAPTER SUMMARY

In general, the motion of a rigid body may be much more complicated than a rotation about a fixed axis; the axis of rotation may change direction, the moment of inertia may change (if the body is not rigid), and so forth. How are the rotational quantities introduced in the last chapter to be extended to the more general situation?

Consider first the motion of a particle under a force $\vec{F}$. If the position of the particle, relative to some origin, is given by $\vec{r}$, we define the torque of the force as

$$\vec{\tau} \equiv \vec{r} \times \vec{F}$$

This definition of torque is consistent with the more restricted one of the last chapter. Define the angular momentum of the particle as

$$\vec{L} \equiv \vec{r} \times \vec{p}$$

where $\vec{p} = m\vec{v}$ is the particle's (linear) momentum. In these terms, Newton's second law for the motion of the particle becomes just

$$\vec{\tau} = \frac{d\vec{L}}{dt}$$

If the particle moves in a uniform circular motion about the origin, its angular momentum is just

$$\vec{L} = mR^2\vec{\omega} = I\vec{\omega}$$

and is constant, as the centripetal force exerts no torque about the center.

Now when we generalize this to an arbitrary system of particles, we find that the torques of internal forces (those exerted by one particle on another) all cancel out, provided that the internal forces are central - that is, directed along the line joining each pair of particles. If this is the case, we have

$$\vec{\tau}_{ext} = \frac{d\vec{L}}{dt}$$

where now $\vec{\tau}_{ext}$ is the resultant torque of all external forces on the system, and $\vec{L}$ is the total angular momentum. Although we derive this from Newton's laws, which hold only in an inertial frame of reference, it is true in general if $\vec{\tau}$ and $\vec{L}$ are measured about the center of mass of the system. In the case of a body which rotates about an axis of symmetry, $\vec{L} = I\vec{\omega}$ and we get

$$\vec{\tau} = I \frac{d\vec{\omega}}{dt} = I\vec{\alpha}$$

just as in the last chapter.

If the resultant external torque on a system is zero, then plainly its total angular momentum does not change with time; this is the law of conservation of angular momentum for an isolated system.

The total angular momentum of an arbitrary system of particles can be written

$$\vec{L} = \vec{L}_{cm} + \vec{R}_{cm} \times M\vec{V}_{cm}$$

where $\vec{L}_{cm}$ is its angular momentum about the center of mass. Notice from this that a body which is simply spinning - rotating about its center of mass - has the same angular momentum about any origin whatever. Correspondingly, any motion of a system can be considered as the motion of its center of mass (determined by the net external force on the system), combined with a rotation about the center of mass (determined by the external torque).

For instance, a body which rolls without slipping on a rough surface rotates about its center of mass with angular velocity V_{cm}/R, so that the point of contact with the surface is instantaneously at rest. A gyroscope is a spinning object which is fixed at one point; if its spin $\vec{L}_{cm}$ is large, an external torque causes a $\Delta\vec{L} \simeq \vec{\tau}\,\Delta t$, and $\vec{L}$ - the spin axis - simply turns in the direction of $\vec{\tau}$. The gyroscope precesses, rather than simply falls over, as it would if it were not spinning. (Some part of the total $\vec{L}$ is due to the motion of its center of mass; this leads to a wobble of the precession called "nutation.")

If a rigid body rotates about an axis which is not a symmetry axis, its angular momentum is not, in general, parallel to its angular velocity. If the body is rotated about a fixed axis, then the direction of $\vec{L}$ is constantly changing; thus $\vec{L}$ is not constant, and there must be a torque exerted on the body by the pivot. Notice that this is true even if the body is pivoted about its center of mass (and so, statically, is in balance). This condition is known as dynamic imbalance.

13.2 CHECK LIST

angular momentum	precession
torque	Atwood's machine
right-hand rule	conservation of angular momentum
vector product	rolling without slipping
cross product	symmetric top
internal and external torques	nutation
spin	dynamic imbalance
gyroscope	static imbalance

13.3 TRUE OR FALSE?

_____1. Rotation about a fixed axis is the most general motion possible to a rigid body.

_____2. A force directed radially from the origin exerts no torque on a particle.

_____3. The vector product is a rule for multiplying two vector quantities, whose result is a vector lying in the same plane.

_____4. The vector product does not commute.

_____5. A given force produces a torque on a body only if the body is constrained to rotate about some axis.

_____6. The angular momentum of a body is its moment of inertia times its angular velocity.

_____7. Angular momentum and torque are both defined relative to some reference point or origin.

_____8. The angular momentum of a body is a vector parallel to the resultant torque on it.

_____9. For a complete description of the motion of a system of particles, we need the law $\vec{\tau} = d\vec{L}/dt$ in addition to Newton's laws of motion.

_____10. In the expression $\vec{\tau} = d\vec{L}/dt$ applied to an arbitrary system of particles, $\vec{\tau}$ is the resultant external torque on the system; internal torques cancel due to Newton's third law.

_____11. The angular momentum and angular velocity of an arbitrary system of particles are parallel vectors.

_____12. If a body is rotating about its center of mass, its angular momentum is the same about any point in space whatever.

_____13. The angular momentum of an arbitrary system of particles is simply that of a particle, having the whole mass of the system, located at and moving with the center of mass.

_____14. A body of mass M and radius R, rotating with linear speed v, has angular momentum MvR.

_____15. If the total angular momentum of an arbitrary system is conserved, the total angular momentum must be also.

_____16. If the total linear momentum of an arbitrary system is conserved, the total angular momentum must be also.

_____17. The theorem $\vec{\tau} = d\vec{L}/dt$ holds even if $\vec{\tau}$ and $\vec{L}$ are referred to an origin which is accelerated.

_____18. Properly speaking, an object cannot roll on a frictionless surface.

_____19. A gyroscope precesses rather than falls over because its spin counteracts the force of gravity.

_____20. A gyroscope supported at its center of mass will not precess.

_____21. The speed at which a top or gyroscope precesses increases as the top is tipped over further from the vertical.

_____22. For a given configuration of a gyroscope, nutation is more pronounced as spin angular momentum increases.

_____23. In general, the angular momentum and angular velocity of a body which rotates about an axis of symmetry are parallel.

_____24. A rotating wheel is balanced if the axis of rotation is through the center of mass.

_____25. If a body is rotating freely - released from any support or whatever - its angular velocity and angular momentum must be parallel.

_____ 26. It is possible for a rotating body to be dynamically, and yet not statically, balanced.

13.4 QUESTIONS

1. In the sketch, a mass is tied through a hole in a frictionless tabletop and set moving in a circular path. If the string is pulled down from below, decreasing the radius of the circular motion, is it linear momentum, angular momentum, or mechanical energy which is conserved? Explain.

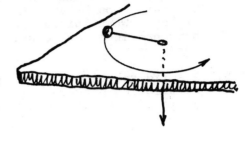

2. A ball, a disk, and a hoop, all with the same mass and radius, are rolled up an incline, all with the same initial velocity. Which goes farthest? If, instead, they are rolled up all with the same initial kinetic energy, which goes farthest?

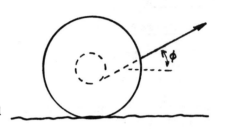

3. A Yo-Yo sits on edge on a rough surface. If its spring is pulled as shown, which way does it roll? Does your answer depend on the angle φ?

4. If the polar icecaps melted tomorrow, what would be the effect on the earth's rotation?

5. The propellor of a light airplane rotates counter-clockwise as seen from the rear. If the pilot pulls up out of a steep dive, but makes no attempt to control his left-right heading, in what direction will the plane tend to turn?

6. A man stands on a frictionless turntable which is rotating. He holds two heavy weights out at arm's length. If he (a) pulls them in to his chest or (b) simply drops them without drawing in his arms, what happens to his rate of rotation?

13.5 EXAMPLES

1. Consider the two vector quantities

$$\vec{A} = 2.4\hat{i} + 3.2\hat{j} + 3\hat{k} \text{ and } \vec{B} = 4.5\hat{i} + 6\hat{j}$$

(a) Find their vector product directly from the components. (b) Find the angle between their directions and show that $|\vec{A} \times \vec{B}| = AB \sin \theta$ gives the same magnitude as you found in (a).

2. For a particle in free fall under gravity, pick some point not on its line of fall as an origin and show that

$$\vec{\tau} = \frac{d\vec{L}}{dt}$$

holds for this motion.

3. A man sits on a frictionless merry-go-round. He and the merry-go-round jointly have a moment of inertia of 7.5 kg-m^2 around its axis. If the man, while at rest, throws a 4-kg brick off tangentially, at a distance 0.7 m from the axis and a speed 9 m/sec, what is the angular velocity which he and the turntable acquire?

4. In the sketch, a man of mass 80 kg
    runs up and jumps on the bottom of a
    ferris wheel whose moment of inertia,
    about its axis, is 1300 kg-m^2. The
    radius of the wheel is 2.4 m, and
    friction in its axle may be neglected.
    The man jumps on and the wheel swings
    him up. What initial speed must he
    have had in order to swing over the
    top?

5. A solid spherical ball rolls down an incline. If the coefficient
    of friction between ball and incline is 0.33, what is the steepest
    angle of the incline for which rolling without slipping is possible?

13.6 ANSWERS

True of False?

1. False - the direction of the rotation axis may change in time.

2. True.

3. False - the vector product is perpendicular to both the vectors
    multiplied.

4. True - $\vec{A} \times \vec{B}$ is in the opposite direction from $\vec{B} \times \vec{A}$.

5. False - the definition of torque does not depend on this.

6. False - or at least not generally true; it's true for a rigid body
    rotating about a fixed axis.

7. True.

8. False - the rate at which angular momentum <u>changes</u> is a vector
    parallel (and equal) to the torque.

9. False - this is a consequence of Newton's laws, not something
    independent of them.

10. False - internal torques cancel only if the internal forces are
    central - Newton's third law isn't enough.

11. False - true in cases such as rotation about a symmetry axis, but
    not general.

12. True.

13. False - this leaves out angular momentum it may have <u>about</u> the center
    of mass.

14. False - unless in some special case all the mass of the body is at
    radius R; this prescription really is meant for a point particle
    moving in a circle.

15. False - what this says is that the resultant external <u>torque</u> is zero.

16. False - the conditions for the two conservation laws aren't the same.

17. False - unless the origin is the center of mass of the system.

18. True - it will simply slide.

19. False - it precesses as a <u>result</u> of the gravitational torque on it,
    and anyway its spin isn't a force.

20. True - in that case there is no gravitational torque.

21. False - the precession rate is independent of angle.

22. False - less pronounced.

23. True.

24. False - this does not guarantee dynamic balance.

25. False - they need not be, in which case the angular velocity wobbles around the fixed direction of angular momentum.

26. True.

Questions

1. Mechanical energy isn't conserved, because the force the string exerts on the mass isn't known to be conservative. Momentum isn't, just because there is a force on it. But the force, since it is radial, exerts no torque about the center, so the thing's angular momentum is constant.

2. The moments of inertia are

   $$\text{ball: } \frac{2}{5}MR^2 \qquad \text{disk: } \frac{1}{2}MR^2 \qquad \text{hoop: } MR^2$$

   If the initial velocity of the center of mass is v_0, its initial angular velocity is v_0/R about the center of mass for rolling. The kinetic energy is

   $$E_k = \frac{1}{2}Mv_0^2 + \frac{1}{2}I\omega_0^2 = \frac{1}{2}(M + I/R^2)v_0^2$$

   Thus if all have the same v_0 the hoop has the greatest kinetic energy, and by conservation of energy it will roll farthest uphill. If, on the other hand, they are rolled up with equal initial kinetic energy, then by conservation of energy all three will reach the same height.

3. This is only confusing because our eye is drawn to looking at the center. Look at the torque about the point where the Yo-Yo sits on the ground - plainly in case A it will roll forward and in case B back, because about that point the string is the only torque that acts on it.

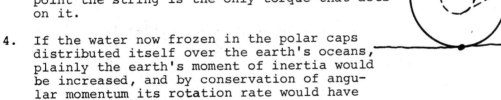

4. If the water now frozen in the polar caps distributed itself over the earth's oceans, plainly the earth's moment of inertia would be increased, and by conservation of angular momentum its rotation rate would have to slow down.

5. The propellor spin is an angular momentum directed opposite to its line of flight, by the right-hand rule. As the plane pulls up, the change of the angular momentum ΔL is directed downward. There must thus be an external torque on the plane, also downward. Again by the right-hand rule, a downward torque tends to rotate the plane to the right; if the pilot doesn't trim it, the plane will turn off to the right.

6. (a) If he pulls them in to his chest, plainly he has decreased the moment of inertia of the system; since there are no external torques about the vertical axis, angular momentum must be conserved, so his

rate of rotation will increase to keep Iω constant. (b) If he simply drops his weights without pulling them in, however, they keep their angular momentum and he keeps his - there is no change in his rate of rotation.

Examples

Partial Solutions (1)

1. In terms of components, the vector product is

$$\vec{A} \times \vec{B} = (A_y B_z - A_z B_y)\hat{i} + (A_z B_x - A_x B_z)\hat{j} + (A_x B_y - A_y B_x)\hat{k}$$

How can you find the angle between the two vectors?

2. Take $\vec{r}$ from the origin of coordinates and let the thing fall from point (x_0, y_0). What is $\vec{r}(t)$ if the thing falls freely from t = 0?

3. This problem is a very direct application of conservation of angular momentum. What is the total angular momentum of the system initially? Why can you say that it stays constant?

4. The thing to be careful about in this problem is what conservation law you try to apply when. Neither conservation of energy nor of angular momentum holds throughout. Angular momentum is conserved while he jumps on, but not afterward. Why?

5. What is the condition that the ball roll without slipping? It will require that the ball have an angular acceleration about its center of mass. What torque causes this angular acceleration? It may not look like it, but you do have enough information to work this.

Partial Solutions (2)

1. With the given components,

(a) $\vec{A} \times \vec{B} = \left[(3.2)(0) - (3)(6)\right]\hat{i} + \left[(3)(4.5) - (2.4)(0)\right]\hat{j}$

$$+ \left[(2.4)(6) - (3.2)(4.5)\right]\hat{k} = -18\hat{i} + 13.5\hat{j}$$

You can find the angle between the two by using $\vec{A}\cdot\vec{B} = |A||B|\cos\theta$.

2. For the particle falling freely we have $x = x_0$, $y = y_0 - \frac{1}{2}gt^2$, so
$$\vec{r}(t) = (x_0)\hat{i} + (y_0 - \frac{1}{2}gt^2)\hat{j}$$
Calculate the torque on the particle, and its angular momentum, around the origin.

3. Initially, everything is at rest, so the total angular momentum of the system is zero. If the turntable is frictionless, there is no torque about the axis of the merry-go-round, so the angular momentum remains zero. The man gives the brick angular momentum

$$L_b = mvr = (4 \text{ kg})(9 \text{ m/sec})(0.7 \text{ m}) = 25.2 \text{ kg-m}^2/\text{sec}$$

If the total remains zero, what angular momentum has the rest of the system acquired?

4. While he is jumping on, the total angular momentum doesn't have time to change much; in other words, we can apply conservation of angular momentum to collision problems even in the presence of external torques. Immediately after he jumps on, let the angular velocity of the wheel (and the man) be ω_0. Then

$$mv_0 R = L = I\omega_0 = (I_{wh} + mR^2)\omega_0$$

since all the man's mass m is at the rim of the wheel. Thus

$$\omega_0 = \frac{mv_0 R}{I_{wh} + mR^2}$$

Now the wheel swings him up over the top. What conservation law can you apply to this part of the problem?

5. A free-body diagram for the ball is sketched at right. If it rolls without slipping, we must have $v = \omega R$ and so $a = \alpha R$. The torque about the center must be due to the frictional force f. But

$$f > \mu_s N = \mu_s mg \cos \theta$$

so the maximum frictional torque possible is

$$\tau = fR > \mu_s (mgR) \cos \theta$$

And you can figure the maximum angular acceleration, and so the maximum acceleration down the plane, for which rolling without slipping is possible.

Partial Solutions (3)

1. With the given components $\vec{A} \cdot \vec{B} = (2.4)(4.5) + (3.2)(6) + (3)(0) = 30$

   but $\vec{A} \cdot \vec{B} = AB \cos \theta$

   for the vectors given, $A = 5.0$ and $B = 7.5$. Thus $\cos \theta = 0.800$, $\theta = 36.9°$, and

   $$|A \times B| = |18^2 + 13.5^2| = 22.5$$
   $$AB \sin \theta = (5)(7.5)(0.600) = 22.5$$

   as required.

2. The force on the particle is $\vec{F} = -mg\hat{j}$, so the torque is

   $$\vec{\tau} = \vec{r} \times \vec{F} = [x_0 \hat{i} + (y_0 - \tfrac{1}{2}gt^2)\hat{j}] \times [-mg\hat{j}] = -(mgx_0)\hat{k}$$

   and the angular momentum

   $$\vec{L} = \vec{r} \times (m\vec{v}) = [x_0 \hat{i} + (y_0 - \tfrac{1}{2}gt^2)\hat{j}] \times [-mgt\hat{j}] = -(mgx_0 t)\hat{k}$$

   and plainly from these
   $$\vec{\tau} = d\vec{L}/dt$$

   as advertised.

3. The rest of the system - man plus turntable - must have acquired an equal and opposite angular momentum:

   $$L = I\omega$$
   so
   $$\omega = L/I = (25.2 \text{ kg-m}^2/\text{sec})/(7.5 \text{ kg-m}^2) = \underline{3.36 \text{ sec}^{-1}}$$

4. If the ferris wheel's axle is frictionless, energy will be conserved. To get Max over the top requires an increase in his potential energy of $2mgR$ (notice the wheel's mass doesn't matter here, because it's symmetric), so at least this much kinetic energy has to be available just after he jumps on the bottom. The kinetic energy is

   $$E_k = \tfrac{1}{2}I_{tot}\omega_0^2 = \tfrac{1}{2}(I_{wh} + mR^2)\omega_0^2 = \frac{(mv_0 R)^2}{2(I_{wh} + mR^2)}$$

   Set this equal to $2mgR$ and solve for

   $$v_0^2 = 4gR\left[\frac{I_{wh} + mR^2}{mR^2}\right]$$

   For the numbers given we get

   $$\underline{v_0 = 18.9 \text{ m/sec}}$$

   about 42 mi/h; Max is quite a runner.

5. The net force down the plane is $mg \sin \theta - f = ma$ so

$$a = \alpha R = g \sin \theta - f/m$$

But $\tau = fR$ so

$$fR = I\alpha = (I/R)(g \sin \theta - f/m)$$

hence we get for f

$$f - \frac{mgI \sin \theta}{I + mR^2}$$

This is the value of f which is required for rolling without slipping. But

$$f < \mu_s mg \cos \theta$$

so

$$\frac{mgI \sin \theta}{I + mR^2} < \mu_s mg \cos \theta$$

or, finally, $\tan \theta < \mu_s (1 + mR^2/I)$

For a solid sphere, $I = \frac{2}{5}mR^2$, so we get $\tan \theta < \frac{7}{2}\mu_s = \frac{7}{2}(0.33) = 1.155$, or $\underline{\theta < 49.1°}$ for rolling without slipping.

CHAPTER 14
Oscillations

14.1 CHAPTER SUMMARY

A periodic motion is one which repeats itself regularly. The simplest
form of periodic motion is simple harmonic motion, in which the position
of a particle is given by

$$x = A \cos (\omega t + \delta)$$

The amplitude A is the maximum displacement (from $x = 0$) in either
direction; δ is a phase constant determined just by when we choose to
call $t = 0$. The cosine function repeats whenever its argument $(\omega t + \delta)$
changes by 2π; hence the period T of the oscillation is

$$T = 2\pi/\omega$$

The number of complete cycles per unit time is called the frequency
$f = 1/T$; ω is called the angular frequency.

For something moving in this manner, plainly

$$v = \frac{dx}{dt} = -\omega A \sin (\omega t + \delta) \qquad a = \frac{d^2x}{dt^2} = -\omega^2 A \cos (\omega t + \delta)$$
$$= -\omega^2 x$$

By Newton's second law, therefore, simple harmonic motion is the motion
which results from a restoring force proportional to the displacement of
the particle:

$$F = -m\omega^2 x = -kx$$

The period and frequency are determined by the force constant k, and in
a given situation are independent of the amplitude of the motion.

There is a very simple relationship between simple harmonic and
circular motion: a single component of a circular motion at constant speed
is a simple harmonic motion. Conversely, a uniform circular motion can
be considered as a combination of simple harmonic motions in two transverse directions.

A mass attached to a stretched spring undergoes a restoring force
proportional to the distance the spring is stretched from its equilibrium
length, thus undergoes a simple harmonic motion. The potential energy
and total energy of the oscillating mass are

$$U = \tfrac{1}{2}kx^2 \qquad \text{and} \qquad E = U + E_k = \tfrac{1}{2}kA^2$$

The total energy is constant, exchanging back and forth between potential
and kinetic as the mass oscillates. A mass on the end of a spring hung
vertically undergoes precisely the same motion, but around the equilibrium
point to which the spring is stretched by gravity.

The oscillation of a pendulum can also be treated as a simple harmonic
motion, provided that the amplitude of the oscillation is small. In the
small-angle limit, the restoring force when the pendulum is pulled aside

an angle θ is proportional to θ, and the motion is thus simple harmonic with

$$\omega^2 = g/L \qquad \text{or} \qquad T = 2\pi(L/g)^{\frac{1}{2}}$$

If the amplitude of the pendulum's motion is not small, the motion is still periodic but is not a simple harmonic motion; in that case the period is no longer independent of the amplitude but increases somewhat with increasing amplitude.

The oscillation of a simple pendulum is independent of the mass of the bob; the period can thus be used as a direct measure of g. The mass independence is a consequence of the equality of gravitational and inertial mass, and thus affords a precise test of their equivalence.

An arbitrary rigid body, suspended from a point and oscillating about it, is spoken of as a physical pendulum. For small amplitudes, its oscillation is a simple harmonic motion of period

$$T = 2\pi(I/MgD)^{\frac{1}{2}}$$

where I is the moment of inertia about the suspension point and D is the distance from the point of suspension to the center of mass of the body. Notice that this can be used to measure the moment of inertia of a given body. As for the simple pendulum, the motion is simple harmonic only in the small-amplitude limit; in general, any case of oscillation about a point of stable equilibrium can, in the limit of sufficiently small amplitude, be considered a simple harmonic motion.

A variety of motions can be understood as a combination of more than one simple harmonic motion. The resultant of two collinear simple harmonic motions - for instance, the distance between two oscillating particles - is also a simple harmonic motion but with an amplitude that depends on the relative phase of the two. Two harmonic motions of the same frequency in transverse directions give a resultant motion which may describe a linear, circular, or elliptic motion, depending on the amplitudes and relative phase of the two components.

14.2 CHECK LIST

oscillation	angular frequency
periodic motion	force constant
simple harmonic motion	turning points
amplitude	gravitational mass
phase constant	inertial mass
relative phase	principle of equivalence
frequency	physical pendulum
period	stable and unstable equilibrium

14.3 TRUE OR FALSE?

_____1.   A periodic motion is any which repeats itself cyclically.

_____2.   Simple harmonic motion is any periodic motion of a particle.

_____3.   Simple harmonic motion is a periodic motion in which the position of a particle varies sinusoidally with the time.

_____4.   The maximum displacement in a simple harmonic motion is called the amplitude.

_____5.   The time it takes for a simple harmonic motion to complete one full cycle is called the phase constant of the motion.

_____6.   The frequency of a periodic motion is the number of complete cycles per unit time.

_____7.   The maximum velocity of a particle undergoing simple harmonic motion is its amplitude times its frequency.

_____8.   At any instant in a simple harmonic motion, the acceleration is directed opposite to the displacement of the particle.

_____9.   The motion of a particle under any force which increases in magnitude with increasing displacement, and which is opposite in direction, is simple harmonic.

_____10. The frequency of a simple harmonic motion is proportional to the square of the amplitude.

_____11. The total distance traversed by a particle in one complete cycle of a simple harmonic motion is twice the amplitude.

_____12. At the point in a simple harmonic motion when the particle's speed is maximum, its acceleration is also maximum.

_____13. One linear component of the motion of a particle undergoing uniform circular motion is a simple harmonic motion.

_____14. A particle which is undergoing simple harmonic motion simultaneously in two perpendicular directions is moving in a circle.

_____15. A particle undergoes simple harmonic motion under a force $F = -kx$; its kinetic energy is $\frac{1}{2}kA^2$, where A is the amplitude of the motion.

_____16. The total energy of a particle undergoing simple harmonic motion is a constant.

_____17. A mass hanging on the end of a spring performs a simple harmonic motion with a frequency which is independent of the mass.

_____18. For a given amplitude of oscillation, the total energy of a mass oscillating on the end of a spring is independent of the mass.

_____19. The frequency of a simple pendulum is independent of its mass.

_____20. In general, the motion of a simple pendulum is a simple harmonic motion.

_____21. The fact that the frequency of a simple pendulum is independent of the mass is a consequence of the principle of equivalence.

_____22. The frequency of a simple pendulum increases slightly with increased amplitude.

_____23. A simple pendulum, with an amplitude large enough so that its motion is not adequately described as simple harmonic motion, is called a physical pendulum.

_____24. For given radius of gyration, the frequency of a physical pendulum is independent of the mass.

_____25. The motion of a particle, sufficiently near a point of stable equilibrium, can always be described as a simple harmonic motion.

_____26. The distance between two particles in one dimension, each of which is in simple harmonic motion at the same frequency, is itself a simple harmonic oscillation.

14.4   QUESTIONS

1. A mass oscillates on the end of spring with a certain frequency. If the spring is cut in half, at what frequency will the same mass oscillate on one of the pieces?

2. How could you use a simple pendulum to trace out a sinusoidal curve on paper?

3. In the graph at right, curve B is the potential energy we assume in approximating the motion of a pendulum as a simple harmonic oscillation, while its actual potential energy is shown in curve A. Use the graphs to explain why, for large amplitude, the period of the pendulum is slightly longer than the simple harmonic motion approximation predicts.

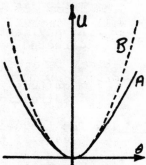

4. A mass on the end of a string is hung over a nail and set swinging as a simple pendulum, with length ℓ. While it is swinging, the string is played out until the length free to swing is 2ℓ. What happens to the frequency of the pendulum? Can you say anything about what happens to its amplitude?

5. Would it have made any difference to our discussion if we had defined simple harmonic motion as one which obeys

$$x = A \sin (\omega t + \delta)$$

rather than the cosine?

6. Two simple pendulums of the same length are swinging with the same amplitude. The mass of the one is three times that of the other. How do the energies of the two compare?

14.5   EXAMPLES

1. The position of a particle undergoing simple harmonic motion as a function of time is shown in the graph on the facing page. For this motion, what is (a) the amplitude, (b) the frequency, (c) the phase constant, (d) the period? If the particle is a 100-gm mass on the end of a spring, what is (e) the force constant of the spring, (f) the total energy of the 100-gm mass?

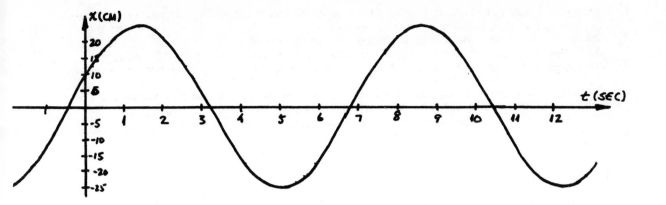

2. A mass hung on the end of a vertical spring, in equilibrium, stretches the spring a distance of 2 cm. If the mass is pulled 5 cm below its equilibrium position and released, at what frequency will it oscillate? What will be its speed as it passes through its equilibrium position?

3. A block is attached to the end of a horizontal spring on a frictionless tabletop. Its mass is 100 gm, and the force constant of the spring is 5.5 N/m. A 50-gm block sits on top of the 100-gm one; the coefficient of static friction between them is 0.38. How far can the blocks be pulled back from their equilibrium position without the upper one slipping when they are released?

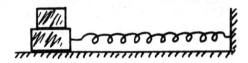

4. A hoop 3 ft in diameter, weighing 12 lb, hangs from a nail on a wall. If it is knocked to one side and set swinging back and forth, at what frequency will it swing? What is the length of the equivalent simple pendulum?

14.6 ANSWERS

True or False?

1. True.

2. False - it is specifically one in which position varies sinusoidally with time.

3. True.

4. True.

5. False - this is the period.

6. True.

7. False - but close, $v_{max} = \omega A = 2\pi fA$.

8. True.

9. False - the force must be proportional to the displacement.

10. False - it is characteristic of simple harmonic motion that the frequency is independent of the amplitude.

11. False - four times the amplitude: x = +A to -A to +A again.

12. False - its acceleration is zero at this point.

13. True.

14. False - it may be a circle, ellipse, or straight line depending on the phase relation of the two component motions.

15. False - this is its total mechanical energy; its kinetic energy isn't constant.

16. True.

17. False - $\omega = 2\pi f = \sqrt{k/m}$.

18. True - $E = \frac{1}{2}kA^2$, where k is the force constant of the spring.

19. True - $\omega = 2\pi f = \sqrt{g/\ell}$.

20. False - only in the limit of small amplitude.

21. True.

22. False - the period increases, the frequency decreases.

23. False - the physical pendulum is something, swinging as a pendulum, which can't be considered a point mass.

24. True - $\omega = 2\pi f = \sqrt{MgD/I} = \sqrt{MgD/MK^2} = \sqrt{gD/K^2}$, if K is the radius of gyration.

25. True.

26. True.

Questions

1. The question is, really, what is the force constant of half the spring? When a force F stretches the whole spring an amount x, each half stretches x/2, so the force constant of each half is thus twice that of the whole, and the frequency is thus increased by a factor $\sqrt{2}$.

2. Attach a pen to the pendulum bob and drag the paper under it at constant speed, at right angles to the plane of oscillation.

3. Mark the total energy on the potential-energy diagram. You see that for every value of x, curve B gives a lower kinetic energy than curve A, thus at given x the real pendulum swings faster than the simple harmonic approximation. However, the pendulum must swing farther in case A, and at the part of its motion where its speed is minimum. Thus in case A - the real pendulum - the cycle takes longer.

4. The period of a simple pendulum is $2\pi\sqrt{\ell/g}$, so its period is increased, its frequency decreased, by a factor $\sqrt{2}$.

    We can use conservation of angular momentum (not conservation of energy - why not?) to treat the question of the amplitude. A flexible string cannot exert any torque about the pivot, and if the pendulum is lowered at the bottom of its arc, the gravitational torque is zero. Conservation of angular momentum will give the speed, from which we can infer the total energy and therefore the amplitude, of the lengthened oscillation.

5. None whatever:

$$x = A \sin (\omega t + \delta) = A \cos (\omega t + \delta - \frac{\pi}{2}) = A \cos (\omega t + \delta')$$

It only changes the phase constant of the description.

6. The total mechanical energy is

$$\frac{1}{2}m\omega^2 A^2 = \frac{1}{2}m(g/\ell)A^2$$

proportional to the mass for given amplitude.

Examples

Partial Solutions (1)

1. Several of the quantities asked for you can pick right off the graph - this is really just asking if you know what they are. At what values of t is x = A?

2. You know how far the spring is stretched if a given mass hangs from it in equilibrium. What is its force constant? Is this enough information to find its frequency?

3. Assume the upper block stays on board, and find whatever limiting conditions this implies. What is the maximum accleration when the two are oscillating?

4. You have a prescription for the angular frequency of a compound pendulum. What is the moment of inertia of a hoop? Do you want the moment of inertia about the center, or about the support point?

Partial Solutions (2)

1.

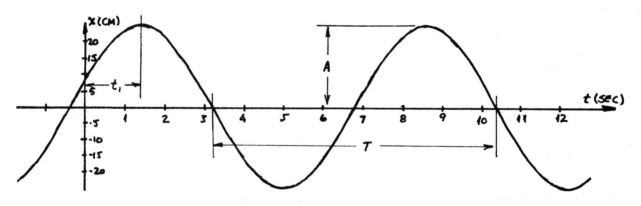

From the graph, directly, you can read off (a) A = 25 cm, (d) T = 7.2 sec, so (b) f = 1/7.2 sec = 0.139 Hz. The particle's displacement has its maximum value at t = 1.4 sec. Find the phase constant from this. The particle's total energy is $\frac{1}{2}kA^2$. How can you find k?

2. In equilibrium, F_{spr} = (k)(2 cm) = mg so mg/k = 2 cm. The angular frequency is

$$\omega = \sqrt{k/m} = \sqrt{(g)/(2\ cm)}$$

What is the particle's maximum speed?

3. The upper block is being accelerated by the frictional force of the lower one. But this cannot be greater than $\mu_s m_1 g$, if m_1 is the mass of the top block. So

$$m_1 a < \mu_s m_1 g \quad \text{or} \quad a < \mu_s g$$

if the upper block is not to slip. The acceleration at any moment is $a = (k/m)x$, where x is the displacement. Where is this maximum?

4. The moment of inertia of a hoop about its axis is obviously MR^2, since all the mass is at radius R. But you want the moment of inertia about the suspension point; by the parallel-axis theorem this is

$$I = MR^2 + MR^2 = 2MR^2$$

Partial Solutions (3)

1. (c) x is maximum when $\cos(\omega t + \delta) = 1$, thus when $\omega t = -\delta$. Here, then,

$$\delta = -\omega t = -2\pi f t = -(2\pi)(0.139 \text{ sec}^{-1})(1.4 \text{ sec}) = \underline{-122 \text{ radians}}$$

(e) We have for any simple harmonic motion, $\omega = \sqrt{k/m}$ or $k = m\omega^2$ — so here

$$k - (0.1 \text{ kg})(2\pi)^2(0.139 \text{ sec}^{-1})^2 = \underline{0.0762 \text{ N/m}}$$

(f) and

$$E = \tfrac{1}{2}kA^2 = \tfrac{1}{2}(0.0762 \text{ N/m})(0.25 \text{ m})^2 = \underline{2.38 \times 10^{-3} \text{ joule}}$$

2. We have already

$$\omega = (9.80 \text{ m/sec}^2)/(0.02 \text{ m}) = 22.1 \text{ sec}^{-1}$$

so

$$f = \omega/2\pi = \underline{3.52 \text{ Hz}}$$

and

$$v_{max} = \omega A = (22.1 \text{ sec}^{-1})(0.05 \text{ m}) = \underline{1.11 \text{ m/sec}}$$

3. Acceleration is maximum (in magnitude) at maximum displacement. If the spring is pulled back a distance A,

$$a = \frac{kA}{m} = \frac{kA}{m_1 + m_2}$$

so

$$\frac{kA}{m_1 + m_2} < \mu_s g, \qquad A < \frac{\mu_s (m_1 + m_2) g}{k}$$

With the numbers given, this gives $\underline{A < 10.2 \text{ cm}}$.

4. The angular frequency of a physical pendulum is $\omega = \sqrt{MgD/I}$, where D is the distance from the point of support to the center of mass. Here $D = R$ and $I = 2MR^2$ so

$$\omega = \sqrt{MgR/2MR^2} = \sqrt{g/2R}$$

Note this is the same as a simple pendulum of length $2R$. Here $R = 1.5$ ft and we get $f = \omega/2\pi = \underline{0.520 \text{ sec}^{-1}}$.

CHAPTER 15
Damped and Forced Oscillations

15.1 CHAPTER SUMMARY

A true simple harmonic motion would repeat itself indefinitely; all
real cases of oscillatory motion eventually die out because energy is
dissipated by frictional forces. We speak of this as a damped oscillation.
The analysis of the dissipative forces in a real situation can be very
messy; a damping force represented by

$$\vec{F}_d = -b\vec{v}$$

where b is a constant, is an adequate approximation in many cases.

If the damping constant b is not too large, we expect the resultant
motion to look very much like the undamped simple harmonic motion, but
with a slowly decreasing amplitude. The damping force dissipates energy
at a rate $\vec{F}_d \cdot \vec{v} = -bv^2$, which is proportional to the energy of the oscillator; hence the oscillator energy and its amplitude (since $E \simeq \frac{1}{2}kA^2$) die
out exponentially with time, and we get for the motion of the damped
oscillator

$$x = A_0 e^{-(b/2m)t} \cos(\omega't + \delta)$$

By substituting into the exact differential equation for the damped
harmonic oscillator, we find

$$\omega' = \omega_0 \left[1 - \left(\frac{b}{2m\omega_0}\right)^2\right]^{\frac{1}{2}}$$

where $\omega_0 = (k/m)^{\frac{1}{2}}$ is the natural (undamped) frequency of the oscillator.
For small damping, ω' is very close to ω_0.

More heavily damped systems - larger b - do not oscillate at all, but
die out monotonically to equilibrium. The smallest value of b for
which this occurs is

$$b_c = 2m\omega_0$$

This is the condition for critical damping - the quickest return of the
displaced mass to equilibrium without oscillation. A system with a still
larger value of b is spoken of as overdamped.

In many situations an oscillator is subjected to an external driving
force. The most important case is that in which the driving force varies
harmonically with time,

$$F_{ex} = F_0 \sin \omega t$$

For this case we find solutions for the motion of the particle of the
form

$$x = A \sin(\omega t - \delta)$$

with

$$A = \frac{F_0}{\{m^2(\omega^2 - \omega_0^2)^2 + b^2\omega^2\}^{\frac{1}{2}}} \qquad \tan \delta = \frac{b\omega}{m(\omega^2 - \omega_0^2)}$$

The mass oscillates with the frequency of the driving force but with an amplitude and a phase lag that depend on the frequency as well as on properties of the oscillator. Notice that the amplitude of the oscillator is maximum at a frequency near ω_0; this phenomenon is known as resonance. (This says simply that you get the maximum response from an oscillating system if you drive it at a frequency near its natural frequency, which isn't surprising.) If the driving frequency $\omega = \omega_0$, the transfer of e energy from the driving force to the oscillator is maximum. The details of the resonance depend on the degree of damping; as b is increased, the maximum in the resonance curve becomes lower and broader and the phase lag δ larger. (In the case of an undamped oscillator, b = 0, there is no phase lag, and the amplitude becomes infinite at resonance - but this is an unphysical case.)

The solution to the driven-oscillator problem discussed above is not the whole story, since it doens't depend on initial conditions; what we have found is the steady-state response to a sinusoidal driving force, after initial transients have died out.

15.2   CHECK LIST

damping	forced oscillator
damped oscillation	resonance
natural frequency	transient and steady-state solutions
critical damping	
underdamped and overdamped oscillator	resonance curve

15.3   TRUE OR FALSE?

Note: in all of the following, unless otherwise specified, a damping force of the form $f = -bv$ and a driving force of the form $F = F_0 \sin \omega t$, as discussed in the text, are assumed.

_____1.   The motion of real oscillatory systems can, at best, be only approximately described as simple harmonic motion.

_____2.   The energy of a harmonic oscillator is proportional to its amplitude.

_____3.   The motion of a weakly damped harmonic oscillator is very nearly just simple harmonic motion with decreasing amplitude.

_____4.   The work done by a damping force on a harmonic oscillator is always negative.

_____5.   For a damping force proportional to velocity, the energy of the damped oscillator decreases exponentially with time.

_____6.   The time it takes for a given fraction of the oscillator's energy to be lost is proportional to b.

_____7.   The frequency of a damped oscillator is always less than its natural (no damping) frequency.

_____8.   A sufficiently strongly damped oscillator does not oscillate at all, but just moves monotonically back to its equilibrium position.

_____9. A given system will oscillate - that is, be less than critically damped - only if the mass is less than $b/2\omega_0$.

_____10. Critical damping is the condition in which the particle returns to equilibrium, without oscillating, most rapidly.

_____11. A __constant__ force applied to a harmonic oscillator always causes a net decrease of its energy with time.

_____12. The driven harmonic oscillator with $b = 0$ oscillates at the frequency of, and in phase with, the driving force.

_____13. For $b = 0$, the driven harmonic oscillator has a maximum amplitude of F_0/m when the frequency of the driving force and the oscillator's natural frequency are equal.

_____14. The fact that a driven harmonic oscillator absorbs maximum power when driven at its natural frequency (or nearly so) is referred to as __resonance__.

_____15. The general solution of the problem of the driven damped harmonic oscillator is an oscillation at the frequency of the driving force.

_____16. A driven harmonic oscillator, with damping, always lags behind the driving force in phase.

_____17. The height of the resonance curve for a driven damped harmonic oscillator - the amplitude, or the power absorbed, at resonance - increases with increasing b.

_____18. The width (in frequency) of the resonance curve increases with increasing b.

15.4 QUESTIONS

1. A certain object falling, under gravity, through the air reaches a terminal velocity v_t. If the same object (in the same air) oscillates on the end of a spring, what is the value of the damping constant b?

2. The form of the damping force we used, proportional to velocity, is chosen mainly for analytic simplicity, although it is a fair representation of the drag on an object moving through a fluid. What effect would it have on our results if we had assumed a different form - for example, a constant magnitude, as for friction between dry surfaces?

3. Are the turning points - the points of maximum displacement, at which the particle is instantaneously at rest - of the damped harmonic oscillator precisely halfway between successive zeros of the displacement?

4. Two oscillators have the same natural frequency; the resonance curve of one, driven by a sinusoidal force, is twice as wide as that of the other. If each is allowed to oscillate without any driving force, how do their times to die out compare? Which damps out more quickly?

5. Soldiers marching in formation are taught to break step when crossing a footbridge. Why?

6. How do the phase of driving force, displacement, and velocity of the driven harmonic oscillator at resonance compare? Comment.

15.5 EXAMPLES

1. A damped harmonic oscillator loses 18% of its total energy in each full cycle of oscillation. By what factor would its damping force have to be increased in order to damp it critically?

2. A 60-gm mass on the end of a spring, with negligible damping, has twice the amplitude when driven at 50 Hz than it has when driven at 60 Hz. What is the force constant of the spring?

3. A damped harmonic oscillator driven at 1.1 times its natural frequency oscillates, in the steady state, with amplitude 1.9 cm; if driven at its natural frequency, its amplitude is 10 cm. The driving force is removed after the oscillator has reached the steady state at frequency $1.1\omega_0$, and its motion gradually damps out. What is its amplitude after 15 cycles?

15.6 ANSWERS

True or False?

1. True - there is some damping, some dissipation of energy, in any real oscillator.

2. False - to the square of the amplitude.

3. True.

4. True.

5. True - it loses a given _fraction_ of its energy in a given time.

6. False - inversely proportional to b, directly proportional to m/b.

7. True - although unless it is near critical damping the frequency difference is very small.

8. True - the onset of this condition is "critical" damping.

9. False - $b = 2\omega_0 m$ is the condition for critical damping, but it will oscillate if the mass is _more_ than this.

10. True.

11. False - over a complete cycle, the work done by any constant force is zero.

12. True.

13. False - with zero damping, the amplitude at resonance goes to infinity.

14. True.

15. False - this is the steady-state solution, after initial transients have died out.

16. False - the relative phase depends on whether the natural frequency is greater or less than the driving frequency.

17. False - the resonance curve is lower (and wider - see next question) for larger b.

18. True.

1. An object falls at a steady terminal velocity when the drag force
    of the air on it equals its weight; thus

$$bv_t = mg$$

or

$$b = mg/v_t$$

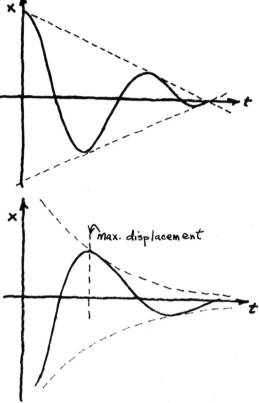

2. The general conclusions, and the
    qualitative description of what
    happens, would be unchanged: the
    amplitude of the oscillations dies
    out with time, more rapidly for a
    larger frictional force. But the
    detailed description of the motion
    would be different; if the fric-
    tional force has constant magni-
    tude, for example, the amplitude
    decreases linearly with the time.

3. Not exactly. This is easiest to
    see on a graph if you look at a
    strongly damped case; see the
    sketch at right. The particle
    takes longer to come back to equil-
    ibrium than it did to go out - if
    you like, because the damping
    force decreases its energy.

4. The one with the wider resonance
    curve has the larger b - the width
    of the peak is proportional to b -
    and thus damps out in half the time
    as does the one with the sharper
    resonance.

5. Because if their pace happened to coincide with a natural resonance
    frequency of the bridge, they could set the bridge vibrating with
    amplitude large enough to damage it.

6. At resonance, the phase difference (δ) between driving force and
    displacement is $\pi/2$; that is, the force has its maximum value as
    the particle passes through its equilibrium position. Thus at
    resonance the force and velocity are in phase; the transfer of
    energy from the driving force is maximum because the force is
    always shoving the particle along in the direction it's already
    going.

Examples

Partial Solutions (1)

1. The condition for critical damping is

$$b = 2m\omega_0$$

    but here we are given none of the constants (k, m, b) of the
    oscillator. How long does it take a damped oscillator to lose a
    given fraction of its energy?

2. Set up the problem by writing the amplitude of an undamped, driven
    harmonic oscillator; from the information given you can find ω_0.
    Having the natural frequency ω_0, how do you find the force constant?

3. Here again you have the amplitude at two different frequencies, this

time for a damped oscillator. Write out the amplitude for the two cases. In order to determine the rate at which the free oscillator - after the driving force is removed - loses energy, what do you need to know?

Partial Solutions (2)

1. The energy decreases with time according to

$$E = E_0 e^{-(b/m)t}$$

and the time required for a full cycle is the <u>period</u>

$$T = \frac{2\pi}{\omega} \simeq \frac{2\pi}{\omega_0}$$

So what follows from the fact that it loses 0.18 of its energy in a full cycle?

2. The amplitude of the undamped forced oscillator is

$$A = \frac{F_0}{m(\omega_0^2 - \omega_2^2)}$$

Here we are given

$$A(50 \text{ Hz}) = 2A(60 \text{ Hz})$$

and want to solve for ω_0. Given the natural frequency, the force constant of the oscillator is

$$k = m\omega_0^2$$

3. The amplitude of the driven damped oscillator is

$$A = \frac{F_0/m}{\sqrt{(\omega^2 - \omega_0^2)^2 + (b\omega/m)^2}}$$

Here we are given, for $\omega = \omega_0$

$$A(\omega_0) = \frac{F}{b\omega_0} = 10 \text{ cm}$$

and for $\omega = 1.1\omega_0$

$$A(1.1\omega_0) = \frac{F_0/m}{\sqrt{(0.21\omega_0^2)^2 + (1.1b\omega_0/m)^2}} = \underline{1.9 \text{ cm}}$$

These can be solved for the combination $m\omega_0/b$.

Partial Solutions (3)

1. For a full cycle,

$$E = E_0 e^{-bT/m} = 0.82$$

so

$$\frac{bT}{m} = -\ln 0.82 = 0.198$$

thus

$$\frac{b}{m} \frac{2\pi}{\omega_0} = 0.198 \quad \text{or} \quad \frac{b}{m\omega_0} = 0.0316$$

For critical damping, $b = 2m\omega_0$; thus the present value of b would have to be increased by

$$\frac{2}{0.0316} = \underline{63.3 \text{ times}}$$

2. We have

$$\frac{A(50\ Hz)}{A(60\ Hz)} = 2 = \frac{\{(2\pi)(60)\}^2 - \omega_0^2}{\{(2\pi)(50)\}^2 - \omega_0^2}$$

so

$$(377\ sec^{-1})^2 - \omega_0^2 = 2(314\ sec^{-1})^2 - 2\omega_0^2$$

Solving gives

$$\omega_0^2 = 5.53 \times 10^4\ sec^{-2} = k/m$$

So
$$k = (0.06\ kg)(5.53 \times 10^4\ sec^{-2}) = \underline{3320\ N/m}$$

3. From the amplitude at ω_0 we have

$$F_0 = (0.1m)(b\omega_0)$$

so

$$A(1.1\omega_0) = 1.9\ cm = \frac{(0.10m)(b\omega_0/m)}{0.0441\omega_0^4 + 1.21(b\omega_0/m)^2}$$

$$\frac{1}{(0.19)^2} = 0.0441\left(\frac{m\omega_0}{b}\right)^2 + 1.21$$

Solving gives

$$\frac{b}{m\omega_0} = 0.0408$$

After the driving force is removed, the oscillator dissipates a fraction

$$e^{-2\pi b/m\omega_0} = e^{-2\pi(0.0408)} = 0.774$$

of its energy in each cycle. The fraction remaining after 15 cycles is then $(0.774)^{15}$ or 0.0214 of the initial energy. But the amplitude initially was 1.9 cm, and amplitude goes as the square <u>root</u> of the energy. Thus after 15 cycles

$$A = (1.9\ cm)\ \sqrt{0.0214} = \underline{0.28\ cm}$$

CHAPTER 16
Gravity

16.1 CHAPTER SUMMARY

The gravitational force exerted by a particle of mass m_1 on another of
mass m_2 is given by Newton's law of gravitation as

$$\vec{F} = -G\,\frac{m_1 m_2}{r_{12}^2}\,\hat{r}$$

where $\vec{r}_{12}$ is the vector (and $\hat{r}_{12}$ the corresponding unit vector) from m_1
to m_2. The force is always attractive.

Newton justified this primarily in terms of the empirical rules
about planetary motion known as Kepler's laws:

1. The planets move in elliptical orbits with the sun at one focus.
2. A line joining a planet to the sun sweeps out equal areas in
   equal times.
3. The square of the period of a planet's orbit is proportional to
   the cube of the planet's mean distance from the sun.

The second of Kepler's laws says only that the force between planet and
sun is central - that the planet's angular momentum is constant; but
the first and third are consistent only with an inverse-square force law.
An inverse-square law also reconciles the acceleration of the moon in its
orbit with the acceleration of gravity at the earth's surface.

The gravitational constant G must be obtained from measurements of
the force between independently known masses. The first terrestrial
measurement was accomplished by Cavendish, using a very delicate torsion
balance. (G being known, the masses of bodies in the solar system can be
inferred from their orbital motion; Cavendish referred to his experiment
as "weighing the earth.")

In some situation, let the force of gravity on a mass m_0 be $\vec{F}$. We
define the gravitational <u>field</u> $\vec{g}$ at the position of m_0 by

$$\vec{F} = m_0 \vec{g}$$

The point is that, in terms of the field, what happens to m_0 depends on
conditions <u>at</u> the position of m_0; this is a way around the conceptual
problem of "action at a distance."

If the field at a point arises from a system of particles, it is
calculated as a direct superposition of the gravitational fields of each
mass. The field due to an extensive body is calculated by integrating
the field due to each mass element, over the whole body.

The gravitational <u>potential</u> at a point is defined as the potential
energy per unit mass: if the gravitational potential energy of a mass
m_0 is U, then its potential is $V = U/m_0$. The gravitational potential
due to a system of point masses is just a sum of that due to each:

$$V = -\sum_i \frac{Gm_i}{r_{i0}}$$

It is often useful to visualize a gravitational field in terms of a map of "lines of force" of the field. Each line at every point indicates the direction of $\vec{g}$ at that point; because the field of a point mass falls off as $1/r^2$, the density of force lines at a point is proportional to the magnitude of the field there. A map of the field of a system of point masses can be made by letting the number of lines that converge on each point mass be proportional to the mass. Several examples of lines-of-force diagrams are illustrated in the text.

A special case of particular importance is that of a mass distribution with spherical symmetry. From the outside, the gravitational field is simply that of a point mass, having the total mass of the system, at the center of symmetry; on the inside of a "spherical shell" of mass, the gravitational field is zero. (This is derived in the text, but can be seen directly from the symmetry of the lines of force of a spherical distribution of mass.)

16.2   CHECK LIST

Newton's law of gravitation

Kepler's laws

central force

inverse-square law

Cavendish experiment

torsion balance

$G = 6.673 \times 10^{-11}$ N-m^2/kg^2

gravitational constant

gravitational field

gravitational potential

lines of force

16.3   TRUE OR FALSE?

____1.   According to Kepler's third law, the cube of a planet's orbital period and the square of its mean distance from the sun are proportional.

____2.   Kepler's second law is equivalent to the statement that the angular momentum of the planet is constant.

____3.   The most general motion of a particle moving under the influence of an inverse-square force is an ellipse with the center of force at one focus.

____4.   For the special case of a circular orbit, the inverse-square force law can be derived from Kepler's laws.

____5.   A confirmation of Newton's law of gravitation is that the acceleration of the moon in its orbit is the same as the gravitational acceleration of objects at the surface of the earth.

____6.   Cavendish's experiment provides a direct measurement of the mass of the earth, from which the gravitational constant G can be inferred.

____7.   The gravitational field at a point is defined as the gravitational force on a unit mass at that point.

123

_____8. The gravitational field is a scalar quantity.

_____9. Changes in the gravitational field are found to propagate as waves, with infinite speed.

_____10. The gravitational force from an arbitrary distribution of mass is the same as if all its mass were concentrated at the center of mass.

_____11. The gravitational potential energy per unit mass is called the gravitational potential.

_____12. A gravitational field can be mapped in terms of lines of force, which at every point give the direction in which a particle is moving.

_____13. A lines-of-force map can be drawn only because the gravitational force follows an inverse-square law.

_____14. The gravitational field **sufficiently** far away from an arbitrary finite distribution of mass must look like that due to a point mass.

_____15. The units of gravitational field are the same as those of acceleration.

_____16. Lines of force cannot intersect.

_____17. The gravitational potential inside a spherical shell of matter is zero.

_____18. A spherically symmetric mass distribution can be approximated as a point mass only at distances large compared to its radius.

16.4 QUESTIONS

1. Some communications satellites hang stationary over one spot on the earth. How is this accomplished?

2. Two satellites of a certain planet have orbits whose diameters are in the ratio 1.7 to 1. What is the ratio of their periods?

3. A gravitational lines-of-force map for some system of point masses is sketched at the right. What can you say about the masses?

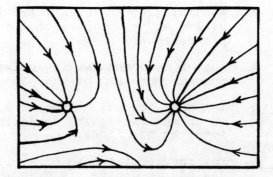

4. Consider the problem of an object dropped through a hole drilled all the way through the earth. Will it drop straight down the axis of the hole? What will be the effect of the earth's rotation?

5. Neglecting air resistance and all the obvious technical difficulties, could an earth satellite be put into a stable orbit around the earth by firing it from a huge cannon on the ground?

6. Two planets have the same density but different diameters. Which has the larger surface escape velocity?

7. Consider observing a distant double star system. You can obviously determine the period of their revolution about one another. What

other observations would be required to infer the masses of the stars?

16.5 EXAMPLES

1. You stand holding a plumb bob next to a large mountain. It is 1.5 km high and 6 km through at the base. Making reasonable assumptions about its gravitational effect, estimate the deflection of the plumb bob from the vertical.

2. We considered the problem of a hole through the earth and showed that an object dropped from the surface undergoes simple harmonic motion in this tunnel, if the earth's density is uniform. A better model of the interior of the earth is a core of radius 3500 km and density 10.3 gm/cm^3, surrounded by a mantle of density 4.5 gm/cm^3. On this assumption, find the speed of an object which has fallen to the center of the earth.

3. You are in a manned satellite, in a circular orbit 500 mi above the earth. You fire rockets directly opposite your direction of motion and increase your speed relative to the earth by 10%, without changing direction. Find the distance from the earth, and the speed, at the farthest point from earth of your new orbit.

4. Find an expression for the gravitational force on the axis of a uniform disk of radius R.

5. An astronaut lands on a planet of radius 0.71 times that of the earth and finds that a simple pendulum of length 1 m has a period of 2.51 sec. What is the mass of the planet?

16.6 ANSWERS

True or False?

1. False - T^2 and R^3 are proportional.

2. True.

3. False - this is true if the particle is in a closed orbit, but unbound - parabolic and hyperbolic - trajectories are possible also.

4. True.

5. False - it is inversely proportional to R^2 - this is the confirmation of Newton's law - but not the same.

6. False - the Cavendish experiment is an independent determination of G, from which the mass of the earth can be inferred; astronomical data give you GM_e.

7. True.

8. False - it is the force per unit mass, a vector quantity.

9. False - they are expected, from theory, to propagate at the speed of light; at present it is arguable whether they have been "found" to do anything at all.

10. False - this is true only if the mass distribution has spherical symmetry.

11. True.

12. False - the direction at any point is that of the gravitational force.

13. False - you could map the force direction in any case; the inverse-square force law allows you to interpret the density of force lines as a measure of the magnitude of the force.

14. True - sufficiently far away, details of the distribution must cease to matter.

15. True - acceleration is force per unit mass.

16. True - the field cannot have more than one direction at a given point.

17. False - the field is zero, so the potential is constant; but its absolute value is arbitrary.

18. False - at any point outside; this is the justification for calculating force at the earth's furface using the distance from the center.

Questions

1. If a satellite is in a circular orbit whose period is equal to that of the earth's rotation, it will appear to be stationary over one place on the surface. The radius of the orbit required works out to about 23,000 mi.

2. T is proportional to $R^{3/2}$, so their periods are in the ratio $(1.7)^{3/2}$ = 2.22 to 1.

3. The number of lines of force is proportional to the mass, so the two point masses shown are in the ratio 3:2. From the appearance of the lines, and their lack of symmetry about the line joining the two point masses, there must be another mass located below and to the right of the region shown.

4. If the hole were drilled along the rotation axis of the earth, an object would drop straight down the middle. Otherwise, as it drops toward the center of the earth, its transverse rotational velocity must decrease; thus it will be pressed against the eastern wall of the shaft.

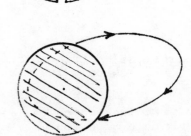

5. No; the launch point - where the cannon is - is a point on the satellite's orbit, so when it comes back around it must intersect the earth. For this reason real satellites take off vertically and turn laterally as they approach orbital altitude.

6. If they have the same density, their masses are proportional to R^3, and so

$$v_e = \frac{2GM}{R} \propto \frac{2GR^3}{R} \propto R^2$$

The bigger one has the higher escape speed.

7. If the size of the system is known, in addition to the period, this suffices to determine the total mass. Compare the formula for a planetary system,

$$T^2 = \frac{4\pi^2 R^3}{GM}$$

Further information, such as the velocity of each, is required to determine the indivudual masses. This kind of analysis of double stars is, in fact, about the only information we have on the masses of stars.

Examples

Partial Solutions (1)

1. This is a problem in which it's only the order of magnitude of the answer that's instructive, so it's appropriate to make as many simplifying assumptions as possible. To estimate the mass of the mountain, approximate it as a cone of the given diameter and height. Also, assume that the gravitational force it exerts is the same as if all its mass were at the center of mass. This isn't true, except for a sphere, but it saves a lot of calculation.

2. The force on a mass m at distance r from the center is

$$F = \frac{G\{M(r)\}(m)}{r^2}$$

where M(r) is the mass <u>inside</u> radius r. Write out what M(r) is. The most direct way to attack this problem is by the work-energy theorem: the work done by this force, from r = R to r = 0, must equal the change in the kinetic energy.

3. The way to attack this is by conservation of energy and angular momentum. If the satellite is at distance r from the center of the earth, and has speed v, its energy is

$$E = -\frac{GMm}{r} + \frac{1}{2}mv^2$$

and, at points A and B <u>only</u> (why?) its angular momentum is

$$L = mvr$$

Use the initial conditions to find L and E, and solve for v and r.

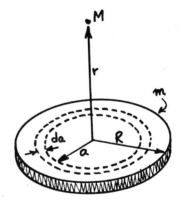

4. The easiest way to set this up is to find the force, at point P, due to a ring of radius a, and consider the disk as made up of concentric rings. You need only consider the component of force along the disk axis. Why is this?

5. What the period of the pendulum gives you is the acceleration due to gravity at the planet's surface. Take it from there.

Partial Solutions (2)

1. The volume of a cone, if you've forgotten, is

$$\frac{1}{3}\pi R^2 h$$

You can locate the center of mass easily enough. But this is just a rough calculation anyway and the height of the center of mass is plainly much less than the radius of the base, so just assume the center of mass is 3 km away, horizontally.

2. Let M_c, R_c, and density ρ_c refer to the core, ρ_m to the mantle. Then for

$$0 < r < R_c \qquad M(r) = \frac{4}{3}\pi\rho_c r^3$$

$$R_c < r < R \qquad M(r) = \frac{4}{3}\pi\rho_c R_c^3 + \frac{4}{3}\pi\rho_m(r^3 - R_c^3)$$

The work done by the gravitational force from surface to center is just

$$W = \int_0^R F(r)\ dr = Gm\int_0^R \frac{M(r)}{r^2}\ dr$$

and this must equal the kinetic energy gain of the falling object.

3. The angular momentum is mvr only if the velocity is directed tangentially - this is true only at the near and far points of the orbit, in general. Before you fired your rocket, the satellite's orbit was circular. For this case

$$\frac{mv_0^2}{r_0} = \frac{GMm}{r_0^2} \qquad so \qquad v_0^2 = \frac{GM}{r_0}$$

Firing increases the speed to $1.1v_0$ still at distance $r = r_0$. Write out E and L at this point; they must be the same at the far point of the orbit, and you can solve for v and r there.

4. Just by symmetry, there can be no force parallel to the plane of the disk. That along the axis is

$$dF \cos\ \theta = \frac{GM \cos\ (\theta)\ dm}{r^2 + a^2}$$

where

$$dm = 2\pi\rho at\ da$$

if t is the thickness of the disk and

$$\rho = \frac{m}{\pi R^2 t}$$

is its density. What is $\cos\ \theta$?

5. The period of a pendulum of length ℓ is

$$T = 2\pi\sqrt{\ell/g}$$

and the acceleration of gravity at the surface of the planet is given by

$$g = \frac{GM}{R^2}$$

M is the mass of the planet, which is what you want to find.

Partial Solutions (3)

1. We have, finally, a mass $\pi\rho R^2 h/3$ approximately a distance R away; the force it exerts is

$$F = \frac{G(\pi\rho R^2 h/3)m}{R^2} = \frac{\pi\rho mGh}{3}$$

A reasonable value for the density of surface soil and rock is 4.5 g/cm³. Then

$$F = \frac{(\pi)(4.5 \times 10^3\ kg/m^3)(m)(6.67 \times 10^{-11}\ N\text{-}m^2/kg^2)(1500\ m)}{3}$$

$$= (4.7 \times 10^{-4}\ m/sec^2)(m)$$

This is approximately at right angles to the force of the earth's gravity, so the angle at which the plumb line hangs is given by

$$\theta = \tan^{-1}\left(\frac{Fmt}{mg}\right)$$

or

$$\theta = \tan^{-1}\left(\frac{4.7 \times 10^{-4}}{9.8}\right) = \underline{0.0027^\circ}$$

2. If the object is dropped from rest at the surface, its kinetic energy at the center is

$$\frac{1}{2}mv^2 = W = Gm \int_0^R \frac{M(r)}{r^2}\, dr$$

so

$$v^2 = \frac{8\pi}{3}G\left[\rho_c \int_0^{R_c} r\, dr + (\rho_c - \rho_m)\int_{R_c}^R \frac{R_c^3}{r^2}\, dr + \rho_m \int_{R_c}^R r\, dr\right]$$

$$= \frac{8\pi}{3}G\left[\frac{1}{2}\rho_c R_c^2 + (\rho_c - \rho_m)R_c^2(1 - \frac{R_c}{R}) + \frac{1}{2}\rho_m(R^2 - R_c^2)\right]$$

In this case we have

$R = 6.37 \times 10^6$ m	$\rho_m = 4.5 \times 10^3$ kg/m^3
$R_c = 3.5 \times 10^6$ m	$\rho_c = 1.03 \times 10^4$ kg/m^3

thus

$$v^2 = (8\pi/3)(6.67 \times 10^{-11}\ \text{N-m}^2/\text{kg}^2)(1.59 \times 10^{17}\ \text{kg/m})$$

$$= 8.88 \times 10^7\ \text{m}^2/\text{sec}^2$$

so

$$v = \underline{9.43 \times 10^3\ \text{m/sec}}$$

3. We have $v_0^2 r_0 = GM$, so just after firing

$$E = -\frac{GMm}{r_0} + \frac{1}{2}m(1.1v_0)^2 = -mv_0^2 + 0.605mv_0^2 = -0.295mv_0^2$$

and

$$L = m(1.1v_0)r_0 = 1.1mv_0 r_0$$

E and L are the same at every point, so at the far end of the orbit

$$-\frac{GMm}{r} + \frac{1}{2}mv^2 = -\frac{mv_0^2 r_0}{r} + \frac{1}{2}mv^2 = E = -0.295mv_0^2$$

and

$$mvr = 1.1mv_0 r_0$$

Eliminate r between these two and solve for v. You get

$$v^2 - 2(\frac{v_0}{1.1})v + (0.59v_0^2) = 0$$

One solution of this is $v = 1.1v_0$, which is where we started; the other is

$$v = 0.718v_0$$

and

$$r = L/mv = \frac{1.1mv_0 r_0}{m(0.718v_0)}$$

$$= 1.53r_0$$

Now

$$r_0 = R_e + 500\ \text{mi} = 7.17 \times 10^6\ \text{m so}\ r = (1.53)(7.17 \times 10^6)$$

$$= \underline{1.10 \times 10^7\ \text{m}}$$

and

$$v_0 = (\frac{GM}{r_0})^{\frac{1}{2}} = 7.45 \times 10^3\ \text{m/sec}$$

so

$$v = (0.718)(7.45 \times 10^3\ \text{m/sec}) = \underline{5.35 \times 10^3\ \text{m/sec}}$$

4. From the diagram,

$$\cos\theta = \frac{r}{\sqrt{r^2 + a^2}}$$

so
$$F = 2\pi GM\rho rt \int_0^R \frac{a\,da}{(r^2 + a^2)^{3/2}} = 2\pi GM\rho rt \left[\frac{1}{r} - \frac{1}{\sqrt{r^2 + R^2}}\right]$$

but
$$m = \pi\rho R^2 t$$

so
$$F = \frac{2GMm}{R^2}\left(1 - \frac{r}{\sqrt{r^2 + R^2}}\right)$$

is the desired expression.

5. The two expressions can be solved for M, giving

$$M = \frac{4\pi^2 \ell R^2}{GT^2}$$

$$= \frac{4\pi^2 (1\text{ m})(0.71)^2(6.37 \times 10^6\text{ m})^2}{(6.67 \times 10^{-11}\text{ N-m}^2/\text{kg}^2)(2.51\text{ sec})^2}$$

$$= 1.92 \times 10^{24}\text{ kg} = 0.322 M_e$$

CHAPTER 17
Temperature

17.1   CHAPTER SUMMARY

Any macroscopic object consists of very many molecules, so many that a description in terms of individual particles is clearly impractical. Instead we can describe it in terms of a few macroscopic properties - temperature, pressure, and so forth - characteristic of the state of the system as a whole. Because very many particles are involved, statements about these average properties become quite precise; the laws of thermodynamics are empirical generalizations about these macroscopic quantities. We first seek careful and general definitions of properties such as the temperature.

When the macroscopic properties of a system are constant, it is said to be in thermal equilibrium; two systems in thermal contact come to such an equilibrium jointly, and are said to be in thermal equilibrium with each other. Empirically, such equilibrium is a transitive relationship: If two systems are each in equilibrium with a third, then they are in equilibrium with each other. (This is spoken of as the "zeroth law" of thermodynamics.) We define temperature by saying that any two systems which would, in thermal contact, be in equilibrium with each other have the same temperature. Common usage is sufficient to say which of two systems not in equilibrium has the higher temperature.

It remains merely to define a quantitative scale. Any property of a system which changes monotonically with temperature can serve as a thermometer in this sense - the pressure of a confined gas, say, or the length of a column of mercury. We calibrate the thermometer by assigning temperature values to one or more reference states and interpolating values linearly,

$$t = aL + b$$

where L is whatever property is serving as the thermometer and a and b are constants. So defined, temperature depends on the detailed variation of the thermometer property. An especially consistent type of thermometer is the gas thermometer at low pressure; the standard reference state for the ideal-gas thermometer is the triple point of water, assigned a value of 273.16°. This will turn out to be identical with the absolute temperature scale; other more or less familiar scales - Celsius, Fahrenheit, Rankine - are defined in terms of it.

An equation describing a thermodynamic system by relating various state variables such as pressure and temperature is an equation of state. In the limit of low pressures, gases obey an equation of state called the ideal-gas law:

$$PV = NkT$$

where N is the number of molecules of the gas and k is a universal constant. (Note that while the dimensions of P are force per unit area, it is often measured in units such as millimeters of mercury or atmospheres.)

The problem of the pressure on the walls of a container of gas has been treated earlier; the product PV is proportional to the average molecular kinetic energy. Comparing this to the ideal-gas law provides us with an interpretation of what temperature means on the molecular scale:

$$(\tfrac{1}{2}mv^2)_{av} = \tfrac{3}{2}kT$$

- T measures the average translational kinetic energy of each molecule.

An object generally expands when its temperature is increased. The expansion of a particular material can be described in terms of its linear expansion coefficient α:

$$\frac{\Delta L}{L} = \alpha\ \Delta T$$

or in terms of a volume expansion coefficient $\beta = 3\alpha$.

17.2 CHECK LIST

degree	zeroth law of thermodynamics
kelvin	thermometer
mm of Hg	ice point
atmosphere	steam point
$k = 1.38 \times 10^{-23}$ J/K	triple point
$R = N_A k = 8.31$ J/mole-K	gas thermometer
thermodynamics	ideal gas
temperature	ideal-gas temperature
heat	reference state
internal energy	absolute temperature scale
microscopic vs. macroscopic description	atmospheric pressure
mole	gauge pressure
pressure	Celsius scale
homogeneous system	Rankine scale
isolated system	Fahrenheit scale
thermal equilibrium	Avogadro's number
state variable	Boltzmann's constant
adiabatic wall	universal gas constant
diathermic wall	equation of state
insulator	coefficient of linear expansion
conductor	coefficient of volume expansion
thermal contact	

17.3 TRUE OR FALSE?

_____1. Thermodynamics treats systems of very many molecules in terms of a few macroscopic variables, because the interactions between molecules are not known in detail.

_____2. Macroscopic variables, such as the temperature or pressure of a system, describe the average conditions of very large numbers of molecules.

_____3. The laws of thermodynamics are derived from the kinetic theory of gases.

_____4. For an isolated system to be in thermal equilibrium with itself means that the macroscopic variables describing its state are constant in time.

_____5. Two variables suffice to describe the state of many homogeneous systems.

_____6. If changes in the state of one system have no effect on the state of another, the two are said to be separated by an adiabatic wall.

_____7. An adiabatic wall can be described as a perfect heat conductor.

_____8. When we say that two systems are in thermal equilibrium with each other, we mean that, if they were connected by a diathermic wall, their states would not change.

_____9. The zeroth law of thermodynamics is the empirical assertion that thermal equilibrium of systems is a transitive property.

_____10. If two gaseous systems are not in thermal equilibrium with each other, the one at the higher pressure is said to have the higher temperature.

_____11. If two gaseous systems not in equilibrium with each other are put in thermal contact, the one whose pressure decreases, at constant volume, has the higher temperature.

_____12. Temperature has no meaning applied to a system not in equilibrium with itself.

_____13. Temperature can, in principle, be defined as any monotonic function of one state variable of the system chosen as a thermometer.

_____14. Assigning temperature values to two reference states of some standard system is necessary and sufficient to fix a temperature scale.

_____15. In the limit of low gas pressures, all gas thermometers agree at all temperatures.

_____16. A single reference state suffices to define the ideal-gas temperature scale.

_____17. The true pressure of a confined gas is called the gauge pressure.

_____18. The Celsius and Rankine temperature scales have the same size degree but different zero points.

_____19. The Rankine and Fahrenheit temperature scales have different zero points but the same size degree.

_____20. The pressure and volume of an ideal gas are directly proportional at constant temperature.

1. Temperature scales that have been defined include Celsius, Rankine, and Fahrenheit. Which of these allow negative temperatures?

2. Treating the molecules of an ideal gas as pure point particles leads us to conclude that the total kinetic energy is $\frac{3}{2}nkT$. How would this conclusion be affected if the molecules are extended bodies and can vibrate and rotate?

3. In an expansion of an ideal gas, the product of pressure and volume remains constant. Has the root-mean-square speed of its molecules increased or decreased?

4. What properties should a system have in order to serve as a good thermometer?

5. The ball with a hole in it, sketched at right, is heated. Does the inside diameter of the hole increase or decrease?

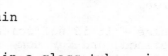

6. In many applications, a thin strip consisting of layers of two different metals bonded together serves as a temperature-sensing element. Explain how this works.

7. If a thermometer of the ordinary sort - liquid in a glass tube - is placed in something hot, it may happen that the liquid column drops briefly before starting to rise. What is happening here?

8. Should we consider the zeroth law of thermodynamics as an independent law of nature, as a definition of temperature, or both? How can a law both define a quantity and say something about the world which is independent of the definition?

17.5 EXAMPLES

1. A sample of gas is in a 3-liter steel container at 20°C and 10 atm. If the temperature is raised to 70°C, (a) what is the pressure? (b) How much does it affect your answer to (a) if you take into account the expansion of the steel vessel? The coefficient of volume expansion for steel is about 3.3 x 10^{-5} °C^{-1}.

2. The coefficient of expansion of mercury over the range 0 - 100°C can be represented by $(1.815 + 0.00057 t_C) \times 10^{-4}$ °C^{-1}. If a mercury thermometer is standardized at 0°C and 100°C, what is the largest amount by which it is in error over this range?

3. The mass of a sample of gas occupying 3 liters at 20°C and 10 atm. pressure is found to be 55 gm. What is the gas?

4. The surface temperature of the sun is 5700 K. What is the root-mean-square speed of a helium atom at this temperature?

17.6 ANSWERS

True or False?

1. False - regardless of whether individual interactions are known, there are far too many of them to allow a complete description.

2. True.

3. False - they are general, although we often illustrate them with ideal

gases because the equation of state of an ideal gas is very simple.

4. True.

5. True.

6. True.

7. False - this is a diathermic wall.

8. True - which ends up meaning that they are the same temperature.

9. True.

10. False - see the next answer.

11. True.

12. True - if we speak precisely; although common usage might assign temperature to parts of a nonequilibrium system which are only slowly changing.

13. True.

14. False - it is sufficient only if the temperature scale is linearly defined, and for some scales, such as the ideal-gas scale, is not necessary.

15. True.

16. True.

17. False - gauge pressure is the difference between true and atmospheric pressure.

18. False - the Rankine degree is the same size as the Fahrenheit.

19. True - $t_R = t_F + 459.7°$.

20. False - inversely proportional.

Questions

1. Negative Fahrenheit and Celsius temperatures are possible. The Rankine scale is the absolute scale with the Fahrenheit-sized degree, and so negative values are not possible.

2. In this case, $\frac{3}{2} NkT$ is the total energy of translational motion; the total kinetic energy includes vibrational and rotational energy also and so is larger.

3. If PV of an ideal gas is constant, so is the temperature; and in this case the root-mean-square speed $\sqrt{3kT/m}$ has not changed either.

4. It depends a great deal on what the thermometer is to be good for, but there are some general requirements that most applications share. Whatever property - length, pressure, electrical resistance - is to be observed should vary linearly, or nearly so, with the "real" (kelvin) temperature; otherwise its scale will agree only at a few points with other thermometers. In most cases it should be physically small, both in order to readily exchange heat and come to equilibrium with the system being measured and also to change the state of the system being measured as little as possible. Other considerations of convenience, useful temperature range and such, will arise in a particular situation.

5. The inside diameter increases. To see this, think of a little strip
    of material running around the perimeter of the hole. Heated, its
    length must increase; but its length is the circumference of the
    hole.

6. As the strip is heated, one of the metals expands, in general, more
    than the other, and the strip curves (toward the one which expands

    less). The degree of curvature depends on the temperature and can
    be used as a thermometer.

7. If this occurs, it is because the glass envelope holding the liquid,
    which gets heated first, expands a little before the temperature of
    the fluid inside has risen. Then, as glass and liquid come to equil-
    ibrium with their surroundings, the liquid rises.

8. It is an empirical law of nature - that is, one observes that the
    equilibrium of different systems is a transitive property - in its
    own right; but its existence makes possible a definition of tempera-
    ture, since if the zeroth law were not true, temperature could not
    be defined unambiguously. The relation between Newton's laws and
    the definition of force is an analogous one.

Examples

Partial Solutions (1)

1. If the system has constant volume, pressure and temperature are
    directly proportional; that is, P/T is constant. If the steel
    vessel also expands, volume is not constant. What combination of
    quantities remains constant in this case?

2. If the coefficient of expansion

    $$\beta = \frac{1}{V}\frac{dV}{dt} = a + bT$$

    then

    $$V \simeq V_0(1 + aT + \frac{1}{2}bT^2)$$

    If the mercury is standardized at 0°C and 100°C and interpolated
    linearly between, how is its reading related to the true temperature
    at points between?

3. Use the ideal-gas law to find the molecular weight of the gas.

4. The atomic weight of helium is 4.00. What is the mass of a helium
    atom?

Partial Solutions (2)

1. In the second case, PV/T is constant for a sample of an ideal gas
    in any event. If β is the volume expansion coefficient, the volume
    of the steel container at temperature t_C is

    $$V = V_0\left[1 + \beta(t_C - 20^\circ C)\right]$$

2. Call the "temperature" interpolated linearly from the volume of
    mercury T*. Then

    $$T* = CV + D$$

$$= (CV_0 + D) + (aC)T + (\tfrac{1}{2}bC)T^2$$

and we are given that $T^* = T$ at $T = 0^\circ C$ and $100^\circ C$; this determines C and D:

$$0 = (CV_0 + D)$$

and

$$100 = (CV_0 + D) + (aC)(100) + (\tfrac{1}{2}bC)(100^2)$$

What we are interested in is the quantity $T - T^*$.

3. We have

$$PV = nRT$$

so

$$n = \frac{PV}{RT}$$

and are given that this number of moles masses 55 gm.

4. The mass of a helium atom is

$$m = \frac{4.00 \text{ gm}}{N_A}$$

where N_A is Avogadro's number; and

$$v_{rms}^2 = \frac{3kT}{m}$$

Partial Solutions (3)

1. In the first case, P/T is constant, so

$$\frac{10 \text{ atm}}{293 \text{ K}} = \frac{P}{343 \text{ K}}$$

or

$$P = 11.71 \text{ atm}$$

In the second, the volume at $70^\circ C$ is

$$V = (3 \text{ liters})\left[1 + (3.3 \times 10^{-5})(50)\right] = 3.0050 \text{ liters}$$

so

$$\frac{(10 \text{ atm})(3 \text{ liters})}{293 \text{ K}} = \frac{(P)(3.0050 \text{ liters})}{343 \text{ K}}$$

$$P = 11.69 \text{ atm}$$

2. From the above, we have

$$CV_0 + D = 0$$

and

$$C = (a + 50b)^{-1} = 5.424 \times 10^3 \ ^\circ C$$

thus

$$T^* = (5.424 \times 10^3)\left[(1.817 \times 10^{-4})(T) + (2.85 \times 10^{-8})(T^2)\right]$$
$$= [0.9846T]\left[1 + 0.000157T\right]$$

and so

$$T - T^* = \delta T = (1.54 \times 10^{-4})(T)(100^\circ C - T)$$

δT is maximum at $T = 50^\circ C$; the value there is

$$\delta T_{max} = (1.54 \times 10^{-4})(50)(50) = 0.385^\circ C$$

3. We have
$$P = (10)(1.013 \times 10^5 \text{ N/m}^2) = 1.013 \times 10^6 \text{ N/m}^2$$
$$V = 3 \text{ liters} = 3.0 \times 10^{-3} \text{ m}^3$$
$$T = 293 \text{ K}$$
$$R = 8.31 \text{ J/K}$$

so

$$n = \frac{(1.013 \times 10^6)(3.0 \times 10^{-3})}{(8.31)(293)} = 1.25 \text{ moles}$$

Its molecular weight is thus

$$NW = \frac{55}{1.25} = 44.0$$

The only common gas of this molecular weight is CO_2.

4.

$$m = \frac{4.00 \times 10^{-3}}{6.02 \times 10^{23}} kg = 6.64 \times 10^{-27} \text{ kg}$$

and so

$$v_{rms}^2 = \frac{(3)(1.38 \times 10^{-23} \text{ J/K})(5.7 \times 10^3 \text{ K})}{6.64 \times 10^{-27} \text{ kg}}$$

$$= 3.55 \times 10^7 \text{ m}^2/\text{sec}^2$$

or

$$v_{rms} = \underline{5.79 \times 10^3 \text{ m/sec}}$$

This is of the same order as the escape velocity of the earth; but that of the sun is much larger ($\sim$600 km/sec).

CHAPTER 18
Heat, Work, and the First Law of Thermodynamics

18.1 CHAPTER SUMMARY

As systems at different temperatures, in thermal contact, come to equilibrium with one another, we say that heat flows between them. Heat cannot
be regarded as an independently conserved entity, since there are many
circumstances in which unlimited amounts of heat can be generated by
doing mechanical work. Instead, we identify heat as a form of energy;
heat and mechanical energy each can be transformed into the other.

Adding heat to an object generally increases its temperature. The
amount of temperature increase depends on the substance as well as on
the mass of the object:

$$Q = mc \; \Delta T$$

c, the specific heat of the material, may depend on the circumstances of
the heat transfer; thus, the specific heat if the heat transfer takes
place at constant volume is, in general, different from the specific
heat at constant pressure. The heat capacity for a given amount (m)
of a substance is mc. An empirical rule, the Dulong-Petit law, says
that the heat capacity per mole of most solids at ordinary temperatures
is near 6 cal/mole-K.

Heat may be added to an object without its temperature increasing if
the material is undergoing a change of phase, such as the boiling of
water. Microscopically, we understand this as the energy that must be
supplied to overcome molecular binding forces without changing the
average kinetic energy of molecules, which determines temperature. In
a pure substance a phase transition occurs at a specific temperature,
and requires a specific amount of heat - the latent heat - for each
unit of mass.

The temperature of a system may be increased by doing work on it
instead of adding heat. Empirically a given change of state of an
isolated system requires a given amount of (adiabatic) work, regardless
of how, in detail, the change is made. Thus we can say that there is
a definite difference of "internal energy" U between two states of a
system; the state, and U, can be changed either by adding heat Q to
it or by its doing work W on its surroundings:

$$\Delta U = Q - W$$

U depends only on the state of a system - it is a state function - but
Q and W depend on the details of the change. The work done by a small
expansion of a gas, for instance, is P dV. We can calculate this only
if the change proceeds quasi-statically, so that P and V are defined at
each point; even so, $\int P \, dV$ plainly depends on the particulars of the

139

change of state. Thus we write the first law of thermodynamics

$$\text{đQ} = dU + \text{đW}$$

to remind ourselves that Q and W are not state functions.

In an ideal gas - the limit of low pressure for real gases - the internal energy U depends only on the temperature. In the Joule experiment, a gas is allowed to expand freely and adiabatically; there is neither heat added nor work done, so U does not change. Experimentally only a very small change in temperature occurs. Since U depends only on T, the heat capacity of an ideal gas at constant volume is

$$c_v = \frac{dU}{dT}$$

The heat capacity at constant pressure is larger as the gas, expanding at constant pressure, does work on its surroundings.

In an adiabatic expansion of an ideal gas, the only change in internal energy is due to the work done by the expanding gas; this yields

$$PV^\gamma = \text{constant}$$

$$\gamma = c_p/c_v$$

for an adiabatic change.

The theorem of equipartition of energy says that the average energy of a molecule will be divided equally among all the degrees of freedom of the motion of molecules in the system. The theorem relates total internal energy to temperature, and thus makes it possible to predict heat capacities for many systems. The difference in heat capacities of gases, for instance, follows from the equipartition theorem, as does the Dulong-Petit law. Observed heat capacities, however, depend on temperature, contrary to the equipartition theorem; this discrepancy is due to quantization of molecular energies and thus reflects a fundamental limitation of the classical treatment.

18.2 CHECK LIST

heat	state function
caloric	internal energy
mechanical theory of heat	quasi-static process
mechanical equivalent of heat	P-V diagram
specific heat	isotherm
heat capacity	isothermal process
molar heat capacity	adiabatic process
specific heat at constant pressure	heat reservoir
specific heat at constant volume	ideal gas
Dulong-Petit law	rotational energy
Debye temperature	Joule experiment
latent heat	1 cal = 4.186 J

change of phase

melting point

boiling point

latent heat of fusion

latent heat of vaporization

first law of thermodynamics

adiabatic work

R = 1.986 cal/mole-K

equipartition theorem

monatomic molecule

diatomic molecule

degree of freedom

quantized energies

18.3   TRUE OR FALSE?

_____1. Heat can be considered as a conserved material substance.

_____2. The observation that heat could be produced in apparently un-limited amounts by mechanical work was a major blow to the caloric theory.

_____3. The experiments of Joule and others established heat as a form of energy.

_____4. The heat capacity of a material is its specific heat per unit mass.

_____5. In general, the specific heat of a substance at constant volume is greater than the specific heat at constant pressure.

_____6. For most solids and liquids under ordinary conditions, the difference between the specific heat at constant volume and the specific heat at constant pressure is negligible.

_____7. The law of Dulong and Petit states that, at high temperatures, the molar heat capacities of all gases are approximately the same.

_____8. The "latent heat" of an object at a given temperature is the amount of heat required to raise it to that temperature from absolute zero.

_____9. A material undergoing a change of phase typically absorbs sub-stantial quantities of heat without any increase in temperature.

_____10. The work required to effect a given change in the state of a system is independent of how the change is made.

_____11. The internal energy of a system is defined so that the internal energy change, in a change of state of the system, is equal to the work done on it, regardless of the heat transfer.

_____12. The internal energy of a system is defined so that the internal energy change, in a change of state of the system, is equal to the heat absorbed by the system, regardless of what work is done on it.

_____13. The internal energy of a system is a state function.

_____14. A quasi-static change of state is one in which no heat is exchanged between system and surroundings.

_____15. The work done by a system in expanding quasi-statically is given by $\int P \, dV$.

_____16. Heat cannot be regarded as a state function.

_____17. The internal energy of a system does not change in an isothermal expansion.

_____18. The theorem of equipartition of energy says that, in a gas, the internal energy is equally divided among all molecules.

_____19. In a real gas it is not strictly true that the internal energy is a function only of the temperature.

_____20. A free adiabatic expansion of a gas is not a quasi-static process.

_____21. At given temperature and pressure, the mass per unit volume of any ideal gas is the same.

_____22. The ideal-gas law is an example of an equation of state.

_____23. The thermal expansivity of an ideal gas is independent of the temperature.

18.4 QUESTIONS

1. Should the theorem of equipartition of energy be expected to apply to the planets of a solar system?

2. The specific heat of most substances common in the earth is substantially less than that of water. The prevailing winds in north temperate latitudes are westerly. Explain why the climate of London is so much more moderate than that of New York.

3. Suppose that in an adiabatic free expansion, the temperature of some gas increased. What could you say about intermolecular forces in this gas?

4. A gas expands at constant temperature and does external work. Does its internal energy change? If not, what is the energy source for the work done? Answer the question again if the expansion is adiabatic.

5. Give an example of a process in which heat is added to a system without causing a change in temperature. Give an example of a process in which the temperature of a system changes even though no heat is added to it.

6. A gas expands quasi-statically to twice its original volume at (a) constant pressure, (b) constant temperature. In which case does it do more work on the surroundings? Why? Relate your answer to the first law of thermodynamics.

7. Distinguish between intensive and extensive variables. Of which kind are: mass, pressure, volume, temperature, internal energy? What about heat?

8. Under what circumstances does the work done on a homogeneous ideal gas, in an adiabatic change, equal the change in total translational kinetic energy of molecules?

18.5 EXAMPLES

1. A piece of ice of mass 30 gm, falling through the earth's atmosphere, reaches a constant terminal velocity of 8 m/sec. Assuming no heat loss to its surroundings, how far would it have to fall in order that all the ice be melted before it hits the ground?

2. In the sketch at right, path (a) is a change of state of a monatomic ideal gas at constant temperature; path (b) is a change at constant pressure, followed by cooling at constant volume. Find the heat input, work done, and internal energy change for 1 mole of an ideal gas, by each path.

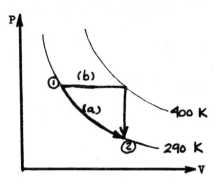

3. A piece of iron of mass 80 gm, at a temperature of 88°C, is dropped into an imperfect calorimeter containing 120 gm of water at 20°C. The specific heat of iron is 0.10 cal/gm-°C. If the system comes to equilibrium at a temperature of 22.8°C, how much heat has been lost to the surroundings?

4. A spherical container of volume 5 liters contains H_2 gas at 1 atm and 30°C. The ratio of specific heats is 1.41. Find the total molecular rotational kinetic energy of the sample of gas. If the same spherical mass of gas could rotate as a rigid body, what angular velocity would it have to have in order to have this much rotational kinetic energy macroscopically?

18.6 ANSWERS

True or False?

1. False - this is the "caloric" idea; heat cannot be considered a conserved quantity.

2. True.

3. True.

4. False - the specific heat is the heat capacity of unit mass.

5. False - if the material expands when heated, the specific heat at constant pressure is greater.

6. True - the thermal expansion of solids and liquids is pretty small.

7. False - the Dulong-Petit observation applies to solids.

8. False - the latent heat is the amount required to effect a phase change.

9. True.

10. False - work is not a state function.

11. False - both work done and heat transfer affect the internal energy.

12. False - both work done and heat transfer affect the internal energy.

13. True.

14. False - it is one made slowly enough so that the system is essentially at thermal equilibrium at every point.

15. True.

16. True.

17. False - this is true of an ideal gas, but is not general.

18. False - equally divided, on the average, among different modes of motion or "degrees of freedom."

19. True.

20. True.

21. False - the number of moles per unit volume is the same, but the mass depends on the molecular weight.

22. True.

23. False - it is 1/T for an ideal gas.

Questions

1. No; the equipartition of energy is a consequence of interactions of the molecules, by which energy is freely exchanged between different degrees of freedom. The interactions between planets of a solar system are very weak, so this exchange takes place only extremely slowly.

2. The higher specific heat of water means that changes in temperature, due to seasonal and daily changes in insolation, of the oceans are substantially less than those of the land. A site where the prevailing wind direction is off the ocean thus, usually, has a more moderate climate - smaller temperature variations - than one where the prevailing winds come to it from over a continent.

3. In a Joule expansion of an ideal gas, the temperature does not change. If the expansion of a real gas is accompanied by a temperature increase, it is because the gas has done positive work on itself in expanding, implying that repulsive forces exist between molecules.

4. If the gas is ideal, there is no change in its internal energy in an isothermal expansion. By the first law, the work done by the gas must equal the heat that was added to it during the expansion to keep the temperature constant. In an adiabatic expansion, no heat is added; the energy source for the work done, in this case, is the internal energy of the gas. This decreases and so the temperature of the gas must decrease.

5. An ideal gas expanding isothermally absorbs heat without temperature change and so does a piece of ice while melting. An ideal gas expanding adiabatically cools even though no heat is added or taken away.

6. The work done by the expanding gas on its surroundings is $\int P\,dV$. If the temperature of the gas is held constant, P decreases during the expansion. Thus the integrand of the work integral is a lower pressure, at each volume, in the case of the isothermal expansion, and less work is done in this case. In terms of the first law, in an expansion at constant pressure, not only the heat absorbed but also the decrease in the internal energy contribute to the work which the gas does on its surroundings.

7. An intensive variable is one which is independent of the mass of a homogeneous system; an extensive variable is proportional to the mass. Mass, volume, and internal energy are extensive, temperature and pressure intensive. Heat is neither: the amount of heat a system "contains" cannot be defined.

8. If the change is adiabatic, the work done on the gas is equal to the change in its internal energy. This will equal the change in the molecular translational kinetic energy, _if_ that's the only kind of internal energy there is - that is, if the gas is monatomic.

Examples

Partial Solutions (1)

1. How much energy is required to melt 30 gm of ice? In the situation described, where does the energy come from?

2. For an ideal monatomic gas, $c_v \simeq \frac{3}{2}R$ and $c_p \simeq \frac{5}{2}R$. The work done by the gas in an isothermal expansion is

$$W = \int_{V_1}^{V_2} P \, dV = nRT \int_{V_1}^{V_2} \frac{dV}{V} = nRT \, \ln\left(\frac{V_2}{V_1}\right)$$

What is the analogous expression for an expansion at constant pressure, for cooling at constant volume? You aren't told the pressures of initial and final states. Do you need them?

3. A certain amount of heat has been released by the metal in cooling; a certain amount has been absorbed by the water, which has been heated from 20°C to 22.8°C. The difference must have been lost to the surroundings.

4. The sample consists of

$$n = \frac{PV}{RT} = \frac{(1.013 \times 10^5 \text{ N/m}^2)(5.0 \times 10^{-3} \text{ m}^3)}{(8.31 \text{ J/K})(303 \text{ K})} = 0.201 \text{ mole H}_2$$

From this, plainly you can work out the number of molecules. What is the rotational kinetic energy per molecule?

Partial Solutions (2)

1. The latent heat of fusion of ice is 80 cal/gm. Thus to melt 30 gm

$$Q = (30 \text{ gm})(80 \text{ cal/gm}) = 2400 \text{ cal} = 1.005 \times 10^4 \text{ J}$$

are required. The kinetic energy of the ice isn't changing, so the source for this energy must be its gravitational potential energy.

2. The two temperatures tell you everything you need. Here

$$P_1 V_1 = P_2 V_2 = nRT$$

and $\qquad P_1 V_2 = nRT'$

At constant pressure,

$$W = P_1 \int_{V_1}^{V_2} d_V = P_1 (V_2 - V_1) = nR(T' - T)$$

and
$$Q = C_p \, \Delta T = \frac{5}{2}nR(T' - T)$$

and
$$Q - W = \Delta U = \frac{3}{2}nR(T' - T)$$

What work is done in a change at constant volume?

3. The heat released by the iron is

$$Q_1 = (80 \text{ gm})(0.10 \text{ cal/gm-}^{\circ}\text{C})(88 - 22.8 = 65.2^{\circ}\text{C}) = 522 \text{ cal}$$

How much has been absorbed by the water?

4. We are given

$$\frac{C_p}{C_v} = \frac{C_v + R}{C_v} = 1 + \frac{R}{C_v} = 1.41$$

hence $\qquad C_v = 2.44R$

and so $\qquad U = 2.44nRT$

if the gas is ideal. How much of this is due to molecular rotation?

Partial Solutions (3)

1. So by conservation of energy, if the ice falls a distance h,

$$mgh = (0.03 \text{ kg})(9.8 \text{ m/sec}^2)(h) = \Delta U = 1.005 \times 10^4 \text{ J}$$

$$\underline{h = 3.42 \times 10^4 \text{ m}}$$

or about 21 mi.

2. In the constant-pressure expansion

$$W = (1)(8.31 \text{ J/K})(400 \text{ K} - 290 \text{ K}) = 914 \text{ J}$$

$$Q = (2.5)(1)(8.31 \text{ J/K})(110 \text{ K}) = 2285 \text{ J}$$

$$\Delta U = Q - W = 1371 \text{ J}$$

When the gas is cooled back to 290 K at constant volume, no work is done; thus

$$\Delta U = Q = C_V n \ \Delta T = \frac{3}{2}nR \ \Delta T$$

$$= (1.5)(1)(8.31 \text{ J/K})(-110 \text{ K}) = -1371 \text{ J}$$

Thus, altogether, along path (b)

$$\underline{\Delta U = 0} \qquad \underline{Q = 914 \text{ J}} \qquad \underline{W = 914 \text{ J}}$$

Path (a) is an <u>isothermal</u> expansion; if the temperature doesn't change, neither does the internal energy of an ideal gas. Thus

$$Q = W = nRT \ \ln \left(\frac{V_2}{V_1}\right) = nRT \ \ln \left(\frac{T'}{T}\right)$$

$$= (1)(8.31 \text{ J/K})(290 \text{ K}) \ \ln (400/290)$$

so by path (a)

$$\underline{\Delta U = 0} \qquad \underline{Q = 775 \text{ J}} \qquad \underline{W = 775 \text{ J}}$$

3. The heat absorbed by the water is

$$Q_2 = (120 \text{ gm})(1.0 \text{ cal/gm-}^{\circ}\text{C})(2.8^{\circ}\text{C}) = 336 \text{ cal}$$

so $\qquad Q_1 - Q_2 = 522 - 336 = \underline{186 \text{ cal}}$

has been leaked to the surroundings.

4. The internal energy must include $\frac{3}{2}nRT$ due to translational kinetic energy; thus the rest is

$$U_{rot} = 2.44nRT - 1.5nRT = 0.94nRT$$

$$= (0.94)(0.201)(8.31 \text{ J/K})(303 \text{ K})$$

$$= \underline{476 \text{ J}}$$

0.201 mole of H_2 gas is $(0.201)(2)(1.008 \text{ gm}) = 0.405 \text{ gm}$, and the radius of a sphere whose volume is 5 liters works out to be 10.6 cm. Thus if we imagine this rotating as a rigid body, its moment of inertia is

$$I = \frac{2}{5}mR^2 = (0.4)(0.405 \text{ gm})(10.6 \text{ cm})^2 = 18.2 \text{ gm-cm}^2$$

$$= 1.82 \times 10^{-7} \text{ kg-m}^2$$

so $\qquad \omega^2 = \dfrac{2U_{rot}}{I} = \dfrac{(2)(4.76 \times 10^2 \text{ J})}{1.82 \times 10^{-7} \text{ kg-m}^2} = 5.23 \times 10^9 \text{ sec}^{-2}$

or $\qquad \underline{\omega = 7.23 \times 10^4 \text{ sec}^{-1}}$

CHAPTER 19
The Availability of Energy

19.1 CHAPTER SUMMARY

According to the first law of thermodynamics, either heating a system or doing work on it contributes to its internal energy. Yet heat and mechanical work are not altogether interchangeable. Mechanical work can be freely converted into heat, as in any system containing friction; it is generally not possible to convert a given amount of heat completely into work.

The second law of thermodynamics is a statement about the direction taken by such irreversible processes. We state it first in terms of the properties of an idealized heat engine which, in a cycle, accepts heat Q_h from a hot reservoir, performs work W, and discards the remaining heat $Q_c = Q_h - W$ to a cooler reservoir. The efficiency of the engine is

$$\varepsilon = \frac{W}{Q_h} = 1 - \frac{Q_c}{Q_h}$$

Run in reverse, the engine becomes a refrigerator. A statement of the second law (Kelvin-Planck) is then: no engine can, with no other effect, extract heat from a reservoir and produce an equivalent amount of work. Another (Clausius) is: no refrigerator can, with no other effect, remove heat from a cooler reservoir and transfer it entirely to a hotter one. The two statements are equivalent in that any engine which violated one could be made to violate the other.

Most processes of nature are irreversible. The conduction of heat from a warmer to a cooler object, for instance - if heat could be made to flow back from the cooler to the hotter object, without some other change being made in the surroundings - this would violate Clausius' statement of the second law. A process can be reversible only if it proceeds quasi-statically and involves neither conduction of heat across a temperature difference nor forces which dissipate mechanical energy as heat.

The most efficient heat engine possible, working between any given pair of reservoirs, is one whose cycle is reversible. This is Carnot's theorem. For the Carnot engine to run reversibly, heat transfer can only take place isothermally; other portions of the cycle must proceed adiabatically. The efficiency of a Carnot cycle can depend only on the two reservoir temperatures. In fact, we can use this to define a temperature scale which is independent of the properties of any material:

$$\frac{T_c}{T_h} \equiv \frac{Q_c}{Q_h}$$

This absolute scale turns out to be identical with the ideal-gas temperature scale already defined.

The second law of thermodynamics makes it possible to define a new
state function, the entropy S of a system, by

$$\Delta S \equiv \int \frac{dQ_r}{T}$$

where dQ_r means heat absorbed reversibly by the system. S is a function
only of the state of a system - thus, for instance, the net entropy
change in a complete Carnot cycle is zero, as the working substance
returns to its original state.

In terms of the entropy, the second law of thermodynamics can be
given a broader statement: the entropy of the universe does not decrease
in any natural process:

$$\Delta S (\text{universe}) \geq 0$$

The entropy change of the universe - system and surroundings - is zero in
a reversible process, and irreversible processes proceed in the direction
which increases the entropy of the universe.

In an irreversible process, $T \Delta S_u$ can be interpreted as the amount
of energy which has become unavailable for use to perform work. T is to
be understood as the lowest reservoir temperature available in a given
situation. For example, if a gas undergoes a free adiabatic expansion,
the work which could have been performed by letting the gas expand
isothermally against a piston can no longer be had. On a microscopic
level, the entropy is thus associated with the degree of disorder of
the system. The energy of ordered motions of all the molecules is
available on the macroscopic scale for doing work; that of random dis-
ordered motion of individual molecules is not all available.

19.2 CHECK LIST

reversible vs. irreversible processes	Carnot engine
second law of thermodynamics	Carnot cycle
heat engine	Carnot's theorem
refrigerator	absolute temperature scale
efficiency	ideal-gas temperature scale
working substance	entropy
heat reservoir	free adiabatic expansion
Kelvin-Planck statement	phase change
Clausius statement	entropy change of the universe
reversibility	available energy
heat conduction	ordered vs. disordered energy
dissipative force	Clausius' inequality

19.3 TRUE OR FALSE?

____1. There are many processes in which the complete conversion of heat
into an equivalent amount of work, although not inconsistent with

the first law of thermodynamics, is not possible.

____2. Most naturally occurring macroscopic processes are reversible.

____3. The conduction of heat across a temperature difference is an irreversible process.

____4. The second law of thermodynamics is a statement as to the direction in which irreversible processes go.

____5. A heat engine is an idealized device in which heat is converted completely into useful mechanical work.

____6. The second law of thermodynamics implies that no heat engine can be 100% efficient.

____7. The Kelvin-Planck statement of the second law applies only to heat engines and is superseded by the more general Clausius statement.

____8. Any process which converts mechanical energy into internal energy of a system is irreversible.

____9. All quasi-static processes are reversible.

____10. Between two given heat-reservoir temperatures, a reversible engine requires the greatest heat input for the production of a given amount of work.

____11. Between two given heat-reservoir temperatures, all reversible heat engines have the same efficiency.

____12. In a reversible engine, heat must be absorbed or rejected isothermally.

____13. The efficiency of a Carnot engine depends only on the two working temperatures.

____14. The absolute temperature scale defined on the basis of a Carnot cycle which uses an ideal gas as a working substance is called the ideal-gas temperature.

____15. The entropy is a state function.

____16. The entropy change of the working substance over one complete cycle of a Carnot engine is Q_h/T_h.

____17. One possible statement of the second law of thermodynamics is that entropy change of the universe, in any possible process, is never negative.

____18. The entropy change of a system in any adiabatic process must be zero since no heat is transferred.

____19. The entropy change of the universe, in an irreversible process, is a measure of the amount of energy which has been made unavailable for useful macroscopic work.

____20. The direction of natural processes is toward increased order.

____21. In an ideal gas, the expression $dU = C_v \, dT$ is valid only for changes made at constant volume.

____22. For nearly all materials, $C_p - C_v \simeq R$.

____23. The temperature change of an ideal gas in an adiabatic expansion is greater than that in an isothermal expansion of the same amount.

____24. The equipartition theorem correctly predicts the temperature dependence of molar heat capacities of elastic solids but not of gases.

____25. The failures of the classical equipartition theorem fundamentally are due to quantization of energy.

19.4   QUESTIONS

1. The conduction of heat across a temperature difference is said to be an irreversible process. So is conversion of mechanical to internal energy, as in the case of an object sliding across a rough tabletop and slowing down. But we can warm one of the objects back up and cool the other one down, and so restore the temperature difference. We can cool the block on the tabletop to its original temperature and set it moving with its original kinetic energy. In what sense are these processes irreversible?

2. In a free adiabatic expansion of an ideal gas, the entropy increases even though no heat is added to the gas. In view of the definition of entropy, how is this possible?

3. Heat Q flows from a hotter (T_1) to a colder (T_2) body. What is the entropy change of the universe? In what sense does this represent energy that has become unavailable for doing work?

4. Imagine a container with just 12 molecules of a gas in it. It must sometimes happen, just by chance, that all of them find themselves in the upper half of the container. Yet this is just the reverse of a free expansion - a process we have declared irreversible. Explain.

5. Can you cool your kitchen on a hot day by leaving your refrigerator door open?

6. The frictional drag of the atmosphere on an orbiting satellite causes it to move closer to the earth and its kinetic energy to increase. In what way has energy become unavailable for doing work in this irreversible process?

7. Is a process in which there is no exchange of heat between system and surroundings necessarily reversible?

8. In talking about the Carnot cycle we say that extracting heat from a reservoir isothermally does not change the entropy of the universe. In a real engine, this limit cannot quite be reached. Why not? In reality, will the entropy of the universe increase or decrease?

19.5   EXAMPLES

1. A not very clever idea for a ship's engine goes as follows: an ideal Carnot cycle extracts heat from seawater at 18°C and exhausts it to evaporating dry ice, which the ship carries with it, at -78°C. The latent heat of sublimation of dry ice is 137 cal/gm. If the ship's engines are to develop 8,000 hp, how much dry ice - neglecting any losses - must it have on board for a day's running?

2. 50 gm of ice at -15°C are dropped into 150 gm of water at 44°C. The specific heats of ice and water may be taken as constant 0.5 and 1.0 cal/gm-°C, respectively. If the system comes to equilibrium without loss of heat to the surroundings, find the entropy change.

3. A certain refrigerator has a motor power rating of 88 W. Consider it

as an ideal reversible refrigerator. If the outside temperature is 26°C, how long will it take to freeze 2.5 kg of water put in at room temperature?

4. Imagine an engine which runs quasi-statically around the cycle sketched at right. The cycle consists of constant-pressure and constant-temperature changes of state. The working fluid is 1.23 moles of an ideal gas for which γ = 1.41. Find (a) the net work done, (b) the net heat absorbed, (c) the entropy change of the gas around one full cycle.

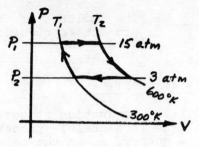

19.6 ANSWERS

True or False?

1. True.

2. False - real processes are thermodynamically irreversible, in general.

3. True.

4. True.

5. False - it is any device that converts heat into mechanical work.

6. True.

7. False - the two statements are equivalent, in that a violation of either also violates the other.

8. True - this is the case of "dissipating energy by friction" or some such.

9. False - although the converse is true.

10. False - it requires the least heat input, its efficiency is largest.

11. True.

12. True - heat conduction across a temperature difference is irreversible.

13. True - $\varepsilon = 1 - T_c/T_h$.

14. False.

15. True.

16. False - a Carnot cycle is reversible and the entropy is a state function; over one full cycle, its change is zero.

17. True.

18. False - consider a Joule expansion, for instance.

19. True.

20. False - toward increasing disorder.

21. False - U is a state function and, for an ideal gas, depends only on the temperature, so this is a valid expression for any state change.

22. False - this is for an ideal gas; for a solid, with very small thermal expansion, the difference is very small.

23. True - there is no temperature change in an isothermal (!) process.

24. False - it says nothing about the temperature difference.

25. True.

Questions

1. To say that a process is irreversible means essentially that the whole universe won't go in the other direction. In the examples given, we can put the "system" back in its original state, but not without making a permanent change in its surroundings.

2. The entropy change is dQ/T for a <u>reversible</u> process. In a free adiabatic expansion, which is <u>irreversible</u>, there is an entropy change, even though dQ/T is zero.

3. The total change in entropy of the two bodies taken together is

$$\Delta S = \frac{Q}{T_2} - \frac{Q}{T_1}$$

and, if this is all that happens, this is the entropy change of the universe. If, instead of just letting the heat flow, we had run a Carnot cycle between these two bodies (as reservoirs), the work we could have gotten from it for heat input Q is

$$Q(1 - \frac{T_2}{T_1}) = T_2 \ \Delta S$$

4. The second law is a probabilistic statement. For 12 molecules, it is possible, though unlikely, for the reverse of a Joule expansion to occur spontaneously. For macroscopic samples - 10^{22} molecules or so - it is so unlikely as to be, in any practical sense, impossible.

5. No; the refrigerator takes heat from inside and exhausts it to the outside - to the room. If you open your refrigerator door the heat you extract from the room is dumped back into the room, with interest.

6. As a satellite moves closer to the earth, its kinetic energy increases; but its potential energy decreases more - twice as much, if the orbit remains nearly circular. Its total mechanical energy has decreased, some of it dissipated to heat in the atmosphere. Since the atmosphere is a great big heat sink, essentially all of this has become unavailable for doing work.

7. No, this is neither a necessary nor a sufficient condition.

8. In any real process, the second law says the entropy of the universe increases. In reality, if everything is exactly at the same temperature, it's all in an equilibrium state and there is no heat flow; there must be some small difference in temperature to cause a heat transfer. But in this case the hotter side's entropy will decrease by an amount always smaller than the increase of entropy of the colder side - the net change of entropy is always an increase. Furthermore, real-world heat reservoirs aren't infinite; extracting heat from something must lower its temperature, even though only slightly.

Examples

Partial Solutions (1)

1. What you need to find, obviously, are the efficiency of a Carnot cycle with the two temperatures given and the amount of work needed for a day's running. The total heat which must be rejected determines how much dry ice you need. A horsepower is 550 ft-lb/sec - watch out for units in this one.

2. If the specific heat of something is constant, its entropy change is

$$\Delta S = \int_{T_1}^{T_2} \frac{dQ}{T} = mc \int_{T_1}^{T_2} \frac{dT}{T} = mc \ln \frac{T_2}{T_1}$$

What is the entropy change of the ice on melting?

3. An ideal reversible engine is a Carnot cycle run backwards; heat Q_c is extracted from a cold reservoir by doing work W, and heat $Q_h = Q_c + W$ rejected to a hotter reservoir. How much heat must you extract to freeze 2.5 kg of water?

4. The work done in an isothermal expansion is

$$W = nRT \ln \frac{V_2}{V_1} = nRT \ln \frac{P_1}{P_2}$$

and in an expansion at constant pressure

$$W = P(V_2 - V_1) = nR(T_2 - T_1)$$

In the same two kinds of processes, what is the heat absorbed? The entropy change?

Partial Solutions (2)

1. The efficiency is

$$\varepsilon = 1 - \frac{T_c}{T_h} = 1 - \frac{195}{291} = 0.334$$

and a horsepower works out to be 746 W.

2. To melt ice requires a heat input of 80 cal/gm at a constant temperature of 273 K, so

$$\frac{\Delta S}{m} = \frac{80 \text{ cal/gm}}{273 \text{ K}} = 0.293 \text{ cal/gm-K}$$

We need also the final equilibrium temperature T_f. The heat gained by the ice is

$$(50 \text{ gm}) \left[(0.5 \text{ cal/gm-K})(15 \text{ K}) + 80 \text{ cal/gm} + (1.0 \text{ cal/gm-K})(T_f - 273 \text{ K}) \right]$$

while that lost by the 150 gm of water is

$$(150 \text{ gm})(1.0 \text{ cal/gm-K})(317 \text{ K} - T_f)$$

Solve for T_f.

3. To freeze 2500 gm of water requires

$$(2500 \text{ gm})(80 \text{ cal/kg}) = 2.0 \times 10^5 \text{ cal} = 8.37 \times 10^5 \text{ J}$$

and, for a reversible engine/refrigerator,

$$\frac{Q_h}{T_h} = \frac{W + Q_c}{T_h} = \frac{Q_c}{T_c}$$

so

$$W = Q_c \left(\frac{T_h}{T_c} - 1 \right)$$

4. For an ideal gas at constant temperature,

$$\Delta U = 0$$

so

$$Q = W = nRT \ln \frac{P_1}{P_2}$$

and

$$\Delta S = \frac{Q}{T} = nR \ln \frac{P_1}{P_2}$$

At constant pressure

$$T = \frac{PV}{nR}$$

so

$$Q = \int nC_p \, dT = nC_p(T_2 - T_1) = \frac{C_p}{R} P(V_2 - V_1)$$

and

$$\Delta S = \int \frac{nC_p \, dT}{T} \quad nC_p \ln \frac{T_2}{T_1} = nC_p \ln \frac{V_2}{V_1}$$

For the gas given, what is C_p?

Partial Solutions (3)

1. The work required for a day's running is

$$W = (8 \times 10^3 \text{ hp})(746 \text{ W/hp})(1 \text{ day} = 8.64 \times 10^4 \text{ sec})$$
$$= 5.16 \times 10^{11} \text{ J}$$

and

$$Q_c = \frac{T_c}{T_n - T_c} W = \frac{195}{291 - 195} W$$
$$= 2.03 \, W = 1.05 \times 10^{12} \text{ J} = 2.50 \times 10^{11} \text{ cal}$$

Melting dry ice provides 137 cal/gm, so for a day's fuel we require

$$\frac{2.50 \times 10^{11} \text{ cal}}{1.37 \times 10^5 \text{ cal/kg}} = \underline{1.82 \times 10^6 \text{ kg}}$$

or about 2000 tons of dry ice.

2. We have

$$(50)(T_f - 185.5 \text{ K}) = (150)(317 \text{ K} - T_f)$$

so

$$T_f = 284.1 \text{ K}$$

The increase of entropy of 50 gm of ice heated from 258 K to 273 K, melted and then heated as water from 273 to 284 K is

$$\Delta S_{ice} = (50) \left[0.5 \ln(273/258) + 0.293 + 1.0 \ln(284/273) \right]$$
$$= (50)(0.028 + 0.293 + 0.040) = 18.05 \text{ cal/K}$$

while the decrease in entropy of 150 gm of water cooled from 317 K to 284 K is

$$\Delta S_{water} = (150) \left[1.0 \ln(284/317) \right] = -16.44 \text{ cal/K}$$

Thus the net change of entropy of the system is

$$\Delta S = 18.05 - 16.44 = \underline{1.61 \text{ cal/K}}$$

3. The work which must be done to extract 8.37×10^5 J of heat from the water is

$$W = \frac{(8.37 \times 10^5 \text{ J})(299 \text{ K} - 273 \text{ K})}{273 \text{ K}} = 7.97 \times 10^4 \text{ J}$$

The refrigerator motor can do work at a rate of 88 J/sec, so the time required is

$$\frac{7.97 \times 10^4 \text{ J}}{88 \text{ J/sec}} = \underline{906 \text{ sec}}$$

This is about 15 min. A real refrigerator, which doesn't achieve ideal (Carnot) performance, might take two or three times as long.

4. Starting from (P_1, T_1) we have first an expansion at constant pressure:

$$W = nR(T_2 - T_1) = (1.23)(8.31 \text{ J/K})(300 \text{ K}) = 3067 \text{ J}$$

If the ratio of specific heats is 1.41, the molar heat capacity at constant pressure is

$$C_p = \frac{1.41R}{1.41 - 1} = 3.44R = 28.6 \text{ J/K}$$

so

$$Q = nC_p(T_2 - T_1) = (1.23)(28.6 \text{ J/K})(300 \text{ K}) = 10{,}550 \text{ J}$$

and

$$\Delta S = nC_p \ln(T_2/T_1) = (1.23)(28.6 \text{ J/K}) \ln 2 = 24.4 \text{ J/K}$$

Next a further expansion isothermally:

$$W = Q = nRT \ln(P_1/P_2) = (1.23)(8.31 \text{ J/K})(600 \text{ K}) \ln 5$$
$$= 9870 \text{ J}$$

and

$$\Delta S = Q/T = (9870 \text{ J})/(600 \text{ K}) = 16.5 \text{ J/K}$$

By the same means, we get for the contraction at constant pressure

$$Q = -10{,}550 \text{ J} \qquad W = -3067 \text{ J} \qquad \Delta S = -24.4 \text{ J/K}$$

and for the repressurization at T_1 to P_1

$$Q = W = -4935 \text{ J} \qquad\qquad \Delta S = -16.5 \text{ J/K}$$

so the totals around one complete cycle are

$$\underline{Q = W = 4935 \text{ J}} \qquad\qquad \underline{\Delta S = 0}$$

CHAPTER 20
Wave Pulses

The many different kinds of wave motion that occur in nature - water waves,
sound waves, waves on a stretched string, electromagnetic waves such as
light - share certain common features. We encounter many of these in
considering wave pulses - finite wave disturbances propagating in one
dimension.

If one end of a stretched string is given a flip, a pulse is produced which travels along it with a speed determined by the properties
of the string. What becomes of the pulse - reflection at the end of
the string, the degree to which its shape spreads out (dispersion) as
it travels - likewise depends on the properties of the medium, the string,
through which the wave is propagated. The pulse carries energy and
momentum but, again, by the motion of the wave disturbance along the
string rather than by actual transport of material parts of it. Each
bit of the string, in fact, is moving perpendicular to the direction of
propagation of the wave; this is a transverse wave. Sound waves, on the
other hand, are longitudinal: the displacement of particles is along the
direction in which the wave propagates.

Many examples of such finite wave pulses occur in nature, and the
more general case of an extended disturbance propagated as a wave can be
thought of as an extended sequence of wave pulses.

A function describing the wave disturbance at each point as a function
of time is a wave function. Functions of the form

$$y(x, t) = y(x \pm vt)$$

describe a shape y(x) moving in the x direction with speed v and so are
appropriate wave functions for waves propagating without dispersion.
In a case in which more than one wave occurs in the same medium, the wave
functions usually simply add; this is the principle of superposition.
Separate waves can thus add to or cancel one another, leading to interference phenomena which are unique to wave motion.

The speed of waves, in general, is a property of the medium that
transmits them. (The exception is that electromagnetic waves - light -
can propagate without any material medium.) The speed in each case is
found by applying the laws of motion to each bit of the medium. For waves
traveling along a stretched string one finds

$$v = \sqrt{T/\mu}$$

where T is the tension, μ the mass per unit length, of the string. This
kind of form - an elastic property divided by a density - is found for

all sorts of mechanical waves; the speed of sound waves in a gas, for instance, is

$$v = \sqrt{B/\rho} = \sqrt{\gamma RT/M}$$

if B is the bulk modulus of the gas and ρ is its density. Compressions of a gas in transmitting a sound wave are so rapid as to take place adiabatically - hence the appearance of γ, the ratio of specific heats of the gas, in the second form.

Propagation of waves, again with the exception of electromagnetic waves in vacuum, is determined by the medium in which they move. When a wave pulse encounters a boundary between different media, as between two strings of different density, only part of it continues across the boundary; part is reflected back. If the wave speed decreases at the boundary - a pulse passing from a lighter to a heavier string, for instance - the image pulse which is reflected back is inverted compared to the original one.

20.2 CHECK LIST

wave motion
mechanical wave
electromagnetic wave
wave pulse
dispersion
transverse wave
longitudinal wave
wave function
interference
superposition principle

nonlinear waves
constructive vs. destructive interference
linear mass density
bulk modulus
speed of sound
frequency
reflection
transmission
image pulse

20.3 TRUE OR FALSE?

_____1. In a mechanical wave motion, momentum and energy are propagated through a material medium without transport of the material itself.

_____2. The propagation of transverse waves along a stretched string is called dispersion.

_____3. The speed at which a wave propagates in a material medium is a property of the medium.

_____4. A wave pulse is a disturbance, propagating as a wave, which is limited in extent and duration.

_____5. A wave motion, in which the disturbance occurs along the direction of propagation, is a transverse wave.

_____6. Sound waves are an example of transverse waves.

_____7. Light - and other electromagnetic - waves are an example of transverse waves.

_____8. A function of the form y(x + vt) describes a shape or pattern y(x) moving in the +x direction at speed v.

_____9. The principle of superposition says that the combined effect of two wave pulses, in the same medium, is just their algebraic sum.

_____10. If two wave pulses traveling in opposite directions along the same string meet, they reflect from one another.

_____11. Superposition is a general principle, always obeyed by most forms of wave motion.

_____12. The speed of wave pulses along a stretched string is proportional to the tension in the string.

_____13. For given pressure, the speed of sound waves in an ideal gas is independent of the temperature.

_____14. For given temperature, the speed of sound waves in an ideal gas is independent of the pressure.

_____15. The pressure variations in the propagation of sound waves through a gas are essentially adiabatic.

_____16. A wave pulse on a stretched string comes to a boundary at which the string becomes less dense; the reflected pulse is inverted.

_____17. In general, a wave pulse encountering a boundary at which the wave velocity becomes smaller is inverted on reflection.

_____18. In general, at a boundary between two media, a wave pulse is partly reflected and partly transmitted across the boundary.

20.4 QUESTIONS

1. All of the following functions describe a shape y(x) moving on the x axis with speed v. Which are and are not useful as descriptions of wave pulses?

(a) $y = Ae^{\frac{-(x - vt)^2}{2a}}$

(b) $y = B \ln (x - vt)$

(c) $y = C(x - vt)^{3/2}$

(d) $y = D$, if $-a \leq x + vt \leq a$
$\quad = 0$, if $|x + vt| \geq a$

2. Pick a familiar example of wave motion and explain how one knows, or can show by experiment, that energy and momentum are transported by the wave and that this occurs without transport of the material medium in which the wave travels.

3. The sketch shows two wave pulses traveling in opposite directions

along a stretched string. Make a few sketches at later times that show what happens as the two pulses encounter one another.

4. Energy and momentum, of course, can be transported by particles as well as by waves. How can we distinguish these two fundamentally different pictures of energy transfer? What experimental means, for instance, could we use to rule out the possibility that sound is transported by invisible material particles?

5. In the upper sketch, two wave pulses approach one another on a string. At a later point in time, the string looks like the lower sketch - the pulses more or less cancel. What has become of the energy that the two pulses (obviously, in the upper sketch) were transporting?

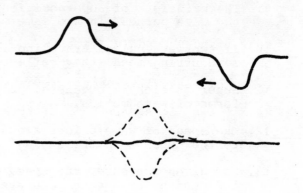

6. The speed of sound waves in a gas is of the same order of magnitude as the mean thermal velocity of the gas molecules. This is not a coincidence but is to be expected. Why?

20.5 EXAMPLES

1. Consider a wave pulse moving on a stretched string and described by the wave function $y = f(x - vt)$, where

$$f(w) = \frac{y_0}{1 + (w/a)^2}$$

(a) Find an expression for the transverse velocity of the string as a function of x and t. (b) If $v = 210$ m/sec, $y_0 = 1.3$ cm, and $a = 5$ cm, what is the <u>maximum</u> speed of the string?

2. You stand on the edge of a canyon 420 m and clap your hands; the echo comes back to you 2.56 sec later. What is the temperature of the air?

3. A certain wire stretches under tension according to

$$\ell = \ell_0 + T/k$$

If the speed of waves on the wire under a tension of 3800 N is twice that under a tension of 1000 N, find k. The length of the wire is 1.32 m, unstretched.

4. In a steel wire, the velocity of longitudinal waves - sound waves traveling along the wire - is 10 times the velocity of transverse waves within the wire under a tension of 6200 N. If the appropriate "bulk modulus" for steel, in this situation, is 2×10^{11} N/m^2, what is the diameter of the wire?

20.6 ANSWERS

True or False?

1. True.

2. False - dispersion is the change of shape of a wave pulse as it propagates.

3. True.

4. True.

5. False - this is a longitudinal wave.

6. False - sound is a longitudinal wave.

7. True.

8. False - this wave function moves in the -x direction.

9. True.

10. False - the principle of superposition is the statement that they pass right through each other, essentially unaffected.

11. False - it is obeyed, except for electromagnetic waves in vacuum, only in the limit of small amplitudes.

12. False - to the square root of the tension.

13. False - it is proportional to the square root of the temperature.

14. True.

15. True.

16. False - the wave velocity on the less dense string is higher.

17. True.

18. True.

Questions

1. (b) and (c) are not bounded; both increase monotonically with (x - vt) and thus do not describe finite wave pulses.

2. Think of ripples spreading on the surface of still water, for instance. As the waves reach it, a bit of trash on the surface of the water is set in motion; energy and momentum have been transported to it from the wave source. But there is no outward physical flow of water taking place, for if you watch the bit of trash you see it just bouncing up and down - it isn't set moving along the wave direction.

3. Something like

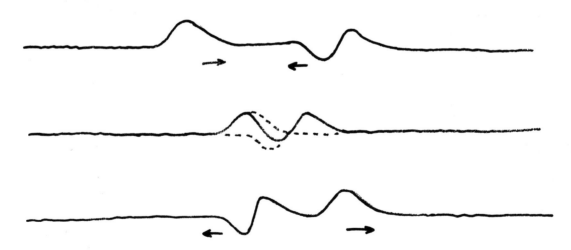

4. You can think of a number of indications, but the most important one, probably, is the   phenomenon of interference. That sound, if carried by a motion of particles, could interfere as waves from separate sources do - especially that, in appropriate circumstances, two sound pulses can cancel out as they encounter one another - is hard to conceive.

5. Nothing has happened to it. Although the string is instantaneously undisplaced, it is in motion; at the instant of the second sketch all the energy is kinetic.

6. Because, on a microscopic scale, the pressure variations in a sound wave must be propagated by collisions between molecules, and so the speed of propagation of the wave must be of the same order as the speed at which molecules move between collisions.

Examples

Partial Solutions (1)

1. The pulse described by this wave function propagates along the string in the +x direction, without change of shape; thus we may watch the time dependence of the displacement at any point. Nothing but complication is lost if we watch it at $x = 0$. Then

$$y(t) = \frac{y_0}{1 + (vt/a)^2} \quad \text{at } x = 0$$

How do we find the time at which the $x = 0$ bit of the string has its maximum velocity?

2. What is the speed of sound in air in this case and how is it related to the temperature?

3. For the given dependence of length on tension, write the speed of sound waves on this wire. The speed at either value of T is unknown, as well as the force constant k. How do you get something you can solve for k?

4. The velocity of sound in a fluid is

$$v = \sqrt{B/\rho}$$

where B is the bulk modulus. For want of anything better, use the same prescription for the steel wire. (What goes in place of B for an elastic solid isn't quite the bulk modulus, but never mind.) What is the speed of transverse waves? Do you need the length of the wire to solve this?

Partial Solutions (2)

1. We can write the displacement of the wire at $x = 0$ as

$$y(t) = y_0 \left[1 + \left(\frac{t}{\tau}\right)^2\right]^{-1} \qquad \tau = \frac{a}{v}$$

and the velocity

$$v_t = \frac{dy}{dt} = \frac{-2y_0 t}{\tau^2}\left[1 + \left(\frac{T}{\tau}\right)^2\right]^{-2}$$

and the velocity has its maximum value at the times when _its_ time derivative is zero.

2. The speed of sound you've measured is

$$v = \frac{840 \text{ m}}{2.56 \text{ sec}} = 328 \text{ m/sec}$$

since the sound of your handclap has to go there _and_ back. The speed of sound in a gas is

$$v = \sqrt{\gamma RT/M}$$

which you can solve for the temperature T.

3. The speed of waves along this wire is given by

$$v^2 = \frac{T}{\mu} = \frac{T\ell}{m} = \frac{T\ell_0}{m}(1 + \frac{T}{k\ell_0})$$

Thus the ratio of speeds at two different tensions, which is what you have to work with here, is

$$\frac{v_1^2}{v_2^2} = \frac{(1 + T_1/k\ell_0)\,T_1}{(1 + T_2/k\ell_0)\,T_2}$$

Solve for k.

4. The speed of transverse waves is

$$v_t = \sqrt{T/\mu}$$

where

$$\mu = m/\ell$$

is the linear density. Thus the ratio of longitudinal to transverse wave speeds is

$$\frac{v_\ell}{v_t} = \sqrt{\frac{Bm}{\rho T\ell}}$$

Where does the diameter of the wire come into all this?

Partial Solutions (3)

1. The velocity found above may be written

$$v_t = \frac{-2y_0 v}{a}(\frac{t}{\tau})\left[1 + (\frac{t}{\tau})^2\right]^{-2}$$

It would look something like the graph at the right. The velocity has an extreme value when

$$\frac{dv}{dt} = 0 = \frac{-2y_0 v}{a}\left\{(\frac{t}{\tau})(-2)\left[1 + (\frac{t}{\tau})^2\right]^{-3}(\frac{2t}{\tau^2})\right.$$

$$\left. + \left[1 + (\frac{t}{\tau})^2\right]^{-2}(\frac{1}{\tau})\right\}$$

$$= \frac{-2y_0 v}{a\tau}\left[1 + (\frac{t}{\tau})^2\right]^{-3}(1 - \frac{3t^2}{\tau^2}) = 0$$

The extrema are thus at

$$t = \pm\,\frac{\tau}{\sqrt{3}}$$

Plugging these times back into the velocity formula gives the maximum transverse speed:

$$v_{tmax} = \frac{-2y_0 v}{a}(\pm\frac{1}{\sqrt{3}})(1 + \frac{1}{3})^{-2}$$

$$= 0.649\,\frac{y_0 v}{a} = 0.649\,\frac{(1.3)(210)}{5} = 34.5\ m/sec$$

2. The temperature is

$$T = \frac{Mv^2}{\gamma R}$$

For air, $\gamma = 1.40$ and $M = 28.8$ gm, so

163

$$T = \frac{(2.88 \times 10^{-2} \text{ kg})(328 \text{ m/sec})^2}{(1.40)(8.31 \text{ J/K})}$$

$$= \underline{266 \text{ K} = -7^{\circ}\text{C}}$$

No wonder you were clapping your hands.

3. We have here $v_2 = 2v_1$, with $T_1 = 1000$ N and $T_2 = 3800$ N. Thus here

$$4 = \frac{(k\ell_0 + 3800)(3800)}{(k\ell_0 + 1000)(1000)}$$

This gives $k\ell_0 = 5.22 \times 10^4$ N

or

$$k = \frac{5.22 \times 10^4 \text{ N}}{1.32 \text{ m}} = \underline{3.95 \times 10^4 \text{ N/m}}$$

4. If the diameter of the wire is d, then

$$\rho = \frac{m}{v} = \frac{4m}{\pi d^2 \ell}$$

so

$$\frac{v_\ell}{v_t} = \sqrt{\frac{\pi d^2 B}{4T}}$$

or

$$d = 2\left(\frac{T}{\pi B}\right)^{\frac{1}{2}} \left(\frac{v_\ell}{v_t}\right) = \underline{1.99 \times 10^{-3} \text{ m}}$$

with the data given here.

CHAPTER 21
Harmonic Waves in One Dimension

21.1 CHAPTER SUMMARY

Any function $y(x \pm vt)$ describes a wave disturbance $y(x)$ propagating at speed v. A highly important special case is a sinusoidal shape:

$$y = y_0 \sin [k(x - vt)] = y_0 \sin (kx - \omega t)$$

Such a wave would be produced if the source of the wave disturbance undergoes simple harmonic motion. The particular importance of these harmonic waves is that this shape alone is not changed by dispersion in propagating through a medium. Other periodic waveforms can be treated as a superposition of harmonic waves; of course there are many cases in nature which closely approximate a pure harmonic wave.

The length of one complete cycle in space, at any instant, is called the wavelength $\lambda = 2\pi/k$. The number of complete oscillations per unit time is the frequency $f = \omega/2\pi$. By these definitions the speed of the wave is

$$v = f\lambda$$

a relation common to harmonic waves of all kinds.

As in all wave motions, we may distinguish transverse and longitudinal harmonic waves. In a transverse wave, the disturbance can occur in either of two perpendicular directions transverse to the wave direction. If it is confined to one of these, or if the two transverse motions are in a definite phase relationship, the wave is said to be polarized. Circular or elliptical, as well as linear, polarizations are possible; a circularly polarized wave has equal amplitudes in the two transverse directions, but the motions are $\pi/2$ out of phase - picture twirling the end of a stretched string in a circle.

In a longitudinal wave the disturbance is directed along the propagation direction, and polarization plainly has no meaning. Sound waves are an example; they may be described either as waves of pressure in the medium or of displacement of the molecules of the medium along the direction of wave motion.

Particularly important interference phenomena arise from the superposition of harmonic waves. The resultant of two waves with the same frequency and wavelength is another wave with the same frequency and wavelength, but with amplitude and phase that depend on the phase difference between the components. Two waves in phase augment one another, while two that are π out of phase cancel each other out. (The amplitude and phase of the resultant can be found by just adding the components, amplitude and phase, by the usual rule of vector addition.) In many interference phenomena the phase difference between two waves which come from the same source, but by different paths, leads to variations in the amplitude of the resultant wave.

An important property of waves of all sorts is the energy they carry. Quite generally the intensity of a wave – the amount of energy transmitted across unit area per unit time – is given by

$$I = \eta v$$

where v is the wave speed and η is the energy density of whatever motion or disturbance is being propagated. In a harmonic wave, each point of the medium undergoes simple harmonic motion; thus the intensity is proportional to the square of the wave amplitude and also to the square of the frequency, as is the energy of a simple harmonic oscillator.

The intensity of a harmonic sound wave, for instance, is thus proportional to the square of the amplitude of the pressure fluctuation. As the ear's response to sound intensity is roughly logarithmic, intensity of sound waves is often measured in decibels:

$$db = 10 \log_{10} \frac{I}{I_0}$$

I_0 being some reference intensity level.

For a given physical system, the wave functions describing waves that can occur are the solutions of a wave equation for that system; the wave equation is derived by applying the laws of motion to each bit of a material medium. The wave equation in general takes the form

$$\frac{\partial^2 y}{\partial x^2} = \frac{1}{v^2} \frac{\partial^2 y}{\partial t^2}$$

Any function y(x, t) of the form y(x ± vt) satisfies this equation. The principle of superposition follows from the fact that this differential equation is linear; in general this is strictly true only for small disturbances y.

21.2 CHECK LIST

harmonic wave

amplitude

wave number

angular frequency

simple harmonic motion

dispersive medium

Fourier analysis

phase difference

wavelength

frequency

period

transverse wave

longitudinal wave

pressure wave

displacement wave

superposition

interference

constructive vs. destructive interference

vector method of addition

phasor

intensity

energy density

decibel

logarithmic scale

166

plane polarization

circular polarization

elliptical polarization

sound waves

partial derivative

wave equation

small-amplitude approximation

21.3 TRUE OR FALSE?

_____ 1. A harmonic wave is one in which the wave function is sinusoidal.

_____ 2. The wave number of a harmonic wave is the number of wave cycles that pass a given point in unit time.

_____ 3. Harmonic waves propagate with unchanged shape regardless of the nature of the medium.

_____ 4. The wavelength of a harmonic wave is the spatial length of one full cycle of the wave.

_____ 5. Fourier analysis is the resolution of a harmonic wave into an infinite succession of individual wave pulses.

_____ 6. Every particle of a stretched string, along which a harmonic wave is traveling, is undergoing simple harmonic motion.

_____ 7. The velocity of any harmonic wave is its wavelength divided by its frequency.

_____ 8. A longitudinal wave is necessarily plane-polarized.

_____ 9. A transverse wave is said to be polarized if there is a definite phase relation between the motions in the two transverse directions.

_____ 10. If the wave motions in the two transverse directions are harmonic but differ in phase by $\pi/2$, the wave is circularly polarized.

_____ 11. Sound waves have no polarization.

_____ 12. A sound wave in a gas can be described either as a displacement or as a pressure wave; the two are $\pi/2$ out of phase.

_____ 13. The ratio of pressure amplitude and displacement amplitude, for a sound wave in a gas, depends on the frequency.

_____ 14. The resultant of two superposed harmonic waves of the same frequency is a harmonic wave of the same frequency, whose amplitude depends on the phase difference of the components.

_____ 15. The resultant of two superposed harmonic waves of the same frequency is a harmonic wave of the same frequency, whose amplitude depends on the phase difference of the components.

_____ 16. Two harmonic waves from the same source, which have reached the same point by different paths, exhibit total destructive interference; the lengths of the two paths must differ by at least a wavelength.

_____ 17. Perfect destructive interference of two harmonic waves requires that they have the same amplitude.

_____ 18. The intensity of a harmonic wave on a string is inversely proportional to its amplitude.

_____ 19. The intensity of a harmonic wave on a string is proportional to the square of the frequency.

_____20. A decibel is a unit of intensity.

_____21. Any function of x and t of the form y(x ± vt) is a solution of the wave equation

$$\frac{\partial^2 y}{\partial x^2} = \frac{1}{v^2} \frac{\partial^2 y}{\partial t^2}$$

_____22. Any wave system described by a wave equation of the form given above possesses the property of superposition.

_____23. For mechanical waves in a material medium, the form of the wave equation given above is equivalent just to F = ma; thus this form applies to <u>all</u> cases of mechanical waves in matter.

21.4   QUESTIONS

1. A harmonic wave moving along a stretched string is given by

$$y = y_0 \sin (kx + \omega t)$$

Find an expression for the particle velocity. Could we equally well describe this as a <u>velocity</u> wave propagating on the string?

2. We say that a wave transports energy and momentum. Can it also transport <u>angular</u> momentum? Explain.

3. A harmonic wave crosses a boundary at which the wave speed changes. Does its frequency, its velocity, or both change? Explain.

4. At a certain point six different harmonic waves are superposed. They have equal amplitude and each differs in phase from the next by the same angle θ. (That is, their phases relative to the first one are θ, 2θ, 3θ, etc.) Draw a phasor diagram for the addition for the cases θ = 45° and 60°.

5. Harmonic waves travel down a stretched string from a source - a tuning fork, say - which provides a fixed power input. Someone pulls on the other end, increasing the tension in the string. The wave speed on the string has plainly increased, yet energy is being transported along the string at the same rate. Explain.

6. In the string of the previous question, the tension was increased by 25%, say. How does the wavelength of waves on the string change?

21.5   EXAMPLES

1. A transverse wave of wavelength 22 cm propagates along a stretched string. If the amplitude of the wave is 1.1 cm and the string is under a tension of 1800 N, find the total energy of a 1-m length of the string. The answer you get is time-independent. How can energy be said to be transported along the string by the wave?

2. A man sits in a room directly between two loudspeakers; he is 1.8 m from one and 3.2 m from the other, at point A in the sketch. The Two speakers vibrate in phase. If the lowest frequency at which he observes maximum destructive interference is 122 Hz, what is the speed of sound in air? He moves to point B, 2.4 m from point A. What then is the lowest frequency for destructive interference?

168

3. The lowest frequency to which the human ear responds is about 30 Hz.
    If sound waves of this frequency have an intensity at the pain
    threshold, what is the displacement amplitude? Assume standard air -
    760 mm Hg at 20°C.

4. A wire consists of two different materials joined together, one of
    them five times as dense as the other. When a traveling wave on
    the wire comes to the boundary (moving from the more to the less dense
    wire), 64% of the incident intensity is transmitted across the
    boundary. If the incident wave's amplitude is 4 cm, find the ampli-
    tude of the reflected and the transmitted waves.

21.6 ANSWERS

True or False?

1. True.

2. False - this is the frequency; the wave number is the number of cycles
    contained in a length of 2 m.

3. True.

4. True - the wave number $k = 2\pi/\lambda$.

5. False - it is the analysis of nonsinusoidal waveforms into harmonic
    components.

6. True.

7. False - the wavelength multiplied by the velocity; if all else fails,
    check the dimensions.

8. False - polarization has no meaning for a longitudinal wave.

9. True.

10. False - I'm being picky; this is an elliptical polarization, but isn't
    circular unless the amplitudes of the two transverse components are
    equal.

11. True - they are longitudinal.

12. True.

13. True - the ratio is proportional to ω^2.

14. False - it is of the same frequency as the two components.

15. True.

16. False - the minimum path length is half a wavelength, since the two
    must be out of phase by an odd multiple of π.

17. True - for complete cancellation.

18. False - it goes as the square of the amplitude.

19. True.

20. False - it measures intensity but can't be said to be a unit, as twice
    the intensity isn't twice as many decibels.

21. True.

22. True - the wave equation is linear.

23. False - this wave equation contains a small-amplitude approximation; for large displacements, mechanical waves are nonlinear.

Questions

1. The particle velocity is plainly

$$v_y = \partial y / \partial t = \omega y_0 \cos (kx + \omega t) = \omega y_0 \sin (kx + \omega t + \pi/2)$$

This is a velocity wave, then, with amplitude ωy_0 and with the same frequency and wavelength as the displacement wave, but 90° out of phase with it. Compare the displacement and pressure waves in the case of sound.

2. Certainly - the most obvious case would be a circularly polarized transverse wave.

3. Consider points just at the boundary, on either side of it. They are oscillating at the wave frequency; this must thus be continuous across the boundary. The wavelength thus changes in proportion to the velocity change, since the frequency is constant.

4.

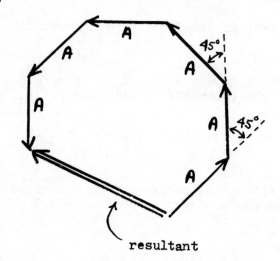

resultant   resultant = 0

5. The intensity of the wave on the string is unchanged, but its speed has increased; the energy density has therefore decreased. The point is that the same energy, delivered to the string in the same time, is carried away faster, so it is spread over a longer length of the string.

6. If the tension increases by 25%, the velocity increases by $\sqrt{1.25}$ or 1.12. Since the source frequency is unchanged, the wavelength (= v/f) also increases by a factor 1.12, that is, by 12%.

Examples

Partial Solutions (1)

1. You could get well and truly bogged in this one if you tried to do it by writing out the wave function and following the motion of a whole meter of the string. Instead just notice that every particle of the string is undergoing simple harmonic motion, with the same frequency,

170

and with amplitude 1.1 cm. What is the total energy of a particle in simple harmonic motion?

2. The difference in path length from the two speakers to point A is 1.4 m. What is the corresponding difference in phase of the two waves? When he has moved to point B, what then is the path length difference from the two loudspeakers?

3. The "pain threshold" usually is taken as 1 W/m^2. In this one you need only plug in and solve for the displacement amplitude.

4. Write out the intensity in terms of velocity, frequency, amplitude, etc.; this last is what you want to solve for. The wave velocity on the wire depends on the tension it is under. How do you get around this? If the transmitted wave has 64% of the intensity incident on the barrier, what is the reflected intensity?

Partial Solutions (2)

1. Consider an element of the string of length dx. Its mass is μ dx, so its total energy in SHM is

$$dE = \frac{1}{2}dm\ \omega^2 y_0^2 = \frac{1}{2}(\mu\ dx)\left[\frac{2\pi v}{\lambda}\right]^2 y_0^2$$

All that you need is to get this in terms of the things you know.

2. For maximum destructive interference, the phase difference between two components must be

$$\Delta\phi = \pi,\ 3\pi,\ 5\pi,\ \ldots$$

So the path difference must be $\frac{1}{2}\lambda$ (or $\frac{3}{2}\lambda$, $\frac{5}{2}\lambda$, etc.)

In the second case, the path length difference is 1.0 m (see the sketch).

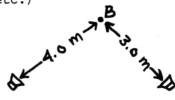

3. The intensity is

$$I = \frac{1}{2}\rho v \omega^2 s_0^2$$

for displacement amplitude s_0, and the speed of sound in a gas is

$$v = \left(\frac{\gamma P}{\rho}\right)^{\frac{1}{2}} = \left(\frac{\gamma RT}{M}\right)^{\frac{1}{2}}$$

4. The intensity is the rate at which energy is being transported along the wire; by conservation of energy the other 36% must be the reflected intensity. The intensity of a transverse wave on a wire is

$$I = \frac{1}{2}\rho v \omega^2 y_0^2 = \frac{1}{2}\left(\frac{m}{A\ell}\right) v \omega^2 y_0^2$$

so

$$I_0 = \frac{\mu v \omega^2 y_0^2}{2A}$$

if the wire has cross-sectional area A. The intensity of the reflected wave is

$$I_r = 0.36 I_0 = \frac{\mu v \omega^2 y_r^2}{2A}$$

if y_r is its amplitude. What is that of the transmitted wave?

Partial Solutions (3)

1. The total energy of the element dx is

$$dE = \frac{2\pi^2 \mu v^2 y_0^2}{\lambda^2} dx = \frac{2\pi^2 T y_0^2}{\lambda^2} dx$$

if T is the tension in the string. Thus the total energy content per unit length is

$$\frac{dE}{dx} = \frac{2\pi^2 (1800 \text{ N})(0.011 \text{ m})^2}{(0.22 \text{ m})^2}$$

$$= \underline{88.8 \text{ J/m}}$$

The fact that this is constant is not inconsistent with the transport of energy along the wire; in a steady state, as much energy flows into each meter of it as flows out.

2. When he is at A,

$$\lambda = (2)(1.4 \text{ m}) = 2.8 \text{ m}$$

so

$$v = (2.8 \text{ m})(122 \text{ m/sec}) = \underline{342 \text{ m/sec}}$$

At B, the path length difference is 1.0 m, so full destructive inter-ference requires a wavelength of 2.0 m, and

$$f = \frac{342 \text{ m/sec}}{2.0 \text{ m}} = \underline{171 \text{ Hz}}$$

3. Here

$$\rho v = (\frac{MP}{RT})(\frac{\gamma RT}{M})^{\frac{1}{2}} = (\frac{\gamma M}{RT})^{\frac{1}{2}} P$$

For standard air, $P = 1.013 \times 10^5$ N/m^2, $M = 28.8$ gm, $\gamma = 1.40$, and $T = 293$ K. Thus

$$s_0 = (\frac{2I}{\rho v \omega^2})^{\frac{1}{2}} = \underline{3.7 \times 10^{-4} \text{ m}}$$

4. The transmitted wave's intensity is

$$I_t = 0.64 I_0 = \frac{\mu' v' \omega^2}{2A} y_t^2$$

where μ' and v' refer to the wire across the boundary; $\mu' = 0.2\mu$. From the above,

$$\frac{\mu v \omega^2 y_r^2}{2A} = 0.36 \frac{\mu v \omega^2 y_0^2}{2A}$$

or

$$y_r = 0.6 y_0 = \underline{2.4 \text{ cm}}$$

and

$$\frac{\mu v' \omega^2 y_t^2}{2A} = 0.64 \frac{\mu v \omega^2 y_0^2}{2A}$$

or

$$y_t^2 = 0.64 y_0^2 \frac{\mu v}{\mu' v'} = 0.64 (\frac{\mu}{\mu'})^{\frac{1}{2}} y_0^2$$

since the wave speed goes as the square root of the density. Thus

$$y_t = 0.8(5)^{\frac{1}{4}} = \underline{4.79 \text{ cm}}$$

Notice that this is bigger than the incident amplitude.

172

CHAPTER 22
Standing Waves

22.1 CHAPTER SUMMARY

When waves propagate on a system of finite size, reflections of the waves
at the boundaries of the system lead to characteristic vibration patterns
called standing waves; among other things these are basic to most musical
instruments.

As an example, again, we take a string fixed at both ends. A wave
on the string reflects at either end and travels up and down it. The
phase difference between successive reflections determines the behavior
of the string; if the extra distance 2L that each successive reflected
wave has traveled is a whole number of wavelengths, then all the reflected
waves are in phase and augment one another. In this case the reflected
waves on the string can build up to a large amplitude (compared to that
of the source driving the string). The particular resonance frequencies
at which this can occur are

$$f_N = Nf_1 = N\frac{v}{2L}, \qquad N = 1, 2, 3, 4, \ldots$$

where v is the speed of the wave on the string and L is its length. f_1
is called the fundamental frequency of the system; the other resonance
frequencies, higher multiples of f_1, are its harmonics.

If the string is driven at a frequency which is not one of the
particular resonance values, the successive reflected waves are out of
phase with one another and cancel to some degree. Large-amplitude
vibrations can be set up on a system only at one of its characteristic
resonance frequencies.

The standing wave on the string consists of components traveling in
both directions; by adding wave functions moving in opposite directions
we find the form of standing-wave functions to be

$$y(x, t) = 2y_0 \cos \omega t \sin kx$$

Note that this describes a constant shape sin kx, whose amplitude oscillates
in time. We determine the possible standing-wave patterns on a given
system by requiring such functions to meet appropriate boundary conditions;
for the string fixed at both ends the requirement that y = 0 at both
ends determines what wavelengths will fit on the string.

If the string is fixed at only one end, with the other end free to
move transversely, the phase relation of successive waves is altered by
the fact that the reflection at the free end does not invert the wave.
In this case, successive reflections augment one another if the extra
distance 2L is half a wavelength (or 1½, or 2½, etc.). The boundary
condition now is that the free end of the string must be an antinode; the

resonance frequencies in this case are

$$f_N = Nf_1 = N\frac{V}{4L}, \qquad N = 1, 3, 5, 7, \ldots$$

That is, the fundamental frequency is half that for the string of the same length with both ends fixed, while the even harmonics are missing.

Another important example is the case of standing sound waves in, for example, a pipe of fixed length. This is a system on which many musical instruments are based. If both ends of the pipe are closed, it behaves as a string with both ends fixed: nodes must occur at either end. If one end of the pipe is open, a pressure node (a displacement antinode) occurs at the open end; its resonance frequencies are those of a string with one end free.

22.2 CHECK LIST

stationary vibration pattern

standing wave

resonance

damping

fundamental frequency

harmonics

harmonic series

natural frequencies

overtones

boundary condition

nodes and antinodes

modes of vibration

22.3 TRUE OR FALSE?

_____1. A standing wave is a stationary vibration pattern on a system of finite size.

_____2. A standing wave is set up when successive reflections at the boundaries of the system are in phase.

_____3. At one of the system's standing-wave frequencies, the amplitude of vibration is approximately equal to that of the wave source.

_____4. Standing waves on a stretched string occur only for wavelengths which are a whole-number multiple of the length of the string.

_____5. The fundamental frequency of a given system corresponds to the longest standing wavelength possible on it.

_____6. If a system is driven at a frequency other than one of its resonance frequencies, successive reflected waves tend to cancel and there is very little response.

_____7. The second overtone is the same as the first harmonic.

_____8. The wave velocity on a certain stretched string, 2.5 ft long, is 400 ft/sec; its fundamental frequency is 160 Hz.

_____9. A displacement of a stretched string given by $y_0 \sin(kx - \omega t)$ is not a standing wave.

_____10. The boundary condition at an open end of a pipe, or a free end of a string, requires an antinode rather than a node.

_____11. The fundamental frequency of a pipe with one end open is the same as that of a pipe of the same length, with closed ends.

_____12. The fundamental frequency of a pipe with one end open is the same as that of a pipe of twice its length, with closed ends.

_____13. A string 4 ft long, fixed at both ends, vibrates at three times its fundamental frequency; there is an antinode 8 inches from either end.

_____14. A string 4 ft long, free at one end, vibrates at three times its fundamental frequency; there is an antinode 16 inches from either end.

_____15. An open end of an air column is a pressure node.

_____16. A pressure antinode is a displacement node.

_____17. In fact, the pressure node at an open end of an air column is a little outside the end of the pipe.

_____18. The fundamental frequency of a given pipe tends to increase with the temperature.

_____19. The odd harmonics of a half-open pipe are missing.

_____20. The amplitude of standing waves on a system, at a resonance frequency, is limited only by damping effects.

22.4 QUESTIONS

1. The fundamental frequency of a certain organ pipe is 240 Hz if the pipe is closed at both ends, 120 Hz if it is open at one end. What is its fundamental frequency if it is open at both ends?

2. Suppose a wave traveling along a string loses 10% of its energy on each reflection from an end. Are there still sharp nodes in a standing-wave pattern on the string?

3. Your G string is flat - that is, your violin sounds below its proper frequency. Do you tighten it or loosen it?

4. How is the pitch of a musical instrument modulated - changed - by fingering its strings?

5. What would happen to the resonant frequencies of an organ pipe if it were sounded in a helium stmosphere?

6. The characteristic tones of musical instruments are determined largely by their content of higher harmonics - components at frequencies above the fundamental note. The even harmonics are largely absent from an oboe's tone, while a clarinet's sound contains both even and odd harmonics. What properties of the two instruments might this fact reflect?

7. The body of a violin acts as a sounding board - that is, it is set vibrating by the vibration of the string and in turn acts as a source of sound waves in the air. Will the vibration of a plucked violin string damp out more or less rapidly if the sounding board is removed?

22.5 EXAMPLES

1. Among the resonant frequencies of a certain stretched string are 560, 160, and 400 Hz. If the mass of the string is 26 gm and it is under a tension of 760 N, how long is it?

2. At an open end of a pipe, the pressure variation cannot fall discontinuously to zero; the pressure node consequently is a little <u>outside</u> the open end. Assume that the effective length of the pipe is consequently

$$\ell_{eff} = (\ell)(1 + d/\lambda)$$

where ℓ is the length and d is the diameter of the pipe. If the first two resonant frequencies of a certain half-open pipe are at 54.6 and 159.8 Hz, and the speed of sound is 337 m/sec, find the dimensions of the pipe.

3. A stretched string vibrates at its fundamental frequency, initially with a maximum amplitude of 4 cm. The tension is then reduced so that the string's frequency decreases by 20%. Assuming that this can be done without loss of energy, what is the string's vibration amplitude thereafter?

22.6 ANSWERS

True or False?

1. True.

2. True - successive reflected waves all augmenting one another add up to a large amplitude.

3. False - it is usually very much larger; see the previous answer.

4. False - the condition is that the length of the string be a whole-number multiple of half the wavelength.

5. True.

6. True.

7. False - the first overtone and the second harmonic are both twice the fundamental frequency.

8. False - the wavelength of the fundamental is <u>twice</u> the length of the string.

9. True - this is a wave traveling toward +x.

10. True - with the quibble that the open end of a pipe requires a <u>displacement</u> antinode, which is a pressure <u>node</u>.

11. False - half the frequency of the closed pipe.

12. True.

13. True - the wavelength is 32 inches.

14. False - there is an antinode 16 inches from the fixed end and <u>at</u> the free end.

15. True.

16. True.

17. True.

18. True - the sound velocity in air goes as the square root of the temperature.

19. False - the even harmonics are missing.

20. True - the limiting condition is that energy is dissipated as fast as the source supplies it.

Questions

1. It is 240 Hz again; if both ends are open, we need a (displacement) antinode at both ends, so the length of the pipe must be any whole number of half-wavelengths, just as for the pipe with both ends closed.

2. No. With a 10% reflection loss, nodes would still be identifiable, but perfect cancellation requires equal amplitudes.

3. You tighten it. Increasing the tension increases the velocity of waves on the string, so increases the frequency for given wavelength.

4. By changing the length of the string so that one of its standing waves - usually the fundamental - has the desired frequency.

5. Other things being equal, the frequencies would increase by about a factor of 2.5 because the speed of sound in a gas is proportional to the square root of its molecular weight.

6. What this says is that an oboe acts like a half-open pipe (the odd harmonics only are responsible for the oboe's characteristic sour tone), while the clarinet acts like an open (or closed) pipe. Since both instruments are open at the lower end, this must reflect the different kinds of mouthpiece and sound source in the two instruments.

7. Without the sounding board the string is very much less efficient at dissipating its energy - as sound - to the surrounding air; this is what the sounding board is there for. Thus without it, it would damp out much more slowly.

Examples

Partial Solutions (1)

1. The standing wavelengths on a stretched string are given by

$$\lambda = \frac{2\ell}{n} \qquad \text{for } n = 1, 2, 3, \ldots$$

   What are the corresponding frequencies?

2. Using the effective length of the pipe, as given, the standing-wave condition for a half-open pipe is

$$\lambda = \frac{4\ell_{eff}}{2n + 1} \qquad \text{for } n = 0, 1, 2, \ldots$$

   or

$$\lambda = \frac{4\ell\,(1 + d/\lambda)}{2n + 1}$$

   The two frequencies given are the two lowest - hence n = 0 and 1.

3. All you need to do this is to know the relation between the vibration amplitude and the total energy content of the vibrating string.

Partial Solutions (2)

1. The corresponding frequencies are

$$f_n = \frac{v}{\lambda_n} = \frac{nv}{2\ell} = nf_1 \qquad n = 1, 2, 3, \ldots$$

Thus all are integer multiples of the fundamental frequency. What is the greatest common divisor of the given frequencies? Is this necessarily the fundamental frequency? Note in passing - I didn't specify; is it possible that this is a string with one end free?

2. The wavelengths corresponding to the given frequencies are

$$\lambda_0 = 4\ell(1 + \frac{d}{\lambda_0}) = \frac{337}{54.6} = 6.17 \text{ m}$$

$$\lambda_1 = \frac{4}{3}\ell(1 + \frac{d}{\lambda_1}) = \frac{337}{159.8} = 2.109 \text{ m}$$

which gives you two equations to solve for the two unknown dimensions of the pipe.

3. We needn't go through the whole calculation. Every particle of the string is in simple harmonic motion, with an amplitude which is a fixed fraction - for a given mode of vibration! - of the maximum amplitude of the vibrating string. Thus the energy of every particle, and thus that of the whole string, is proportional to the square of the frequency and the square of the amplitude.

Partial Solutions (3)

1. The greatest common divisor of the given frequencies is 80 Hz. This isn't necessarily f_1 - that could be any integer fraction of 80 Hz, 40 Hz for instance.

Now

$$f_1 = \frac{v}{2\ell} = \frac{1}{2\ell}\sqrt{\frac{T}{\mu}} = \frac{1}{2\ell}\sqrt{\frac{T\ell}{m}} = \frac{1}{2}\sqrt{\frac{T}{m\ell}}$$

so

$$\ell = \frac{T}{4mf_0^2} = \frac{760 \text{ N}}{(4)(0.026 \text{ kg})(80 \text{ sec}^{-1})^2} = \underline{1.14 \text{ m}}$$

The string can't have one free end, as in that case the resonance frequencies are odd-integer multiples of the fundamental. The given values, in the ratio 7 : 2 : 5, can't fit this pattern.

2. Eliminating d between the two equations leaves

$$\lambda_0 - \lambda_1 = \frac{\lambda_0^2 - 3\lambda_1^2}{4\ell}$$

$$\ell = \frac{\lambda_0^2 - 3\lambda_1^2}{4(\lambda_0 - \lambda_1)} = \underline{1.522 \text{ m}}$$

And you can plug back in to either equation to get d; this gives

$$\underline{d = 8.1 \text{ cm}}$$

3. If

$$E \propto (fy_0)^2 = \text{constant}$$

- as we are assuming - then fy_0 is constant and

$$y_0' = \frac{fy_0}{f'} = \frac{fy_0}{0.8f} = 1.25y_0 = \underline{5 \text{ cm}}$$

CHAPTER 23
The Superposition of Waves of Different Frequency

Further phenomena of interest arise when waves in a system whose frequencies are different are superposed. If two waves are added which differ only slightly in frequency and wavelength, the resultant wave has essentially the same frequency and wavelength as either component, but its amplitude is modulated by a factor whose frequency is $\frac{1}{2}\Delta f$. This is the origin of audible beats in the case of sound waves. Two tuning forks, or piano strings, of slightly different frequency produce a sound whose loudness varies from maximum to minimum with a frequency Δf; among other things, this phenomenon can be used to tune musical instruments.

We should notice that, in this case, the speed of the modulating factor or envelope may not be the same as that of the individual waves. This group velocity is

$$v_g = \frac{\Delta\omega}{\Delta k}$$

In a dispersive medium, the speed of harmonic waves depends on frequency; in this case, the modulating shape factor does not move at the same (phase) velocity as the component waves.

Periodic waveforms more complex than pure harmonic waves can be represented as a combination of harmonic waves of different frequencies. This is Fourier's theorem: any periodic waveform can be written as a sum of harmonic waves with frequencies f, 2f, 3f,..., with appropriately chosen amplitudes. The determination of the amplitude and phase of the components of a given messy waveform is harmonic analysis. Even nonperiodic waveforms - wave pulses - can be represented as a combination of sinusoidal waves, but in this case an integral over a continuous range of frequencies is required, rather than a harmonic series. A fundamental characteristic of the synthesis of wave packets in this way is that the spatial extent of the packet, and the range of wave numbers of its component harmonic waves, are inversely related:

$$\Delta x \; \Delta k \sim 1$$

This very general relation is important in communications theory; in quantum theory, where the motion of particles is represented by the propagation of a wave whose wavelength is related to the particle's momentum, this becomes the Heisenberg uncertainty principle.

As for the superposition of two waves, the speed at which a wave packet, or pattern, resulting from the superposition of many harmonic components moves is not in general the same as the speed of individual harmonic components. If the speed v_p of harmonic waves in a medium depends on wavelength, the group velocity v_g is

$$v_g = v_p + k \frac{dv_p}{dk}$$

In this case the medium is dispersive; a wave pulse does not maintain its shape as it propagates since individual components of the pulse propagate at different speeds. Light waves in transparent materials are generally dispersive; a prism refracts the different wavelengths (colors) contained in white light differently.

By the same approach, vibrations of finite systems with more complex shapes, such as the triangular shape of a plucked string, can be treated as Fourier combinations of the natural harmonic vibrations of the system.

23.2 CHECK LIST

superposition	Doppler effect
beats	Moiré pattern
synthesis of harmonic waves	tone quality
wave packet	Fourier's theorem
dispersion	harmonic synthesis
Fourier analysis	harmonic analysis
modulation	uncertainty principle
envelope	refraction
phase velocity	dispersion relation
group velocity	boundary condition
dispersion	

23.3 TRUE OR FALSE?

_____1. The superposition of two harmonic waves of nearly equal frequency and wavelength results in a wave of about the same frequency and wavelength.

_____2. The amplitude of the resultant wave, in this case, is the sum of the amplitudes of the component waves.

_____3. Beats in the resultant wave occur if the components have frequencies which are in whole-number ratio to one another.

_____4. The "phase velocity" of the resultant wave is the rate at which the relative phase of the two components changes in time.

_____5. The "group velocity" of the resultant wave is the speed at which the pattern of modulation of its amplitude moves.

_____6. If piano strings of frequency 257 and 261 Hz are sounded together, one hears beats at a rate of 2 beats/sec.

_____7. For sound waves in air, the group velocity is always less than the phase velocity.

_____8. Water waves are dispersive.

_____9. If two musical instruments are sounding the same note, they are generating approximately identical sound waveforms.

_____10. Fourier's theorem states that any periodic waveform may be written as a superposition of harmonic components.

_____11. If a periodic waveform has period T, all its Fourier components have periods given by T/n, where T is an integer.

_____12. A small width in space of a wave packet corresponds to a narrow range of wavelengths.

_____13. The Fourier representation of a nonperiodic waveform contains a continuous distribution of wavelengths.

_____14. In quantum mechanics, particles such as electrons are represented as wave packets.

_____15. A "dispersive" medium is one in which the wave speed depends on the mechanical properties of the medium.

_____16. The group velocity may be written as dv_p/dk.

_____17. If a wave pulse propagates without change of shape, $v_g = v_p$.

_____18. Light waves propagating in transparent media are dispersive.

_____19. The harmonics of a real - i.e., not perfectly flexible - piano string are slightly sharp - slightly higher in frequency than a true harmonic series.

_____20. A vibrating string of arbitrary shape may be considered as a superposition of harmonic standing waves.

23.4 QUESTIONS

1. If two harmonic waves are superposed, the resultant may be written

$$2y_0 \cos (\tfrac{1}{2}\Delta k\ x - \tfrac{1}{2}\Delta\omega\ t)\ \sin (\bar{k}x - \bar{\omega}t)$$

   The factor modulating the wave amplitude has frequency $\tfrac{1}{2}\Delta f$; why, then, do we say the beat frequency is not this but Δf?

2. When we play chords on the piano, several notes are sounded at once. Why don't we hear beats?

3. What is the dispersion relation, for a given wave propagation, if the group velocity is twice the wave velocity?

4. We use dispersion to mean both "the change of shape of a wave pulse as it propagates" and "the dependence of wave velocity on wavelength." In terms of Fourier synthesis of complex waveforms, relate these two meanings.

5. The speed of surface waves on shallow water depends on the ratio of their wavelength to the water depth. Can you think of any familiar consequences of this fact?

6. A superheterodyne radio receiver - almost all commercial broadcast receivers are superhet - mixes the incoming signal with one produced by a "local oscillator" in the set to produce a fixed beat frequency of 440 kHz. Further amplification, etc., in the receiver works on this 440-kHz signal. If the radio is tuned to a station at 1.16 MHz, what is the local oscillator frequency? Can you think of any advantages in doing this trick, rather than just working with the incoming signal?

7. Information from computers, etc., is transmitted along telephone wires as brief pulses. If the sending and receiving equipment are limited to frequencies below 250 kHz, what limitation does this impose on the rate at which pulses can be sent?

23.5 EXAMPLES

1. Two identical strings in your piano are tuned to middle C (256 Hz). Each is under a tension of 1300 N. If one string loosens to the point where, when middle C is sounded, you hear beats at the rate of one every 1.4 sec, by how much has the tension in that string decreased?

2. What range of wavelengths is present in a pulse, 0.01 sec long, of radio waves of frequency 30 MHz?

3. On a certain not perfectly flexible wire, phase and group velocities are related by

$$v_g = v_p + \frac{a}{\lambda}$$

If the wire is 1.5 m long and the first two standing-wave frequencies are 40.0 and 79.2 Hz, find the next higher two or three frequencies of the wire.

23.6 ANSWERS

True or False?

1. True - if one really wanted to pick, the resultant wave is not exactly a harmonic wave because its amplitude varies - it isn't precisely sinusoidal.

2. False - the amplitude varies in time at the "beat frequency."

3. False - whenever the frequencies are different.

4. False - it is the velocity at which the (nearly) harmonic wave, as opposed to the modulation pattern, propagates.

5. True.

6. False - 4 beats/sec.

7. False - sound waves in air are essentially nondispersive.

8. True.

9. False - they merely have the same frequency; the waveforms may be very different, corresponding to differences in tone quality.

10. True.

11. True - they have frequencies that are integer multiples of the fundamental frequency.

12. False - to a wide range of wave numbers and therefore of wavelengths.

13. True.

14. True.

15. False - this is true of any mechanical wave motion; a dispersive

medium is one in which wave velocity is not independent of the wavelength.

16. False - it is $d\omega/dk$.

17. True - this is a nondispersive wave motion.

18. True.

19. False - slightly flat; see the example in the text chapter.

20. True.

Questions

1. Because we perceive a beat whenever the modulating factor varies from zero to an extreme value and back; this happens twice per cycle of frequency $\frac{1}{2}\Delta f$, thus Δf times per second.

2. Well, really we do. The beat frequencies, however, are not in the 1-or-2-beats/**sec** range where we perceive them as amplitude modulations, but of the same order as the fundamental frequencies that are being sounded. These "difference tones," however, are present in the combination of sounds that we hear.

3. If $v_g = 2v_p$, then

$$2v_p = v_p + k\frac{dv_p}{dk}$$

$$\frac{dv_p}{dk} = \frac{v_p}{k}$$

which plainly is satisfied if $v_p \propto k$ or $\omega \propto k^2$.

4. Any wave pulse can be represented as a Fourier-integral combination of harmonic waves. If the wave speed varies with wavelength, the Fourier components travel at different speeds and the pulse "comes apart" because the relative phase of the components changes as it moves.

5. The most familiar consequence would be the building up and breaking of waves as they move onto shore. As the water depth decreases (approaching the beach) the wave velocity decreases and the waves pile up to large amplitude.

6. The local oscillator would have to be at

$$1160 - 440 = 720 \text{ kHz}$$

in this case. The chief advantage - aside from the fact that lower frequencies are somewhat easier to work with - is that tuning the receiver to a particular frequency, as you change stations, has to be done at only one point in the circuit; all the rest of it works at a fixed frequency.

7. The range of frequencies contained in each pulse is limited to 250 kHz, and

$$\Delta\omega \, \Delta t \simeq 2\pi$$

Thus the duration of each pulse can't be less than about 2.5×10^{-5} sec; to distinguish one from the next you can't send them faster than about 40,000 per second.

Examples

Partial Solutions (1)

1. One of the strings has loosened, so its frequency has decreased. By how much? How do you relate the frequency change to the change in the tension?

2. For a wave packet,

$$\Delta x \, \Delta k \simeq 1$$

from which you can find Δk. Now all you need is to get from this to the uncertainty in wavelength. What is the length (Δx) of the pulse in space?

3. In general, the relation between phase and group velocity is

$$v_g = v_p + k \frac{dv_p}{dk}$$

From the given relation, integrate to find the phase velocity on this wire. Given the phase velocity, what are the standing wave frequencies of the wire?

Partial Solutions (2)

1. The difference in frequencies is the rate at which beats are heard, so here

$$\delta f = \frac{1}{1.4 \text{ sec}} = 0.71 \text{ Hz}$$

Since we are talking about small changes in f and T, we may put

$$\delta T \simeq \frac{dT}{df} \, \delta f$$

and the fundamental frequency of a stretched string is of course

$$f_1 = \frac{v}{2\ell} = \frac{1}{2\ell} \sqrt{\frac{T}{\mu}}$$

2. Radio waves propagate at speed c, so the length of the pulse in space is

$$\Delta x = c \, \Delta t = (3.0 \times 10^8 \text{ m/sec})(0.01 \text{ sec}) = 3.0 \times 10^6 \text{ m}$$

The wave number

$$k = \frac{2\pi}{\lambda}$$

Here we are talking, again, about small changes in k and λ, and we may put

$$\Delta k \simeq \frac{dk}{d\lambda} \Delta \lambda = \frac{-2\pi}{\lambda^2} \Delta \lambda$$

Put these together and solve for the wavelength spread $\Delta \lambda$.

3. From the given dispersion relation,

$$v_p + \frac{a}{\lambda} = v_p + k \frac{dv_p}{dk}$$

Then

$$\frac{dv_p}{dk} = \frac{a}{\lambda k} = \frac{a}{2\pi}$$

and so

$$v_p = v_0 + \frac{a}{2\pi} k = v_0 + \frac{a}{\lambda}$$

Standing-wave frequencies on a string of length ℓ are

$$\lambda = \frac{2\ell}{n} \qquad f = \frac{v_p}{\lambda} = \frac{n v_p}{2\ell} \qquad n = 1, 2, 3, 4, \ldots$$

Given f_1 and f_2, we can solve these relations for v_0 and a.

Partial Solutions (3)

1. The tension is

$$T = 4\ell^2 \mu f_1^2$$

and so

$$\delta T \simeq \frac{dT}{df_1} \delta f = 8\ell^2 \mu f_1 \delta f = \frac{2T}{f_1} \delta f$$

or, here,

$$\delta T \simeq 2 \frac{1300 \text{ N}}{256 \text{ Hz}} 0.71 \text{ Hz} = \underline{7.2 \text{ N}}$$

2. From what we have above,

$$\Delta x \, \Delta k = \Delta x \left(\frac{2\pi}{\lambda^2}\right) \Delta \lambda \simeq 1$$

or

$$\Delta x \, \Delta \lambda \simeq \frac{\lambda^2}{2\pi}$$

here

$$\lambda = \frac{c}{f} = \frac{3 \times 10^8 \text{ m/sec}}{30 \times 10^6 \text{ Hz}} = 10 \text{ m}$$

and so

$$\Delta \lambda = \frac{\lambda^2}{2\pi \, \Delta x} = \frac{(10 \text{ m})^2}{(2\pi)(3.0 \times 10^6 \text{ m})} = \underline{5.3 \times 10^{-6} \text{ m}}$$

is the range of wavelengths, around the central value of 10 m, contained in this pulse.

3. The standing-wave frequencies on this string are then

$$f = \frac{v_p}{\lambda} = \frac{n v_p}{2\ell} = \frac{n v_0}{2\ell} + \frac{n^2 a}{4\ell^2}$$

and we are given

$$f_1 = \frac{v_0}{2\ell} + \frac{a}{4\ell^2} = 40 \text{ Hz}$$

$$f_2 = \frac{v_0}{\ell} + \frac{a}{\ell^2} = 79.2 \text{ Hz}$$

Solving these two equations simultaneously gives

$$\frac{a}{2\ell^2} = -0.8 \text{ Hz} \quad \text{and} \quad \frac{v_0}{2\ell} = 40.4 \text{ Hz}$$

Plugging these back into the frequency equation gives

$$f_n = 40.4n \left(1 - \frac{n}{101}\right) \text{ Hz}$$

the next few values of which are $\underline{f_3 = 117.6 \text{ Hz}}$, $\underline{f_4 = 155.2 \text{ Hz}}$, $\underline{f_5 = 192 \text{ Hz}}$, etc.

CHAPTER 24
Spherical and Circular Waves

24.1 CHAPTER SUMMARY

Up to now we have talked about various properties of waves propagating in one dimension. There are many properties of real waves, however, that appear only in the motion of waves in two or three dimensions.

In three-dimensional space, consider a wave spreading uniformly out in all directions from a point source. The intensity of the wave must decrease as the square of the distance from the source, since at greater distances the energy put out by the source is spread over a larger area. As the intensity of a harmonic wave is proportional to the square of the amplitude, we may write such a uniform spherical wave function

$$\Psi(r,\ t) = \frac{A}{r} \sin\ (kr - \omega t + \delta)$$

At any time t, the phase $kr - \omega t + \delta$ is constant on spherical wavefronts (constant r) surrounding the source. Far from the source the wavefronts are nearly parallel planes. Such a plane wave, moving in a particular direction x, can be written

$$\Psi(x,\ t) = A \sin\ (kx - \omega t + \delta)$$

That is, it moves just as a one-dimensional wave; but any obstructions that the wave encounters will destroy the plane-wave symmetry.

We often speak of the motion of wavefronts in terms of rays, which are lines drawn perpendicular to the wavefront. A spherical wave is thus represented as rays spreading uniformly out from the source in all directions.

The propagation of a wave motion is determined not by its source, but by the medium in which it moves. If a wave source, or whatever receives the wave, is in motion relative to the medium which transmits the wave, the result is an alteration of the frequency of the wave, known as the Doppler effect. This is the source, for instance, of the apparent change of pitch of a passing car's horn. The received frequency is

$$f' = f_0 (1 + \frac{v_r}{v}) \qquad \text{or} \qquad f' = f_0 (1 - \frac{v_s}{v})^{-1}$$

where the receiver moves toward the source with speed v_r, or the source toward the receiver with speed v_s, and f_0 is the frequency emitted by the source. The two cases are not quite the same because motion relative to the medium transmitting the waves, and not just the relative motion of source and observer, is what matters. (For electromagnetic waves, which can propagate in the absence of any material medium, slight corrections must be made to these formulas.) If the source moves faster than the wave speed in the medium, the waves are confined to a cone behind the source; for electromagnetic waves in a material medium, this effect is known as Čerenkov radiation.

If waves in a medium are generated by two or more sources, there is a phase difference in the waves which arrive at some other point due to the difference in path from the sources. The resultant wave thus varies in amplitude from point to point; the result is an interference pattern. In certain directions from the sources, the difference in path length is a whole number of wavelengths, and the two components add. Other directions differ by half a wavelength; the two waves are π out of phase and cancel one another. The interference maxima are in directions (θ) from the source given by

$$m\lambda = d \sin \theta \qquad\qquad m = \text{integer}$$

if d is the distance between the two sources. At the maxima, the intensity is greater than the sum of intensities of the two waves separately.

If we consider three or more equally spaced sources of waves, the interference maxima occur at the same angles (for the same separation of sources), but are narrower and of greater maximum intensity.

The result above holds if the two (or more) sources of waves are vibrating in phase. This need not be, but notice that for an interference pattern to be observable there must be a definite phase relationship between the sources - that is, they must be coherent. For mechanically generated waves, such as sound, this is fairly easy to arrange, but two coherent light sources are very hard to come by, as the emission of light by most sources is the result of very many unrelated atomic-scale events.

24.2 CHECK LIST

refraction	line wave
diffraction	ray
Doppler effect	wave function
interference	Čerenkov radiation
coherence	theory of relativity
wavefront	principle of relativity
uniform spherical wave	Young's experiment
plane wave	coherent vs. incoherent sources

24.3 TRUE OR FALSE?

_____ 1. The intensity of a uniform spherical wave is inversely proportional to the distance from the wave's source.

_____2. A wavefront is a surface over which the phase of the wave is constant.

_____3. A wave propagating outward in all directions from a point source, in <u>two</u> dimensions, is a plane wave.

_____4. The frequency of a wave from a moving source is greater than the source frequency.

_____5. If the observer is at rest relative to the wave source, the frequency he receives is unaffected by motion of the medium.

_____6. The Doppler shift of a wave depends <u>only</u> on the relative speed of observer and source.

_____7. Sufficiently precise measurement of the Doppler effect for light would permit determination of absolute motion relative to empty space.

_____8. If a wave source moves through a medium faster than the wave speed in the medium, no waves reach an observer behind the source.

_____9. If an observer moves through a medium faster than the wave speed in the medium, he receives no waves from a source behind him.

_____10. According to the special theory of relativity, there is no Doppler effect for light.

_____11. Čerenkov radiation is electromagnetic radiation emitted by a charged particle which moves through a medium faster than the speed of light in the medium.

_____12. Two wave sources are coherent if there is a definite phase relation between them.

_____13. For constructive interference between two point sources, the path-length difference from the sources must be an integer multiple of π.

_____14. Nodal lines or surfaces are those on which the interference of two point sources is destructive.

_____15. Young's experiment is the demonstration of interference of two point sources of sound waves.

_____16. At an interference maximum, in the waves from two sources, the intensity is twice that of either wave alone.

_____17. The interference maxima from four sources in phase, spaced a distance d apart, are twice as close together as those from two sources with the same spacing.

_____18. The interference maxima produced by N equally spaced sources in phase are N^2 times as intense as would be the wave from one source alone.

_____19. Two sources not in phase do not produce an interference pattern.

_____20. Sources must be coherent in order to produce interference.

24.4 Questions

1. The Doppler effect is determined not only by the motion of the source relative to the observer, but by its absolute velocity

188

relative to the medium in which the waves propagate. Briefly,
explain why.

2. From the cases of three or four sources, discussed in the text,
    how would you expect the interference pattern from very many
    equally spaced in-phase sources to look?

3. In Young's experiment - the two-source interference experiment for
    light - one always uses light from a single source, split somehow
    and made to travel by different paths, rather than two separate
    sources. Why?

4. If Young's experiment is done for light containing many different
    frequencies, what will the interference pattern look like?

5. Consider the interference between two sources in phase, separated
    by a distance d. Is there a minimum wavelength below which de-
    structive interference cannot be observed? Is there a maximum
    wavelength?

6. A tuning fork, vibrating at a fixed frequency, is moving back and
    forth along the direction toward and away from you. What do you
    hear? What do you hear if it is moved back and forth in the trans-
    verse direction?

24.5 EXAMPLES

1. Police radar measures the speed of a moving vehicle by the amount
    of the Doppler frequency shift in waves reflected from the vehicle.
    What is the frequency shift in electromagnetic waves of wavelength
    12 cm, reflected from an object moving at 60 mi/h? Assume the
    object moves directly toward the radar source.

2. Light of a sharp wavelength, emitted by a luminous object which is
    rotating, is observed broadened into some range of wavelengths by
    the Doppler effect. Why? A distant star, known somehow to have a
    diameter of 1.1×10^6 km, is rotating; if the red hydrogen light
    in its spectrum (656.3 nm) is observed to be spread into a band
    0.12 nm wide, what is the star's period of rotation?

3. You want to set up a two-slit interference experiment as a demon-
    stration for an elementary physics class, using yellow sodium light
    (589 nm). If you want interference fringes 2 cm apart on a screen
    2.5 m from the slits, what must be the slit separation?

4. Find an expression for the intensity of the resultant of two
    harmonic waves of the same frequency and wavelength, but different
    in phase and amplitude. If the two waves, each acting alone, would
    have intensities in the ratio 3:1, what are the minimum and
    maximum intensity of the resultant?

24.6 ANSWERS

True or False?

1. False - inversely proportional to the square of the distance.

2. True.

3. False - a plane wave is one whose wavefronts are parallel planes;
    it is propagating "all in one direction."

4. False - it may be greater or less, depending on which way the source
    is moving.

5. True.

6. False - this holds only when their relative speed is zero.

7. False - this is what the Doppler formulas derived for waves in a material medium would imply, but these do not apply exactly to light.

8. False - waves propagate backward with a fixed speed relative to the medium.

9. True - he is outrunning the waves, which, again, move at a fixed velocity relative to the medium in which they propagate.

10. False - it is not quite the same as the classical Doppler effect, but it is there.

11. True.

12. True.

13. False - if the two sources are in phase, it must be an integral multiple of the wavelength.

14. True.

15. False - for light.

16. False - the amplitude is twice that from either source, so the intensity is four times as much.

17. False - the principal maxima are at the same positions, but narrower and more intense; there are secondary maxima also, of course, but the spacing is not 2:1.

18. True.

19. False - the location of maxima and minima will be different, but as long as the phase difference is fixed there is interference.

20. True.

Questions

1. Because, for mechanical waves in a material medium, such as sound, the speed of wave propagation is determined by, and relative to, the medium. The Doppler effect for light in free space does depend only on the relative motion of source and observer.

2. The principal maxima are at the same location (for the same spacing between adjacent slits), but are very much sharper and more intense. For N slits, there are N - 1 minima between every two principal maxima, and the latter are N^2 times as intense and on the order of $1/N$ as wide as for two slits.

3. Because it is essentially impossible to arrange two separate light sources which are coherent.

4. Near the central (straight-ahead) maximum it makes very little difference - you see alternately bright and dark bands on a screen, for instance. As you look at higher orders, one wavelength is interfering constructively where another is destructive, and the pattern shows colored bands. In the case sketched below, for instance, you would see a red stripe at A and a blue stripe at B.

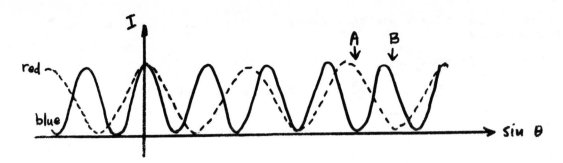

5. The first interference minimum is at

$$\sin \theta = \frac{\lambda}{2d}$$

Since $\sin \theta < 1$, you plainly cannot observe this unless $\lambda < 2d$. There is no minimum wavelength, although as the wavelength gets very small compared to d the interference fringes become closer together and eventually reach a point where your detector - whatever it may be - cannot resolve them.

6. You hear its pitch alternately rise and fall as it moves toward you or away from you, but only a steady pitch as it moves transversely.

Examples

Partial Solutions (1)

1. The easiest approach to the Doppler shift in reflection from a moving object is to look at it in two stages. Waves from the source, first, are received by the object (as a moving "observer") at some Doppler-shifted frequency f'. In the reflection, waves of this frequency are returned to the source from the object, which now acts as a moving source. The original source gets them back with a frequency f". Note in this case the object (the car) moves very much more slowly than the radar waves (speed c); this simplifies things a fair amount.

2. Light is emitted by the whole surface of the star, but different parts of its surface have velocity components, along the line of sight to the observer, anywhere between +v and -v, where v is the equatorial rotation speed. The observer thus sees the corresponding range of shifted frequencies. Find the rotational speed from the observed wavelength broadening, and from that figure its period of rotation.

3. How is position on the screen related to the angle at which light leaves the slits, if the slits are a known distance from the screen?

4. In this case we have waves of the same frequency and wavelength but differing in phase and amplitude. Use the phasor trick to find an expression for their resultant and go on from there.

Partial Solutions (2)

1. Because the car's speed is enormously less than c, we may use the ordinary (nonrelativistic) Doppler formulas. The frequency with which the wave arrives at the reflecting object is

$$f' = f(1 + \frac{v}{c})$$

For the return to the sender, we have a "source" sending out waves at frequency f' by a moving source; they are thus received back at frequency

$$f'' = \frac{f'}{1 - v/c}$$

Combine, simplify, and find the net frequency shift

$$\delta f = f'' - f$$

if the car moves toward the radar gear at 60 mi/h.

2. As the wavelength shift is very much less than the wavelength, we can assume again that we have $v \ll c$, and use the nonrelativistic Doppler formulas. Thus

$$f' = \frac{f}{1 \pm v/c}$$

and

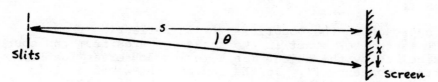

$$\delta f = f' - f = \frac{\pm v}{c - v} f \simeq \pm\frac{v}{c} f$$

The wavelength $\lambda = c/f$ and so the wavelength shift corresponding to a (small) Doppler shift in the frequency is

$$\delta\lambda \simeq \frac{d\lambda}{df} \delta f = \frac{-c}{f^2}\delta f = \frac{\pm v}{f} = \pm\frac{v}{c}\lambda$$

Solve for v from the data given.

3. If the screen is at distance s from the slits, then (see the sketch)

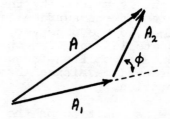

the position on the screen is

$$x = s \tan\theta \simeq s \sin\theta \qquad (\text{small } \theta)$$

What angles θ give constructive interference?

4. A phasor diagram for this situation is sketched at the right. If the ampli- tudes are A_1 and A_2 and the relative phase of the two waves is ϕ, then by the law of cosines

$$A^2 = A_1^2 + A_2^2 + 2A_1A_2 \cos\phi$$

What is the relation of the <u>intensities</u>?

Partial Solutions (3)

1. Combining the "two shifts" gives

$$f'' = f \frac{c + v}{c - v}$$

As $v \lll c$, we may approximate this by

$$f'' = f \frac{1 + v/c}{1 - v/c} \simeq f(1 + \frac{v}{c})^2 \simeq f(1 + \frac{2v}{c})$$

so then

$$\delta f = f'' - f = \frac{2vf}{c} = \frac{2v}{\lambda}$$

Here we have $\lambda = 0.12$ m, $c = 3.00 \times 10^8$ m/sec, and $v = 60$ mi/h = 26.9 m/sec. These values give

$$f = \frac{(2)(26.9 \text{ m/sec})}{0.12 \text{ m}} = \underline{449 \text{ Hz}}$$

2. Opposite limbs of the star are moving in opposite directions relative to the observer, so the <u>range</u> of wavelength shifts observed is from $-\delta\lambda$ to $+\delta\lambda$. Therefore,

$$1.2 \times 10^{-10} \text{ m} = 2\frac{v}{c}\lambda$$

which, for $\lambda = 6.563 \times 10^{-7}$ m, gives

$$v = (9.14 \times 10^{-5})(c) = 2.74 \times 10^4 \text{ m/sec}$$

Now if the star's radius is R and its period of rotation is T, then plainly

$$T = \frac{2\pi R}{v} = \frac{(2\pi)(1.1 \times 10^9 \text{ m})}{2.74 \times 10^4 \text{ m/sec}} = \underline{1.26 \times 10^5 \text{ sec}}$$

or about 1.5 days.

3. Constructive interference occurs for angles given by

$$n\lambda = d \sin \theta$$

where d is the slit spacing. Thus

$$n\lambda \simeq \frac{dx}{s} \quad \text{or} \quad d = \frac{s\lambda}{\Delta x}$$

Here, then,

$$d = \frac{(5.89 \times 10^{-7} \text{ m})(2.5 \text{ m})}{2.0 \times 10^{-2} \text{ m}} = \underline{7.36 \times 10^{-5} \text{ m}}$$

4. The intensity of each wave is proportional to the square of its amplitude; then

$$I = I_1 + I_2 + 2\sqrt{I_1 I_2} \cos \phi$$

Here we are given $I_2 = 3I_1$, so

$$I = 4I_1 + 2\sqrt{3I_1^2} \cos \phi$$

The phase difference (ϕ) can have any value. Maximum resultant intensity occurs for angles where $\cos \phi = +1$, giving

$$I_{max} = I_1(4 + 2\sqrt{3}) = 7.46 I_1$$

and minimum for $\cos \phi = -1$, giving

$$I_{min} = I_1(4 - 2\sqrt{3}) = 0.54 I_1$$

CHAPTER 25
Wave Propagation

25.1 CHAPTER SUMMARY

The relatively simple wave functions of Chapter 24 describe plane or spherical waves propagating in a uniform medium. The situation is more complicated when the wave encounters obstacles or obstructions.

For example, consider a wave impinging on a barrier with a hole in it. If the hole is very much larger than the wavelength, the wave propagates through very nearly unaltered except for being cut off by the barrier, but there is always some degree of bending, or diffraction, of the wave at the edges of the obstruction. In the other extreme, when the hole is very small compared to the wavelength, the wave spreads out essentially as from a point source at the hole. This is reasonable enough; the oscillations of each bit of the medium are the cause of what happens to the next bit.

The extension of this notion is Huygens' principle: that each point on a wavefront can be considered a source of new waves, the envelope of these wavelets defining the next wavefront. The simplest case to which we can apply this is the diffraction of a plane wave incident on a barrier with an aperture of width a in it. Each point on the wavefront in the aperture is a new wave source; this problem is then just an extension of the interference of equally spaced sources. The pattern of maximum and minimum intensity of the diffracted wave in various directions is calculated from a vector addition diagram for many equally spaced sources; the minima of the diffraction pattern are at angles (θ) from the incident direction given by

$$a \sin \theta = m\lambda \qquad m = 1, 2, 3, \ldots$$

far away from the aperture. This (Fraunhofer) treatment is much simpler than the more general (Fresnel) case.

In general, if in a given case we need never consider a piece of a wavefront which is not very much larger than the wavelength, diffraction is unimportant and the ray approximation is valid. The wavelength of light is quite small and the ray approximation for light therefore broadly useful; for sound waves, with very much longer wavelengths, it is not.

The laws of reflection and refraction of waves at boundaries between media can also be deduced from Huygens' principle. In reflection at a plane boundary, the angle of incidence and the angle of reflection are equal. The refraction of the part of the wave transmitted across the boundary depends on the two wave speeds:

$$\frac{\sin \theta_i}{v_i} = \frac{\sin \theta_r}{v_r}$$

The bending of light rays by either reflection or refraction leads to the formation of images - the waves appear to be coming, after reflection or refraction, from some point other than their actual source. Reflection and refraction at plane boundaries form virtual, rather than real, images.

Beyond a certain critical angle, refraction of a wave incident in the medium with the slower wave speed cannot occur; the wave in this case is totally reflected.

An obstacle very much smaller than a wavelength acts essentially as a point source of reflected waves; this is a model of the scattering of light by atoms. The reflection of a wave by a regular array of scatterers, such as the scattering of light by atoms of a crystalline solid, depends on the phase relation of the scattered waves. If the separation of scatterers is very much smaller than a wavelength, as for visible light on atoms of a solid, phase differences between different scatterers are not important; reflection can take place at any angle of incidence. If the wavelength is of the same order of magnitude as the separation of scattering obstacles, however, the reflection will be strong only at certain angles at which interference of the reflected waves from different layers of scatterers is constructive. This is the case for x-rays on a crystalline solid. The angles at which reflection takes place in this case are given by

$$2d \sin \phi = m\lambda \qquad m = 1, 2, 3, \ldots$$

25.2 CHECK LIST

diffraction

Huygens' method

Huygens' principle

wavelets

phase difference

Fraunhofer diffraction

Fresnel diffraction

ray approximation

x-rays

de Broglie wavelength

Planck's constant

law of reflection

image point

$h = 6.63 \times 10^{-27}$ erg-sec

virtual image

real image

spherical abberration

reversibility

law of refraction

Snell's law

index of refraction

critical angle

total internal reflection

barrier penetration

crystal

Bragg scattering

25.3 TRUE OR FALSE?

_____ 1. If a plane wave encounters some obstruction, the unobstructed parts of the wavefront propagate straight on past it.

_____ 2. A wave encountering a barrier with a very small hole in it propagates outward from the hole in all directions, as if from a point source.

____3. The bending of "rays" around an obstruction is called "diffraction."

____4. Diffraction is important only for obstructions, apertures, etc., that are large compared to the wavelength.

____5. Huygens' principle states that a wave propagating past an obstruction looks as if the edge of the obstruction were itself a wave source.

____6. Huygens' construction, taken at face value, would predict a diffracted wave moving backwards, as well as forewards, from an aperture.

____7. The laws of reflection and refraction, for light, must be derived in the ray approximation.

____8. Huygens' principle applies only to mechanical waves in a material medium.

____9. Diffraction at a single aperture, in Huygens' treatment, is equivalent to the interference of many point sources distributed over the aperture.

____10. The first minimum in the single-slit Fraunhofer diffraction pattern occurs where the waves from the edges of the aperture are π out of phase.

____11. Secondary diffraction maxima from a single slit of width d occur at the same places as the minima of the interference pattern of two slits separated by d.

____12. Fraunhofer diffraction is that which is observed very far away from the apertures or obstructions at which diffraction occurs.

____13. The ray approximation to wave propagation holds as long as we need never look at a piece of a wavefront which is not large compared to λ.

____14. De Broglie waves are the same thing as x-rays.

____15. An electron has a de Broglie wavelength determined by its momentum.

____16. The rays of waves reflected from a barrier make the same angle with the normal to the barrier as do the incident rays.

____17. The direction of waves reflected from a barrier can be inferred from Huygens' principle.

____18. Waves from a point source reflected by a plane barrier appear to come from an "image" point at the same distance behind the barrier.

____19. The image of a point source in reflection from a barrier is always a virtual image.

____20. In refraction across a boundary at which the wave speed changes, the waves leaving the boundary make the same angle to it as the incident waves.

____21. Rays crossing a boundary at which the wave speed increases are bent away from the normal to the boundary.

_____22. When a wave propagates across a boundary at which the speed changes, its wavelength is changed but its frequency remains the same.

_____23. Total internal reflection can occur only at a boundary at which the wave speed increases.

_____24. When a plane wave encounters a very small obstacle, the reflected wave propagates uniformly outward from the obstacle as if from a point source.

_____25. "Reflection" of a wave from a regular array of point scatterers occurs only at certain definite angles.

25.4 QUESTIONS

1. Why is it that we can hear, but not see, around corners?

2. Is there a maximum wavelength for which the maxima and minima of the diffraction pattern from a single aperture can be observed? A minimum wavelength?

3. In Young's experiment, what, if anything, would be the effect of the finite size of the slits?

4. Give a brief qualitative explanation as to why the intensities of the secondary maxima of a single-slit diffraction pattern decrease as $1/N^2$, approximately.

5. Under what circumstances might "angle of incidence equals angle of reflection" fail to describe reflection at a plane barrier? Explain.

6. Distinguish between diffraction and interference.

7. Why is it that visible light, reflecting from a crystalline solid, displays no Bragg pattern?

25.5 EXAMPLES

1. Find at what points the central peak of the single-slit diffraction pattern has half its maximum intensity. Then under what conditions does this occur at 90° from the direction of incidence? Take your result as a rough index of the aperture size at which the directionality of the diffraction pattern is lost. For what size aperture does this occur with sound waves of frequency 440 Hz (concert A)?

2. In a single-slit diffraction pattern using white light, for what wavelength does the second subsidiary maximum coincide with the second minimum of hydrogen red (656.3 nm) light?

3. The transparent slab shown has index of refraction n = 1.32. For what range of angles (θ) does total internal reflection at the vertical face of the slab occur?

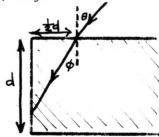

4. A continuous spectrum of x-rays with wavelengths ranging from 0.09 to 0.21 nm falls on the face of a crystalline material as sketched below. The reflected x-rays contain only the wavelengths 0.104 and 0.156 nm. Assuming these to be due to the planes identified in the sketch (are there other possibilities?) what is the spacing (a) of the crystal?

25.6 ANSWERS

True or False?

1. False - the wave bends around the obstruction; this is diffraction.

2. True.

3. True.

4. False - for apertures or obstructions not much larger than θ.

5. False - every point on a wavefront is to be considered a source of new "wavelets" whose envelope constitutes the next wavefront.

6. True - either the Huygens wavelets are constructed so that they vanish in the back direction, or else the back direction is just ignored.

7. False - it is derived in the text from Huygens' construction.

8. False - it applies equally well to light, although its physical plausibility is more obvious in a material medium.

9. True.

10. False - waves from the edges are 2π out.

11. True - at angles θ given by $\sin \theta = m\lambda/d$.

12. True.

13. True.

14. False - de Broglie waves are those associated with the motion of subatomic particles such as electrons.

15. True.

16. True - this is the "law of reflection."

17. True.

198

18. True.

19. False – the image in a plane barrier is always virtual, in the sense that there is no physical point from which the reflected waves are diverging; but real images may be formed by curved barriers.

20. False – it is refracted at any such boundary.

21. True.

22. True – that its frequency be unchanged is required by Huygens' principle.

23. True.

24. True.

25. True.

Questions

1. Because many of the obstacles, apertures, and so forth that surround us in everyday circumstances – doorways, corners, etc. – are not very large compared to the wavelength of audible sound, but they are all very large compared to that of visible light.

2. The first minimum in the single-slit diffraction pattern is given by

$$\sin \theta = \lambda/d$$

if d is the width of the slit. As $\sin \theta$ cannot exceed 1, plainly this can be observed only for $\lambda < d$. The minimum wavelength limit is a practical one: as the wavelength becomes much smaller than d, diffraction effects become unobservably small.

3. If the slits are each of nonzero width, each is the source of a single-slit diffraction pattern, rather than acting as a point source. The intensity of the light from each slit, available to interfere with that from the other one, at any given angle will be determined by the diffraction pattern; thus a single-slit diffraction pattern _modulates_ the two-slit interference pattern, giving something like what is sketched.

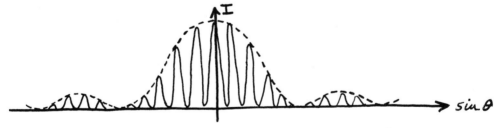

4. Imagine the aperture (width a) divided into segments of width b, such that

$$b \sin \theta = \lambda$$

Then the Huygens wavelets from the segment b of the wavefront, spanning 2π in phase, add to zero; the remainder of the wavefront is all that contributes to the diffracted intensity. A diffraction maximum occurs when this "remainder" has width $\frac{1}{2}b$ – and thus at the Nth secondary maximum, the amplitude is due to a fraction $1/(N + \frac{1}{2})$ of the

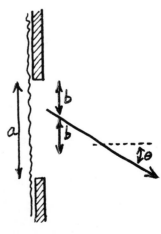

whole wavefront, and the intensity goes as this, squared.

5. If the reflecting barrier is not large compared to the wavelength, the wave reflected from it will look just like the diffracted wave from an aperture of the same size, coming from the "image source" behind the barrier. In this case there is no unique angle of reflection.

6. Diffraction refers to the bending of wave "directions" by obstructing parts of wavefronts; interference is cancellation and augmentation of waves from two sources due to their phase difference.

7. The wavelength is so large - several thousand times the crystal lattice spacing - that the spacing of adjacent Bragg maxima is unobservably small.

Examples

Partial Solutions (1)

1. The intensity of the single-slit Fraunhofer diffraction pattern may be written in the form

$$I = I_0 \{ \frac{\sin \xi}{\xi} \}^2$$

where

$$\xi = \frac{\pi a}{\lambda} \sin \theta$$

So what you want is to find where the factor in curly brackets has the value $1/\sqrt{2}$.

2. Simply write out the second minimum, and the second subsidiary maximum, for the appropriate wavelengths, and require that they occur at the same diffraction angle.

3. What are the limitations on whether total internal reflection occurs? There is obviously some requirement on the angle ϕ, in terms of the critical angle of the material. Is there any other?

4. Strong reflection of the incident rays occurs only if the Bragg condition,

$$m\lambda = 2d \sin \phi \qquad m = 1, 2, 3, \ldots$$

is met. For what wavelengths will this be the case at $\phi = 40°$?

Partial Solutions (2)

1. This amounts to solving

$$\sin \xi = \frac{\xi}{\sqrt{2}}$$

This cannot be done exactly; you would have to use some approximation method. Making a careful graph can easily give you a result to two significant figures, as can simply playing with numbers in a table of sines and cosines. If you are familiar with them, there are more powerful approximation methods such as Newton's method. In any case, the equation is satisfied for $\xi = 1.392$. To what diffraction angle - in terms of a, λ, etc. - does this correspond?

2. The minima of the single-slit diffraction pattern are at angles given by

$$m\lambda = a \sin \theta \qquad m = 1, 2, 3, \ldots$$

200

The secondary maxima are <u>approximately</u> at

$$(m + \tfrac{1}{2})\lambda = a \sin \theta$$

For hydrogen red light we are given

$$2(6.563 \times 10^{-7} \text{ m}) = a \sin \theta$$

Set up the other (unknown) wavelength the same way.

3. By Snell's law,

$$\sin \phi = \frac{\sin \theta}{n}$$

The angle of incidence at the interval
face is obviously

$$\phi' = \frac{\pi}{2} - \phi$$

Thus the requirement for total internal
reflection is

$$\sin \phi' = \cos \phi \geq \frac{1}{n}$$

The other limitation on the angle of
incidence is that the internal ray must
intersect the vertical face - that is, ϕ must not be so small that
the internal ray leaves the <u>bottom</u> of the slab. Thus, from the
diagram,

$$\frac{d}{2} \cotan \phi \leq d$$

These two conditions bound the acceptable angles of incidence.

4. We have

$$2a \sin 40^{\circ} = 1.286 \, a = m$$

If order m is wavelength 0.156 nm, then

$$(m)(0.156 \text{ nm}) = 1.286 \, a$$

and likewise

$$(m')(0.104 \text{ nm}) = 1.286 \, a$$

and we need to figure out what m and m' are in order to find a.

Partial Solutions (3)

1. We get

$$\frac{\pi a}{\lambda} \sin \theta = 1.392$$

or

$$\sin \theta = 0.443 \, \frac{\lambda}{a} = 1$$

if this is to be the condition at $\theta = 90^{\circ}$. Thus for the conditions
specified, the aperture size must be given by

$$\lambda = 2.26 \, a$$

If we take the speed of sound in air to be 340 m/sec, the wavelength corresponding to 440 Hz is

$$\lambda = \frac{340 \text{ m/sec}}{440 \text{ sec}} = 0.773 \text{ m}$$

so

$$a = \frac{0.773}{2.26} = \underline{0.342 \text{ m}}$$

or a little over 1 ft.

2. At the second subsidiary maximum,
$$2.5\lambda = a \sin \theta = 1.313 \times 10^{-6} \text{ m}$$
Hence
$$\lambda = 5.25 \times 10^{-7} \text{ m} = \underline{0.525 \text{ nm}}$$

3. From the first condition we get
$$\cos \phi \geq \frac{1}{1.32} = 0.758 \qquad \text{or} \qquad \phi \leq 40.7^{\circ} .$$
and from the second,
$$\text{cotan } \phi \leq 2 \qquad \text{or} \qquad \phi \geq 26.6^{\circ}$$

Using Snell's law to translate these back into angles of incidence, we find that total internal reflection occurs at the vertical face of the slab if

$$\underline{36.2^{\circ} \leq \theta \leq 59.5^{\circ}}$$

If θ is bigger than this, the internal ray gets out through the end; if θ is smaller, it misses the vertical face altogether.

4. Plainly $2m' = 3m$; since m' and m must both be integers, this means $m' = 3$ and $m = 2$, giving

$$\underline{a = 0.243 \text{ nm}}$$

This has to be the answer because the problem specifies <u>only</u> these two wavelengths, in this range anyway, reinforce. $m' = \overline{6}$ and $m = 4$ would do just as well for the two given wavelengths, but in that case $\lambda = 0.125$ nm would also be reflected.

There are very many other possible sets of parallel planes of atoms in the crystal; a couple of other sets are indicated below. The x-ray scattering spectrum would be a good deal more complicated than this problem has implied.

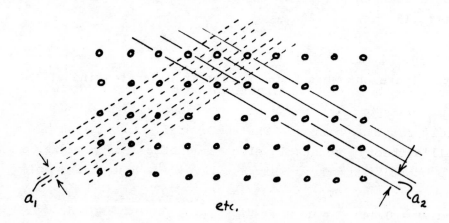

CHAPTER 26
Light

The microscopic nature of light was a lively debate in physics for
centuries. Newton, with most of his contemporaries, held light to
consist of particles of some kind, largely because of the apparent
absence of diffraction of light. In the 18th and 19th centuries,
many interference and diffraction phenomena were observed, showing
light to be a wave of very small wavelength. The culmination of the
wave theory was the identification of light with the electromagnetic
waves predicted by Maxwell. Difficulties with this theory, such as
the properties of the photoelectric effect, have in the present century
left us with a dual theory of the nature of light: it propagates as a
wave, but interacts with matter more as a stream of particles called
photons.

Light waves, then, are a propagation of electric and magnetic
fields through space as a wave. All wavelengths are possible, but
there are important differences in the ways electromagnetic waves are
generated, or detected, in different regions of wavelength, leading to
different names - radio waves, light, x-rays - for different parts of
the electromagnetic spectrum. The source of electromagnetic waves
is accelerated electric charge, a particularly important example being
an oscillating electric dipole.

The speed of light is very large; substantial travel-time lags
are observable only over astronomical distances, and the first measurements of the speed of light were in fact based on astronomical observations. Terrestrial methods of measurement require measurement of
very small time intervals by, for instance, interrupting a beam of
light with a rapidly rotating mirror. The speed of light can also be
related, by Maxwell's theory, to static electromagnetic measurements.

The general properties of waves which we have been discussing hold
as well for light waves. Reflection and refraction of light at
boundaries follow the laws already derived; the law of refraction for
light is Snell's law,

$$n_1 \sin \theta_1 = n_2 \sin \theta_2$$

where n is the index of refraction of each medium. These laws for
light can also be deduced from Fermat's principle: that light traveling
between any two points follows the fastest possible path. Details of
reflection and refraction at boundaries depend on the polarization of
the incident light; there is one angle at which the reflected light
is completely polarized. Transparent media are dispersive; n depends

on the wavelength. Microscopically the reflection and refraction of light must be understood in terms of absorption and reradiation of the light by individual molecules of the medium.

Diffraction occurs, as for any wave, if light encounters obstacles not very large compared to its wavelength, and we calculate diffraction patterns by the same approach as for any wave. Diffraction of light by a circular aperture is of great importance to the behavior of optical instruments.

Interference phenomena likewise are observed for light waves. A difficulty is that coherent sources of light are very hard to come by, and interference experiments are usually done by dividing light from a single source, as with Lloyd's mirror or Young's two slits. As before, interference maxima are given by

$$m\lambda = d \sin \theta \qquad m = 0, 1, 2, 3, \ldots$$

where d is the effective separation of the two sources. In the Young experiment, if the slits are of finite size, the interference pattern is modulated by the diffraction pattern of each slit. The most familiar interference phenomena arise from interference of light reflected at each surface of a transparent film - giving rise of Newton's rings, and to the colors in reflection from an oil film, for instance. The condition for constructive interference in this case is

$$\frac{2nt}{\lambda} = m + \tfrac{1}{2} \qquad m = 1, 2, 3, 4, \ldots$$

where t is the thickness and n the refractive index of the film.

The extension of interference to the case of very many spaced slits is the diffraction grating. This is an important tool for the spectroscopic analysis of light; its resolution is proportional to the total number of slits.

Many important optical phenomena arise from the polarization of light. Unpolarized light, in general, can be partially or wholly polarized by absorption, reflection, refraction, or scattering. Some materials (polaroids) can be made to absorb selectively light of a particular state of polarization. Some media, including most crystalline materials, are birefringent: the different states of polarization of light incident upon such media obey different laws of refraction and propagate at different speeds in the medium. A piece of birefringent material can be made to pass only one polarization component of the incident light (Nicol prism) or to alter its state of polarization (wave plates).

26.2 CHECK LIST

h = 6.63×10^{-27} erg-sec

c = 3.00×10^{8} m/sec

particle theory of light

Huygens' principle

polarization

Brewster's angle

wave theory of light

reflection

refraction

diffraction

electromagnetic wave

photoelectric effect

quantization

photons

dual nature of light

electromagnetic spectrum:

   γ-rays

   x-rays

   ultraviolet light

   infrared light

   microwaves

   radio waves

electric field

electric dipole

dipole radiation

speed of light measurements:

   Roemer

   Fizeau

   Foucalt

   Michelson

Fermat's principle

Snell's law

optical path length

dispersion

index of refraction

Rayleigh criterion

coherent sources

Lloyd's mirror

Young's experiment

Newton's rings

diffraction grating

spectroscope

resolving power

linear polarization

circular polarization

elliptical polarization

birefringence (double refraction)

optic axis

polaroid

polarizer and analyzer

scattering

anisotropic material

Nicol prism

quarter-wave plate

half-wave plate

26.3   TRUE OR FALSE?

_____1. Newton believed light to be a stream of particles emitted by the source, principally because of the absence of diffraction.

_____2. A particle model can explain the law of refraction, but requires that the speed of light in transparent materials be greater than it is in air.

_____3. Snell's law of refraction can be inferred from either a particle or a wave model of light.

_____4. In the present century, phenomena such as the photoelectric effect, which the wave theory cannot explain, have reestablished the particle, instead of the wave, theory of light.

_____5. The energy of electromagnetic waves is exchanged only in fixed discrete amounts, proportional to their frequency.

_____6. Radio waves are electromagnetic waves with wavelengths much shorter than those of visible light.

_____7. Visible light is an electromagnetic wave with wavelength on the order of several times 10^{-7} m.

_____8. The wave function for electromagnetic waves is the electric field.

_____9. Any motion of electric charge radiates electromagnetic waves.

_____10. An oscillating point charge radiates electromagnetic waves with the frequency of oscillation.

_____11. Electric dipole radiation is unpolarized.

_____12. The first successful measurements of the speed of light were based on astronomical measurements.

_____13. Precise terrestrial determinations of the speed of light date back to Galileo.

_____14. In Maxwell's electromagnetic theory, the speed of light can be inferred from static electric and magnetic measurements.

_____15. Fermat's principle states that light follows the shortest path between any two points.

_____16. The laws of both reflection and refraction follow from Fermat's principle.

_____17. Reflection at a boundary between transparent media depends only on the speeds of light in the two media.

_____18. For reflection at a boundary between two transparent media, there is a particular angle of incidence at which the reflected light is completely polarized.

_____19. Light encountering a boundary between transparent media, moving from the medium with the higher speed of light to the lower, is reflected with a 180° phase shift.

_____20. If light falls on a boundary at Brewster's angle, both the reflected and the refracted light are completely polarized.

_____21. Light from any two sources of the same frequency can be made to interfere.

_____22. Propagation of light waves in a transparent medium is dispersive.

_____23. Diffraction constitutes a limitation on the precision of optical instruments.

_____24. Lloyd's mirror is a device exploiting reflection at Brewster's angle to produce polarized light.

_____25. In general, the interference in the reflection of light from the two faces of a thin film, whose thickness is half the wavelength, is destructive.

_____26. Properly speaking, a diffraction grating is an interference, rather than a diffraction, device.

_____27. Light is emitted from an electric discharge in a gas at discrete wavelengths.

_____28. For given line spacing, a larger grating is capable of better resolution.

_____29. Light is polarized if the phase difference between the two transverse components of the electric field is constant.

_____30. Brewster's angle is that angle of incidence on a boundary, such that incident and refracted rays are perpendicular to each other.

_____31. The sky is blue because light is polarized in scattering.

_____32. The optical axis is the direction, in a briefringent material, along which the difference in the speeds of O and E rays is greatest.

_____33. Snell's law does not hold for the E ray in a birefringent medium.

26.4 QUESTIONS

1. Arguments can be invented to explain - rather unconvincingly - the phenomenon of diffraction on the basis of a particle theory of light. Do you think interference - as in Young's experiment, for instance - could be similarly explained away?

2. How should a dipole broadcast antenna be oriented?

3. There are situations in which light travels through a medium with a continuously varying index of refraction. The index of refraction in a gas, for instance, is proportional to its density, so the refractive index of the atmosphere decreases with increasing altitude. What would the path of a ray of light in such a situation look like?

4. In the interference pattern of two slits of width a, separated by a distance d, the (d/a)th interference maximum is missing. Why? What other maxima will be missing from the pattern?

5. The surface of a piece of glass is wet with water. As it dries, the glossy reflections from the surface become much less noticeable, then reappear. What is going on here?

6. If nonreflective coatings for lenses and such are made very thin - compared to the wavelength of light - they must have an index of refraction which is more than that of glass. Why?

7. At night, looking out at a street lamp through a sheer curtain, one can see a cross-shaped pattern of spots of light with the lamp at its center. How does this come about?

8. Unpolarized light is incident on two sheets of polaroid with their axes crossed at an angle θ; the fraction of its intensity that gets through is $\cos^2 \theta$ in this case. Is the same true of plane-polarized incident light? Circularly polarized light?

9. What is the effect of a quarter-wave plate on already circularly polarized light?

10. How should the polarizing material in glare-reducing sunglasses be oriented?

26.5 EXAMPLES

1. The gadget sketched on the next page is Fresnel's double mirror. Light reflected from the two inclined mirror surfaces onto the screen in the direction indicated produces an interference pattern. If the angle between the two mirrors (α) is 0.01° and the distance R is 60 cm, find the separation of interference fringes of light of wavelength 620 nm on a screen 4 m away.

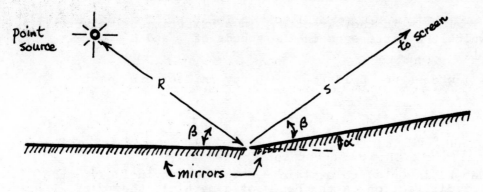

2. You are designing a diffraction grating to examine the visible spectrum from green to red (500 to 660 nm). You want this portion of the spectrum to fall within an angular range of 15° in third order, with resolution no worse than 0.01 nm. What line spacing is indicated, and what width of the grating must be illuminated?

3. A glass lens (n = 1.42) is coated with a thin layer of transparent material (n = 1.59). Light of wavelength 495 and 660 nm is absent from the reflected light. If the film is the thinnest possible that meets the given conditions, what wavelengths are brightest in the reflected light?

4. A certain sheet of mica (indices of refraction 1.6049 and 1.6116) is a quarter-wave plate for light of wavelength 600 nm and a half-wave plate at 540 nm. How thick is it?

5. Light is incident on a clean slab of glass of uniform thickness, along the normal to the surface of the galss. If the slab's refractive index is 1.49, what fraction of the incident intensity is transmitted by the slab? Include the effect of multiple reflections at the surfaces of the glass.

26.6 ANSWERS

True or False?

1. True.

2. True - thus the measurement of the speed of light in a dense medium would have been a crucial experiment.

3. True.

4. False - all the interference phenomena, etc., that established the wave theory in the 19th century didn't go away in 1905; we have to regard light as possessing aspects of both the wave and the particle behavior.

5. True.

6. False - with much longer wavelength.

7. True.

8. True - the electric or the magnetic field, for that matter.

9. False - an accelerated charge radiates.

10. True.

11. False - it is polarized with the electric field and the dipole axis coplanar.

12. True - Römer's observations of the moons of Jupiter.

13. False - they have been possible only since the early 19th century.

14. True.

15. False - at least, if "shortest" means distance; Fermat's principle says light finds the route which takes the shortest <u>time</u>.

16. True.

17. True - the refractive index is the ratio of speeds of light.

18. True - this is Brewster's angle.

19. True - as for instance from air into glass.

20. False - the refracted light is only partially polarized.

21. False - light from two separate sources is practically impossible to make interfere because it cannot be made coherent.

22. True.

23. True - the resolution limit (Rayleigh limit) of a telescope is the obvious instance.

24. False - Lloyd's mirror is an interference experiment.

25. False - no such general statement can be made; it depends on the angle of incidence and on the refractive indices of both the film and the media surrounding it.

26. True - it is interference from many slits.

27. True.

28. True - it has the greater total number of lines.

29. True.

30. False - such that reflected and refracted rays are perpendicular.

31. False - because blue light is more readily scattered than red.

32. False - the speeds of O and E rays along the optical axis are the same.

33. True.

Questions

1. I don't think so; in an interference pattern, light from two sources cancels out at some places and adds (to more than the sum of its parts) at others. If this isn't beyond a particle picture, then nothing is.

2. Vertically, since the intensity, or power, of the emitted radiation is greatest in the median plane. This, of course, is assuming that you want to broadcast horizontally.

3. A ray of light is sketched in a medium in which the refractive

index increases downward. Thinking of
the medium as the earth's atmosphere,
you can see that this affects the
observation of objects in the sky,
near the horizon.

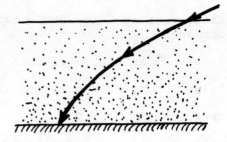

4. The first minimum of the single-slit
    diffraction pattern (for width a) is
    given by

$$a \sin \theta = \lambda$$

However, this is also the condition for
the (d/a)th maximum of the two-slit interference pattern. Thus,
at this θ, because of diffraction, there isn't any light there to
interfere. The (2d/a)th, the (3d/a)th, etc., maxima will likewise
be at diffraction minima.

5. As the film of water evaporates, it reaches, then passes, a thickness
    at which the thin-film interference is predominantly destructive;
    it forms a temporary nonreflecting coating.

6. Because in this case the 180° phase shift for destructive interfer-
    ence must come from reflections at the two surfaces; thus you have
    to have one fast-to-slow and one slow-to-fast boundary.

7. The threads of the curtain fabric form a two-dimensional diffraction
    grating; you are looking at an interference pattern.

8. The same would be true of circularly polarized incident light,
    because on a time-average it is unpolarized. Plane-polarized
    incident light, however, would have a transmission which must also
    depend on the angle between the polarization direction of the light
    and the axes of the polarizers.

9. Since a quarter-wave plate changes the relative phase of the two
    transverse components by 90°, it would give linearly polarized
    light.

10. Most of the glare you want to reduce is reflection off horizontal
    surfaces - that of the sun off a highway, say. Thus the lenses
    are oriented to pass light polarized in the vertical plane.

Examples

Partial Solutions (1)

1. What happens here is that the images of the source, in the two plane
    mirrors, are, in effect, two point sources in a definite phase
    relationship to one another. In general, they will not be in phase,
    but that doesn't matter much.

    Essentially, you have a geometry problem to do, to find the separation
    of the two "point sources." After that, it's just a two-source
    interference experiment, and how the sources got where they are
    doesn't signify. Remember that the image of a point source in a
    plane mirror is a point an equal distance behind the plane of the
    mirror.

2. Constructive interference from a grating occurs at angles given by

$$m\lambda = d \sin \theta \qquad\qquad m = 1, 2, 3, \ldots$$

where d is the grating spacing. Here you want to look in order
m = 3. What is it that determines the resolution of the lines
produced by a diffraction grating?

3. Write out the condition for destructive interference in reflection

from a thin film. What phase shifts occur at the two surfaces? The thickness of the film is found from the given destructive wavelengths.

4. In a quarter-wave plate, a phase <u>difference</u> of $\pi/2$ is introduced between the E and the O rays in transmission through a birefringent material; in a half-wave plate the difference is π. This doesn't say, however, that the plate is only a quarter- (or a half-) cycle thick. How thick must the plate be in this case?

5. The fractional reflection <u>each</u> time the light encounters the boundary between glass and air is determined by the index of refraction of the glass. But part of the beam may be reflected internally many times. What difference does this make? You aren't meant to be worrying about interference effects in this one - the glass slab isn't necessarily uniform in thickness to less than a wavelength - just reflection.

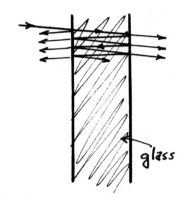

Partial Solutions (2)

1. The geometry is sketched below. A little thought will make it apparent that - since each image is as far behind its mirror as the source is in front - the real source and its two images are all three at the same distance R from the junction of the mirror planes (O).

From the diagram,

$$\beta' = \beta + \alpha$$

$$\phi = 2\beta' - 2\beta = 2\alpha$$

Thus the source separation d is the base of an isosceles triangle of side R and apex angle ϕ. Therefore

$$d = 2R \sin \tfrac{1}{2}\phi = 2R \sin \alpha$$

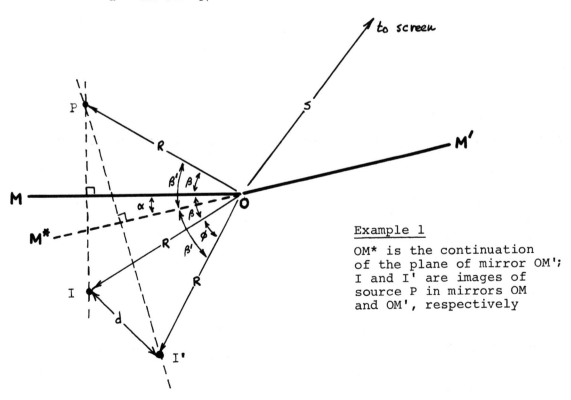

Example 1

OM* is the continuation of the plane of mirror OM'; I and I' are images of source P in mirrors OM and OM', respectively

2. For third order (m = 3)

$$(3)(5.0 \times 10^{-7} \text{ m}) = d \sin \theta_1$$

$$(3)(6.6 \times 10^{-7} \text{ m}) = d \sin \theta_2$$

and we specify that

$$\theta_2 = \theta_1 + 15^\circ$$

These equations can be solved for the angle θ, then in turn for the required grating spacing d. It is the total number of lines that determines resolution - and thus, for given line spacing, determines the width of the grating that must be illuminated.

3. In this case, the surface layer is optically more dense than the medium on either side of it; thus the phase changes of the two reflections are opposite, and we have

$$\frac{2nt}{\lambda} + \frac{1}{2} = m$$

for constructive, and

$$\frac{2nt}{\lambda} = m \qquad\qquad m = 1, 2, 3, 4, \ldots$$

for destructive interference. Putting in the two given wavelengths,

$$(6.6 \times 10^{-7} \text{ m}) = \frac{(2)(1.59)(t)}{m} = \frac{3.18t}{m}$$

$$(4.95 \times 10^{-7} \text{ m}) = \frac{3.18t}{m'}$$

are the conditions for destructive interference. Plainly

$$m' = \frac{4}{3} m$$

What value of m results in the <u>thinnest</u> layer possible?

4. For 600-nm light the sheet is a quarter-wave plate; that is, one of the rays is retarded by a quarter cycle compared to the other one:

$$\frac{tn_e}{\lambda} - \frac{tn_o}{\lambda} = m + \frac{1}{4} \qquad m = 0, 1, 2, 3, \ldots$$

So

$$t = (m + \frac{1}{4})\frac{\lambda}{\delta n} \qquad\qquad \delta n = n_e - n_o$$

At wavelength 540 nm we get a half-wave plate, so for that wavelength

$$t = (m + \frac{1}{2})\frac{\lambda'}{\delta n} = (m + \frac{1}{2})\frac{0.9\lambda}{\delta n}$$

but the thickness is the same in both cases.

5. The fraction transmitted on a <u>single</u> encounter with the boundary is

$$f = 1 - (\frac{n_2 - n_1}{n_2 + n_1})^2 = 0.961$$

The fraction going straight through the slab is thus f^2. But there is also some transmitted light which reflected off both boundaries once and was transmitted on its second try; since the fraction reflected at each encounter is $1 - f$, this is a fraction

$$f^2(1 - f)^2$$

of the incident intensity. There are also higher-multiple reflections to be considered. Altogether, what fraction is transmitted?

1. Plainly from the sketch, the distance to the screen is approximately $R + s$. Thus if the separation of interference fringes on the screen is to be some value x,

$$\frac{x}{R + s} \simeq \sin \theta_1 \simeq \frac{\lambda}{d}$$

so

$$x = \frac{(R + s)\lambda}{2R \sin \alpha}$$

For the data given, this is $\underline{x = 1.36 \text{ cm}}$.

2. We divide the two interference conditions to give

$$1.32 = \frac{\sin (\theta_1 + 15^\circ)}{\sin \theta_1} = \cos 15^\circ + (\sin 15^\circ)(\cotan \theta_1)$$

or

$$1.32 = 0.966 + 0.255 \cotan \theta_1$$

giving $\cotan \theta_1 = 1.368$ or $\theta_1 = 36.2^\circ$

Plugging this back into either interference condition gives

$$\underline{d = 2.54 \times 10^{-6} \text{ m}}$$

The resolution of a grating is

$$\frac{\delta\lambda}{\lambda} \simeq \frac{1}{3n}$$

Thus for 0.01 nm in 660 we need 22,000 lines or a width of

$$(22,000)(2.54 \times 10^{-6} \text{ m}) = \underline{5.6 \text{ cm}}$$

of the grating.

3. The thinnest layer has $m' = 4$, $m = 3$; this requires a thickness of 6.23×10^{-7} m. If we put this value back into the condition for constructive interference, we find the wavelengths most strongly reflected are

$$\lambda = \frac{2nt}{m - \frac{1}{2}} = \frac{1980 \text{ nm}}{m - \frac{1}{2}} \qquad m = 1, 2, 3, \ldots$$

The members of this series in the visible range are $\underline{566 \text{ nm}}$ and $\underline{440 \text{ nm}}$, so we expect these to be most strongly reflected.

4. The expression found above boils down to

$$m' + \frac{1}{2} = \frac{10}{9}(m + \frac{1}{4})$$

The lowest integer solution of these is $m = m' = 2$. We have also $\lambda = 600$ nm and $\delta n = 1.6116 - 1.6049 = 0.0067$. Thus the thickness must be

$$t = \frac{(2\frac{1}{4})(6 \times 10^{-7} \text{ m})}{0.0067} = 2.01 \times 10^{-4} \text{ m}$$

5. By extending the above argument, we can see that the entire fraction transmitted is

$$f^2 + f^2(1 - f)^2 + f^2(1 - f)^4 + \ldots = \frac{f^2}{1 - (1 - f)^2}$$

from the binomial expansion of $(1 - x)^{-1}$. For $f = 0.961$, this says a fraction $\underline{0.925}$ of the incident intensity is transmitted.

CHAPTER 27
Geometric Optics

27.1 CHAPTER SUMMARY

On the scale of everyday objects, the wavelength of light is very small; consequently, many phenomena can be treated satisfactorily in the ray approximation. The most important such phenomena, dealing with image formation by reflection and refraction of light at boundaries, constitute geometric optics.

A plane mirror forms a virtual image: that is, light does not actually diverge from the image point. A spherical mirror can form a real image: incident light parallel to the mirror axis is reflected to a point on the axis. The distance from the mirror to this point (its focal length) is half the radius of curvature. In general, light from a point distant s from the mirror forms an image at a distance s' from the mirror, where

$$\frac{1}{s} + \frac{1}{s'} = \frac{1}{f}$$

If we adopt the convention that a negative focal length refers to a convex mirror and a negative distance s' to a virtual image, this formula works for either real or virtual images.

A lens forms an image by refraction of light. The formula above applies to a thin lens as well as to a mirror. The focal length of a thin lens is determined by its radii of curvature and refractive index:

$$\frac{1}{f} = (n - 1)\left(\frac{1}{R_1} - \frac{1}{R_2}\right)$$

A diverging lens has a negative, and a converging lens a positive, focal length; note that, for a lens, a real image (positive image distance) is formed on the opposite side of the lens from the light source.

The image of an extended object is formed by point-to-point imaging of each point of the object. In general image and object are not the same size. The magnification of a single mirror or lens is

$$m = -\frac{s'}{s}$$

In many cases graphical construction of a few rays suffices to locate the image. A few special rays, for both mirrors and lenses, can be drawn without calculation. For either, a ray parallel to the axis is reflected, or refracted, through the focal point; a ray from the focal point is reflected or refracted parallel to the axis; a ray through the center of symmetry of a lens is undeviated; and a ray through the center of curvature of a spherical mirror reflects back on itself.

Exact point-to-point imaging holds only for paraxial rays; departure from this limit lead to various aberrations of mirrors and lenses. Focal length changes slightly with distance from the axis, for example, leading to the blurring of the image called spherical aberration. In addition to these geometric aberrations, lenses exhibit chromatic aberration because the lens material is dispersive. Aberrations can be reduced by using combinations of optical elements or by making them with nonspherical surfaces (e.g., the parabolic mirror).

In the eye, light from objects without is focused on the light-sensitive retina, at the back of the eyeball by a lens in front. The focal length of the lens is variable to accommodate the eye to objects at different distances.

A simple magnifier is a converging lens used to view objects more closely than the eye can accommodate to, so increasing the angle subtended at the eye by the object. Its magnifying power is inversely proportional to its focal length. In the basic forms of both the telescope and the compound microscope, the eyepiece is a simple magnifier used to view real images of distant, or small, objects produced by an objective lens.

27.2 CHECK LIST

geometric optics	aberration
real vs. virtual image	spherical aberration
spherical mirror	chromatic aberration
paraxial rays	parabolic mirror
focal point	pupil
focal length	retina
magnification	accommodation
image and object distance	near point
lens	simple magnifier
virtual object	angular magnification
thin lens	eyepiece
lensmaker's formula	ocular
erect vs. inverted image	telescope
converging vs. diverging lens	compound microscope
reversibility	objective

27.3 TRUE OR FALSE?

____1. The image formed by a plane mirror is the same size as the object.

_____2. A real image is one in which light actually emanates from the image point.

_____3. A virtual image cannot be seen directly but must be projected on a screen.

_____4. Paraxial rays are rays parallel to the axis of a mirror or lens.

_____5. A focal point of a mirror or lens is the point at which light from a source infinitely far away is brought to a focus.

_____6. The focal length of a spherical mirror is half its radius of curvature.

_____7. A ray coming from, or passing through, the focal point of a spherical mirror is reflected back on itself.

_____8. Only real images can be located by drawing ray diagrams.

_____9. The eye does not distinguish real from virtual images.

_____10. The image of a real object, formed by a convex mirror, is always virtual.

_____11. A negative image distance is taken to mean a virtual image.

_____12. An image on the same side of a single lens as the object is a real image.

_____13. Refraction at a plane boundary does not form images.

_____14. A thin lens is one in which the refractive index is not very different from 1.

_____15. A ray incident on a lens from one focal point is refracted through the other focal point.

_____16. The "lensmaker's equation" gives the focal length of a lens in terms of its physical properties.

_____17. A diverging lens has a negative focal length.

_____18. A spherical mirror, unlike a thin lens with spherical surfaces, is free of spherical aberration.

_____19. A parabolic mirror focuses all light, which is incident parallel to its axis, to a single point.

_____20. Focusing of light in the eye is accomplished by the pupil.

_____21. An eye which is nearsighted has its near point nearer the eye than is normal.

_____22. The magnifying power of a simple magnifier depends on the distance of most distinct vision of the user's eye.

_____23. A given object, twice as far away from the eye, forms half as big a retinal image in the eye.

_____24. A simple magnifier is a positive lens of short focal length.

_____25. The image formed by a simple magnifier is virtual.

_____26. The objective lens of a telescope is a magnifier used to view the real image formed by the ocular.

____27. The objective of a telescope would ordinarily be a negative lens of long focal length.

____28. The magnifying power of a telescope depends only on focal lengths of its objective and eyepiece.

____29. The magnifying power of a compound microscope depends only on the focal lengths of its objective and eyepiece.

27.4 QUESTIONS

1. Under what circumstances - if any - does a convex spherical mirror form a real image?

2. Explain what happens to the properties of a lens immersed in a fluid such as water. Is it possible that an ordinarily converging lens becomes a diverging lens under these conditions? Why is your vision blurred underwater?

3. It appears that a plane mirror forms an image in which left and right are inverted, but not up and down. Why is this?

4. What is the cause of chromatic aberration?

5. What is the difference between a lateral magnification of +1 and one of -1? Under what circumstances does the lateral magnification of a thin lens have each of these values?

6. The objectives of the largest astronomical telescopes are always mirrors rather than lenses. Why is this?

7. As we have described it, the final image of a telescope is virtual. How, then, is it possible to take telescopic (e.g., astronomical) photographs by allowing the image to fall on photographic film?

27.5 EXAMPLES

1. A concave spherical mirror has radius of curvature 60 cm. Where must an object be placed if its image is to be virtual and three times the size of the object?

2. A biconvex lens consists of two spherical surfaces of radii R_1 and R_2. Its thickness along the axis is t, and its diameter is d. Show that, if the lens is thin, the focal length may be written

$$f \simeq \frac{d^2}{8(n-1)t}$$

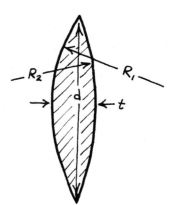

If such a lens, of diameter 7 cm, is made of glass of refractive index 1.42 and has a focal length of 56 cm, how thick is it?

3. From a ray diagram for a converging lens with a real object and a real image, show that

$$\frac{1}{s} + \frac{1}{s'} = \frac{1}{f}$$

4. A light source is 1 m from a screen. A lens placed at either of two points between them focuses an image of the source onto the screen. The image with the lens in one position is three times the size that it is with the lens in the other position. What

is the focal length of the lens?

5. A compound microscope has an overall length of 26 cm, an overall
    magnification of 40, and uses an eyepiece whose focal length is
    4 cm. What is the focal length of the objective lens?

27.6 ANSWERS

True or False?

1. True.

2. True.

3. False - only a real image can be projected on a screen, as in a
    virtual iamge there is no real point at which light from a point
    source converges, but the eye does not distinguish.

4. False - they are rays sufficiently near the axis (but not
    exactly parallel to it) that we may use small-angle approximations
    to analyze their reflection and refraction.

5. True.

6. True.

7. False - this is true of a ray through the center of curvature.

8. False - either kind may be; there is no real convergence of rays
    to, but only an apparent divergence from, a virtual image.

9. True.

10. True.

11. True.

12. False - virtual; there could not be a real convergence of light
    by a single lens to a point on the same side of the lens as
    the source.

13. False - if it didn't, you couldn't see the fish underwater at all.

14. False - a thin lens is one whose thickness is small compared to
    all other significant dimensions.

15. False - it is refracted parallel to the lens axis.

16. True - in terms of its refractive index and radii of curvature.

17. True.

18. False - spherical aberration afflicts them both, as do the other
    geometric aberrations; the mirror, of course, has no chromatic
    aberration.

19. True - no spherical aberration.

20. False - this is the function of the lens; the pupil is a variable-
    size aperture which controls the amount of light admitted.

21. False - it is one in which the relaxed lens focuses in front of
    the retina; "too near" a near point is no defect at all.

22. True - the magnifying power is this distance divided by the focal

length of the lens.

23. True - this is the way in which apparent size varies with distance.

24. True - the focal length must be shorter than the distance of most distinct vision, or it is no magnifier at all.

25. True.

26. False - it's the other way around; the ocular is the eyepiece.

27. False - a positive lens, to form a real image that is viewed by the eyepiece.

28. True.

29. False - it depends also on their separation.

Questions

1. A convex mirror has a negative focal length. From the focusing equation, then, if the image is to be real, the <u>object</u> distance (s) must be negative - that is, it must be a virtual object. This case is illustrated in the sketch.

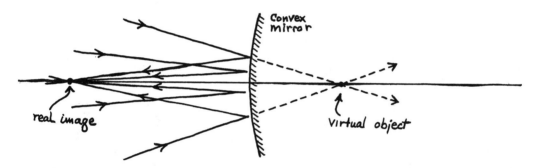

2. The focusing power of a lens depends on the <u>difference</u> in refractive index; see the lensmaker's equation. The difference between glass and water is much less than the difference between glass and air; consequently the lens's focal length underwater will be much longer. If the lens is immersed in a fluid of refractive index higher than its own, its sign changes - a converging lens becomes a diverging one, for instance.

   Focusing in the eye is due primarily to refraction at its front surface (the cornea). Thus when immersed in water - which is not very different from the material of the eye - most of its focusing power is lost. This is why, if you want to see underwater, you wear a face mask - to keep an <u>air</u> boundary at the eye's surface.

3. Well, really, it does neither. If your head is up, so is your image's; if your left hand - the one wearing the ring - is pointing west, so is your image's. What really happens is that the image is inverted front to back: you are facing north, your image is facing south.

4. Chromatic aberration is due to dispersion of light in the lens material; the speed of light in any transparent material is a function of the wavelength, and wavelength is color. Thus the focal length of a lens for blue light is a little different than it is for red.

5. The lateral magnification is

$$m = \frac{-s'}{s} = \frac{-f}{s - f}$$

for a thin lens. A positive magnification means an erect image, a negative magnification an inverted one. From the formula, magnification -1 plainly occurs for $s = 2f$ and magnification +1 for $s = 0$. In the latter case, the object is at the lens and its image coincides with it.

6. A mirror can be fround with a paraboloidal surface and thus be free of spherical aberration, and mirrors of course do not exhibit chromatic aberration in any case. The determinative factors, however, are mechanical rather than optical; only one side of a mirror matters, and it can be supported from the other. A lens must be free on both sides - it can be supported at the edges only - mounting very large ones becomes enormously difficult.

7. What one does is to put the film at the position of the real image formed by the objective and dispense with the eyepiece. The essential function of a big telescope in this case is its light-gathering power, not its magnification.

Examples

Partial Solutions (1)

1. The relative sizes of object and image are given. What do these tell you? Set up the focusing equation for the mirror and solve for the object distance. Don't forget to include the fact that the image formed is a virtual one.

2. Imagine the lens divided into two spherical "caps," as sketched, by a plane passing through its perimeter. You need the thickness of each piece; it can be deduced from its diameter and the radius of the sphere from which it is sliced.

    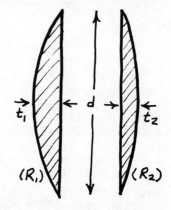

    Note that the lens is given as thin - what this means is that you can feel free (but not too free - why?) to approximate that angles are small, that t is much less than other dimensions, and so on.

3. The readily drawable rays are:
   (a) One through the near focal point, bent parallel to the axis
   (b) One leaving the object parallel to the axis, refracted through the far focal point
   (c) One through the center of symmetry of the lens, undeviated
   How many of these do you need to prove what you want to prove?

4. One can set this up and brute-force solve for the two lens positions. Is this really necessary? What can you tell about the two lens positions without doing this? Think about reversibility. You are given, not the magnification in either position, but the ratio of magnifications in the two positions.

5. In the text, the magnifying power of a compound microscope is given as

$$M = \frac{(25 \text{ cm})(\ell)}{f_0 f_e}$$

where f_0 and f_e are the focal lengths of objective and eyepiece. What is ℓ?

Partial Solutions (2)

1. The magnification is

$$m = -\frac{s'}{s} = +3$$

here. The positive sign is used because the image is (given) virtual and hence erect. Therefore

$$s' = -3s$$

is the image distance. Plug this in the focusing equation and solve for s.

2. The geometry problem here is to find the "sagitta" of an arc of a circle. In the sketch below

$$u = R - t = R \cos \alpha$$

while

$$d = 2R \sin \alpha$$

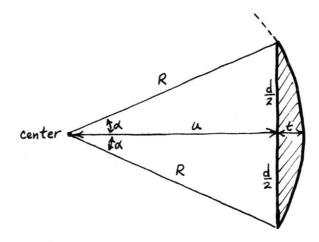

Thus

$$\sin^2 \alpha + \cos^2 \alpha = 1 = (1 - \frac{t}{R})^2 + (\frac{d}{2R})^2$$

or

$$\frac{d^2}{4R^2} - \frac{2t}{R} + \frac{t^2}{R^2} = 0$$

which gives

$$d^2 = 4t(2R - t)$$

If the lens is thin, however, the second term in the parentheses can be dropped, and so

$$t \simeq \frac{d^2}{8R}$$

Now put your lens together - it is just two such slices.

3. Any two of these rays suffice to locate the image; thus any two ought to suffice for you to prove where the image is. Rays (b) and (c) for a converging lens, with real object and image, are sketched below.

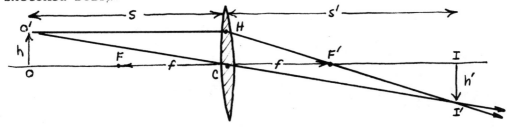

221

Triangles O'OC and I'I$_C$ are plainly similar, so corresponding sides are in proportion:

$$\frac{h}{s} = \frac{h'}{s'}$$

Find another equation of the same sort relating s' and s, eliminate h'/h between them, and you are home.

4. The magnification of a single lens is

$$m = -\frac{s'}{s}$$

and here we are given that

$$\frac{m_1}{m_2} = 3$$

if 1 and 2 refer to the two lens positions; so

$$\frac{s_1' s_2}{s_1 s_2'} = 3$$

But - reversibility! - if an object at A gives an image at B, then with the same lens, an object at B must give an image at A. This means that, as there are only two focusing positions, the image distance in one must be the object distance in the other. That is,

$$s_1' = s_2$$

and vice versa.

5. In this prescription, ℓ is the distance from the far focal point of the objective to the real image formed by the objective; this in turn is placed at the focal point of the eyepiece.

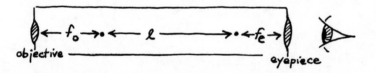

Therefore

$$f_0 + f_e + \ell = 26 \text{ cm}$$

and

$$\frac{(25 \text{ cm})(\ell)}{f_0 f_e} = 40$$

You know f_e; solve for f_0.

Partial Solutions (3)

1. If s' = -3s, we have

$$\frac{1}{s} - \frac{1}{3s} = \frac{2}{R}$$

or

$$\frac{2}{3s} = \frac{2}{R}$$

so s = R/3 = <u>20 cm</u> from the mirror.

2. To be consistent with the sign convention we are using, we call R_2 negative for a biconvex lens. Since t is positive, put

$$t_2 \simeq -\frac{d^2}{8R_2} \qquad\qquad t_1 \simeq \frac{d^2}{8R_1}$$

The thickness of the lens is therefore given by

$$t = t_1 + t_2 = \frac{d^2}{8}\left(\frac{1}{R_1} - \frac{1}{R_2}\right)$$

But

$$\frac{1}{f} = (n - 1)\left(\frac{1}{R_1} - \frac{1}{R_2}\right)$$

is the lensmaker's equation. Therefore

$$t = \frac{d^2}{8(n - 1)f} \qquad\qquad f = \frac{d^2}{8(n - 1)t}$$

as advertised. For the numbers given,

$$t = \frac{(7\ cm)^2}{(8)(0.42)(56\ cm)} = \underline{0.26\ cm}$$

3. From similar triangles F'HC and I'F'I we have

$$\frac{h}{f} = \frac{h'}{s - f}$$

Therefore

$$\frac{h'}{h} = \frac{s' - f}{f} = \frac{s'}{s}$$

so

$$s(s' - f) = s'f \qquad or \qquad f(s' + s) = ss'$$

and finally, solving this for 1/f gives

$$\frac{1}{s} + \frac{1}{s'} = \frac{1}{f} \qquad\qquad\qquad Q.E.D.$$

4. We have, then,

$$\left(\frac{s_1'}{s_1}\right)^2 = 3$$

so that

$$s_1' = \sqrt{3}\, s_1$$

but also

$$s_1 + s_1' = d$$

if d is the distance between source and screen. Solving, we get

$$s_1 = \frac{d}{1 + \sqrt{3}} \qquad and \qquad s_1' = \frac{\sqrt{3}\, d}{1 + \sqrt{3}}$$

the thin-lens equation is thus

$$\frac{1 + \sqrt{3}}{d} + \frac{1 + \sqrt{3}}{\sqrt{3}\, d} = \frac{1}{f}$$

Solving this gives

$$f = \frac{\sqrt{3}}{(1 + \sqrt{3})^2}\, d = 0.232\, d = \underline{23.2\ cm}$$

5. The eyepiece focal length is 4 cm; therefore

$$f_0 + \ell = 22\ cm$$

and

$$\frac{\ell}{f_0} = \frac{(40)(4\ cm)}{25\ cm} = 6.4$$

Thus $\ell = 6.4 f_0$ and $7.4 f_0 = 22$ cm or $\underline{f_0 = 2.97\ cm}$.

CHAPTER 28
Special Relativity

28.1 CHAPTER SUMMARY

The special theory of relativity consists essentially of the consequences of two fundamental postulates, originating with Einstein:

1. Absolute, uniform motion cannot be detected.

2. The speed of light is independent of the motion of the source.
The theory grew out of inconsistencies in classical ideas of the
propagation of light. All but electromagnetic waves require some
physical medium in which to propagate. It was assumed that a quasi-
physical medium called the "ether," through which light travels,
existed throughout the universe. The experiment of Michelson and
Morley attempted to measure, by interferometric methods, the motion
of the earth relative to the ether. It yielded a null result: no
motion through the "ether" could be detected. The result is consistent with the postulates of relativity, in that an absolute state of
motion is not measurable.

It follows from the postulates that all observers measure the
same speed of light in vacuum, regardless of their relative motion.
This contradicts our ordinary experience of velocity addition; it
implies that the observers' measurements of space and time intervals
depend on their relative motion. As this conclusion is independent of
the measuring apparatus, we imagine for convenience measurements based
on a "light clock," which measures the travel time of a flash of
light. Since all observers find the same speed of light, the interval
between ticks of a light clock will depend on its motion relative to
the observer. We call the time interval between two events, according
to an observer for whom they occur in the same place, the proper time
interval. In any other frame of reference, the time interval between
the same events is longer by a factor γ

$$\Delta t' = \gamma \, \Delta t$$

where

$$\gamma \equiv \frac{1}{\sqrt{1 - v^2/c^2}}$$

and v is the relative velocity of the observers. Likewise, an object
observed in motion is shorter along the direction of motion, by the
same factor γ, than if observed at rest. These effects can be observed
directly in some cases; muons generated by cosmic rays in the atmosphere
would mostly decay before reaching the ground, if it were not for the
relativistic time dilation.

The essential point is that the Einstein postulates imply that

224

the synchronization of clocks and the simultaneity of events, depend on the motion of the observer. If two clocks a distance L apart are synchronized in their rest frame, then in the reference frame of an observer moving at speed v they are out of synchronization by an amount Lv/c^2. We may attack the general question of two inertial observers, in relative motion; the relation between their versions of events, which is consistent with the Einstein postulates, is the Lorentz transformation:

$$x' = \gamma(x - vt)$$

$$y' = y$$

$$z' = z$$

$$t' = \gamma(t - vx/c^2)$$

if their relative motion is in the x direction. The corresponding transformation of velocities is

$$u'_x = \frac{u_x - v}{1 - u_x v/c^2}$$

Note that the Lorentz transformation reduces to our ordinary notions (the "galilean transformation") at speeds v<<c.

A well-known illustration is that of the two twins, one of whom stays home while the other indulges in a round trip at high speed to some distant planet. On his return, the traveller finds he is younger - he has aged less - than his twin. This is consistent with special relativity; it sometimes appears as a paradox because the roles of the two twins seem symmetric. They are not, however, as only the stay-at-home twin has remained in an inertial reference frame throughout.

The Doppler effect, for waves in a mechanical medium, depends on whether it is the source or the observer that moves. For light waves, no such distinction is possible; the relativistic Doppler effect depends only on their relative motion.

The postulates of relativity require redefinition of the basic dynamic quantities as well. Classically we define momentum as $\vec{p} = m\vec{u}$ essentially because it is a conserved quantity. But using correct relativistic expressions we find that $m\vec{u}$ is not conserved in collisions; we redefine momentum therefore as

$$\vec{p} = \frac{m\vec{u}}{\sqrt{1 - u_2/c_2}} = \gamma m\vec{u}$$

which is conserved in collisions and reduces to the usual form for u<<c. (If we like, we can continue to call $\vec{p} = m'\vec{u}$ and say that the mass of the particle, m', increases with speed.) Having redefined $\vec{p}$, we redefine kinetic energy by means of the work-energy theorem, using $\vec{F} = d\vec{p}/dt$ to calculate the work. This yields

$$E_k = (\gamma - 1)mc^2$$

We may interpret this to say that the total energy of the particle consists of E_k plus a term mc^2 which is independent of its motion. In fact this is not arbitrary; we find that this "rest energy" must be considered as a part of the total energy of the particle. Neither (rest) mass nor (kinetic) energy is conserved individually, but their sum

$$E = E_k + mc^2 = \gamma mc^2$$

is conserved jointly. This is of practical importance primarily in nuclear interactions; a measurable fraction of the rest mass of a system of nucleons may be "gained" or "lost" in a nuclear reaction. The mass difference between a stable nucleus and the sum of individual particle masses measures the nuclear binding energy.

28.2 CHECK LIST

u = 1.66 x 10^{-27} kg $\leftrightarrow$ 931.5 MeV
apecial theory of relativity
relativistic kinematics
relativistic dynamics
principle of relativity
Michelson-Moreley experiment
ether
Michelson interferometer
electromagnetic waves
time dilation
Lorentz contraction
light clock
proper time
lifetime of muons
clock synchronization
simultaneity

Doppler effect
Lorentz transformation
galilean transformation
inertial reference frame
velocity transformation
twin paradox
relativistic momentum
conservation of momentum
elastic collision
relativistic mass
rest mass
relativistic kinetic energy
total energy
rest energy
binding energy
nuclear reaction

28.3 TRUE OR FALSE?

_____1. The speed of light in free space is the same for all observers.

_____2. The luminiferous ether was a material medium assumed responsible for the propagation of light.

_____3. The Michelson interferometer is a device for precise measurements of the speed of light.

_____4. The Michelson-Morley experiment requires a Michelson interferometer with arms of exactly the same length.

_____5. The result of the Michelson-Morley experiment showed that the sun is stationary with respect to the ether.

_____6. Einstein developed the special theory of relativity in an effort to explain the null result of the Michelson-Morley experiment.

_____ 7. A rapidly moving object appears contracted in the direction of motion because light from the front and back of the object takes different times to reach the observer.

_____ 8. A "light clock" is a hypothetical device in which the measurement of time intervals is based directly on the speed of light.

_____ 9. It is impossible for an observer to conclude that the <u>relative</u> speed of two objects, each in motion with respect to him, is greater than c.

_____ 10. A moving clock runs faster than would the same clock at rest.

_____ 11. The <u>proper time</u> interval between two events is the time interval as measured in a frame of reference in which the two events occur at the same place.

_____ 12. Two observers in motion relative to one another agree as to their relative speed.

_____ 13. Because of the time dilation, muons produced by cosmic rays in the atmosphere mostly decay before reaching the ground.

_____ 14. If the proper time interval between two events is zero, they are simultaneous in all frames of reference.

_____ 15. Two clocks not in the same place are necessarily out of synchronization because of the time L/c which light takes to travel between them.

_____ 16. Two clocks synchronized in their own rest frame, but not in the same place, are always out of synchronization in a frame of reference in which they are moving.

_____ 17. Because it is impossible to distinguish between motion of the source and motion of the observer, there can be no Doppler effect for light in free space.

_____ 18. The Lorentz transformation is the relation between events, as measured by observers in relative motion, which is valid for speeds very much less than that of light.

_____ 19. The relativistic velocity transformation is such that a motion at speed c in one frame of reference has speed c in any other frame moving relative to the first.

_____ 20. The idea of the "twin paradox" is, so far at least, beyond experimental verification.

_____ 21. In the "twin paradox," the one who remains, throughout, in an inertial frame of reference will always be the older of the two when they get back together.

_____ 22. Momentum is redefined in the special theory of relativity because the classical definition $\vec{p} = m\vec{u}$ is not a quantity which is conserved in collisions.

_____ 23. $\vec{F} = m \cdot \vec{a}$ is not relativistically valid.

_____ 24. The "relativistic mass" of an object in motion is always greater than its rest mass.

_____ 25. The difference between the "relativistic mass" of a moving object and its rest mass is a measure of its kinetic energy.

_____ 26. The kinetic energy of a moving object can still be written $\frac{1}{2}mv^2$ if m is the <u>relativistic</u> mass.

____27. A system of two particles bound together by an attractive force has a mass greater than the sum of the two rest masses, because of the mass of the binding energy.

28.4 QUESTIONS

1. Imagine a man in a spaceship which is moving at a speed near that of light. He holds some rectangular object such as a shoebox or a book. As he turns it in different directions, does its shape appear to change due to the Lorentz contraction along the direction of motion?

2. Human lifetimes are ordinarily under 100 years, and nothing can move faster than light. Explain how, even so, it is possible (in principle) for a man to travel to a star 150 light-years away.

3. How is it possible that each of two observers find that the other's meter stick is shorter than his own?

4. Imagine someone running into his barn carrying a ladder, at a speed near that of light. The rest length of the ladder is the same as that of the barn. It is easy to see that, because the ladder is Lorentz-contracted, it fits inside the barn   you could prove this with cameras at each door, for instance. But, according to the guy carrying the ladder, it is the barn that is Lorentz-contracted, while his ladder is full length; so clearly it can't fit inside at any moment. Who is right?

5. Under what circumstances do two observers agree as to the velocity of something which is in motion relative to both of them?

6. For which is the actual "relativistic mass increase" greater - a proton or an electron, each with 10-MeV kinetic energy? For which is the fractional mass increase greater?

7. Two globs of putty are thrown directly toward each other, collide, and stick together. Each has a rest mass of 1 gm, and each, before the collision, had a relativistic mass of 2 gm. After the

collision, the two, stuck together, must be at rest in the laboratory. Why? Is the rest mass of this resulting glob 2 gm or 4 gm?

28.5 EXAMPLES

1. The lifetime of a free neutron is 12 min. If neutrons are made in the center of the sun, how fast - on the average - must they be traveling to reach the earth?

2. A rocket ship departs the earth at a speed of 0.35c. Ten seconds after leaving - according to its own clocks - it launches a missile back toward the earth at a speed of 0.9c. According to clocks on the earth, when was the missile launched, and when does it strike the earth?

3. If a meter stick is moving, lengthwise, directly at you with a speed 0.6c, what length would you <u>see</u> it as having? Assume you can tell the distance of a point by looking at it, but don't forget that light takes some finite time to travel to your eye.

4. A certain line in the emission spectrum of hydrogen gas has a wavelength, in the laboratory, of 656.29 nm. You observe this line in the spectrum of one member of a double-star system to vary between 656.10 and 656.48 nm, with a period of 9.06 days. If you assume that the star you are looking at is much smaller than the other member of the system, what is the radius of its orbit?

5. K mesons and π mesons are subnuclear particles with rest masses of 498 MeV/c^2 and 135 MeV/c^2, respectively. A K meson in flight decays into two π mesons. If the total energy of the original K was 680 MeV, find the kinetic energies of the two π's.

28.6 ANSWERS

True or False?

1. True.

2. True - although I suppose one could argue about the word "material."

3. False - an interferometer measures differences in optical path length, although in some circumstances it is applied to measure small changes in the speed of light.

4. False - the difference in fringe shift as the interferometer is rotated, thus exchanging the roles of the two arms, is observed rather than the absolute fringe shift.

5. False - it failed to detect any motion of the earth relative to the other.

6. False - according to Einstein, he was hardly aware of the experiment at the time.

7. False - the object is <u>observed</u> to be contracted, after any such time lags are allowed for.

8. True - at least, as directly as possible; in the kind we usually talk about, there is a length measurement involved also.

9. False.

10. False - slower.

11. True.

12. True - they must, if one's frame of reference is just as good as the other's.

13. False - it is because of the time dilation that many survive to reach the ground.

14. True - two such events are called "coincident."

15. False - if they are at rest relative to one another, there is no problem in allowing for the time lag in synchronizing them.

16. True.

17. False - all this says is that there's no difference in the Doppler effect for moving source and moving observer.

18. False - that is the "galilean" transformation.

19. True.

20. False - the basic idea is verified in experiments on the decay of elementary particles in flight.

21. True.

22. True.

23. True - at least, not without substantial reformulation of what $\vec{F}$ and $\vec{a}$ are.

24. True.

25. True.

26. False.

27. False - less than the sum; if they are bound, energy (which "has mass") must be added to the system to separate them.

Questions

1. Of course not - the book isn't moving at high speed relative to the guy that's observing it.

2. All he has to do is to travel fast enough so that the 150 light-years to the star is Lorentz-contracted to, say, a manageable 15 light-years. From the point of view of an observer on the earth the star is still 150 light-years away, but all the pilot's clocks are running slow, and he ages more slowly.

3. There is nothing puzzling about this if we can get over the tacit assumption of simultaneity. Each observer would conclude that the other did something wrong in measuring the first observer's stick - he measured where the front and back ends were at different times, or he timed its passage with a clock that was running slow, or something. And each would be right - in his own frame of reference.

4. Again, there is an apparent paradox only because we tend to assume the absoluteness of simultaneity without thinking about it. Suppose in the frame of reference of the ground, you take pictures simultaneously at the front and back doors and find that at some moment the ladder was in the barn. In the frame of reference of the moving ladder, the (contracted) barn came at you; the front camera took its picture after the rear camera did, so the ladder was never all in the barn at any one moment.

barn frame

230

ladder frame

5. When - and only when - whatever it is moves at the speed of light.

6. The "relativistic mass increase" is the kinetic energy divided by c^2, so it is $10\,\text{MeV}/c^2$ for a 10-MeV anything. The rest mass of an electron is much less than that of a proton, so the <u>fractional</u> mass increase of a 10-MeV electron is much larger.

7. The rest mass of the resulting glob is 4 gm - it is <u>total</u> energy, not rest or kinetic, that is conserved. The glob is <u>at rest</u> by conservation of momentum or, if you prefer, just by the symmetry of the situation; thus its total energy is all rest energy.

Examples

Partial Solutions (1)

1. The neutrons must be traveling fast enough to reach the earth in 12 min - on their <u>own</u> clocks. Presuming that they travel fast enough for it to be significant, don't overlook the Lorentz contraction of the sun-earth distance, in a frame moving with the neutrons.

2. This isn't very hard, but there is a little potential for confusion about what is relative to what. You can usually avoid such confusion if you set everything up carefully and use the Lorentz transformation. Call the earth the unprimed frame and the rocket ship the primed frame. The relative speed is 0.35c, so

$$\gamma = \frac{1}{\sqrt{1 - (0.35)^2}} = 1.068$$

The Lorentz transformation gives

$$x' = \gamma(x - 0.35ct)$$
$$t' = \gamma(t - 0.35x/c)$$

3. The point here is that light from the two ends of the stick takes different times to reach your eye. Let the two ends of the stick be at x_1 and x_2. Then if it moves toward you at speed v,

$$x_1 = x_0 - vt$$
$$x_2 = x_0 + L - vt$$

Be careful - what is L? If the light reaches your eye at time t*, when did it leave each end of the stick?

4. You need to make a couple of assumptions to make this a simple problem. If you assume that the star is orbiting around a stationary primary - this was the point of assuming it is much smaller than its primary - and if you are in the plane of the orbit, the star alternately approaches you and recedes from you at orbital velocity. This you can find from the Doppler shift of the hydrogen line.

5. Conservation of total energy and conservation of momentum give you two equations that can be juggled to find the velocities of the two π mesons. Another equation that simplifies things somewhat is

$$E^2 = (pc)^2 + E_0^2$$

where E is the total energy and $E_0 = m_0c^2$. This applies to anything.

Partial Solutions (2)

1. If τ is the neutron lifetime, at rest, its lifetime in the earth frame is $\gamma\tau$. Let d be the earth-sun distance; then for the neutron to reach the earth,

$$v > \frac{d}{\gamma\tau}$$

Solve for v.

2. According to observers on board the rocket, the missile is fired at $t_1' = 10$ sec. This event takes place at $x_1' = 0$ in the rocket frame - that is, at the rocket. If, still in the rocket frame, the missile hits the earth at time t_2'

$$(0.9c)(t_2' - t_1') = (0.35c)(t_2')$$

so

$$t_2' = 16.36 \text{ sec}$$

Where does this event happen?

3. L is the length of the stick in your frame of reference - that is, contracted. Let the time at which the light that reaches your eye at t* leaves the front end of the stick be t_1; the back end, t_2. Then

$$t^* - t_1 = \frac{x_1(t_1)}{c} = \frac{x_0 - vt_1}{c}$$

which gives

$$t_1 = \frac{ct^* - x_0}{c - v}$$

At this moment, where was it? Do the same for the back end of the stick.

4. If a light source whose frequency, it its own rest frame, is f_0 moves toward you at speed v, the frequency you observe is

$$f = \sqrt{\frac{c + v}{c - v}}\, f_0$$

In this case, you have f_0 and f, and want to find v.

5. The total energy available to the two pions is 680 MeV; the total momentum is given by

$$(680 \text{ MeV})^2 = (pc)^2 + (498 \text{ MeV})^2$$

or

$$p = 463 \text{ MeV/c}$$

Conservation of momentum and energy thus give

$$E_1 + E_2 = 680 \text{ MeV}$$

$$p_1 + p_2 = 463 \text{ MeV/c}$$

and for each π, we have also

$$E^2 = (pc)^2 + (135 \text{ MeV})^2$$

Solve for p_1 and p_2.

Partial Solutions (3)

1. We have

$$v > \frac{d}{\tau}(1 - \frac{v^2}{c^2})^{\frac{1}{2}}$$

so

$$(\frac{v\tau}{d})^2 > 1 - \frac{v^2}{c^2}$$

solving for v gives

$$\frac{v}{c} > [1 + (\frac{c\tau}{d})^2]^{-\frac{1}{2}}$$

With τ = 12 min = 7.2×10^2 sec and d = 93×10^6 mi = 1.50×10^{11} m, this gives

$$\underline{v > 0.570c = 1.71 \times 10^8 \text{ m/sec}}$$

2. Still in the rocket frame, the position at which the missile hits earth is

$$x'_2 = (0.35c)(16.36 \text{ sec}) = -(5.73 \text{ sec})(c)$$

since the earth has been moving away at $0.35c$ for time t'_2. What we want are the times at which these two events occur, in the <u>earth</u> frame of reference. Solving the Lorentz transformation for <u>t</u> gives

$$t = \gamma(t' + \frac{ux'}{c^2}) = (1.068)(t' + \frac{0.35x'}{c})$$

Thus

$$t_1 = (1.068)(10 \text{ sec}) = \underline{10.68 \text{ sec}}$$

is the time at which the missile was fired, and

$$t_2 = (1.068)[16.36 \text{ sec} - (0.35)(5.73 \text{ sec})] = \underline{15.33 \text{ sec}}$$

the time at which it struck the earth.

3. At time t_1, the front end of the stick is at

$$x_1(t_1) = x_0 - vt_1 = x_0 - v\left[\frac{ct* - x_0}{c - v}\right] = \frac{c(x_0 - vt*)}{c - v}$$

The analysis for the back end of the stick is identical, except that x_0 is replaced by $x_0 + L$. Thus at time $t*$ you are seeing the back end of the stick when it was at

$$x_2(t_2) = \frac{c(x_0 + L - t*)}{c - v}$$

The difference is the length you <u>see</u> the stick as having:

$$L* = x_2(t_2) - x_1(t_1) = \frac{c}{c - v} L = \frac{L}{1 - 0.6} = 2.5L$$

However, the stick is moving at $0.6c$, so $L = 0.8L_0 = 0.8$ m; so

$$L* = (2.5)(0.8 \text{ m}) = \underline{2.0 \text{ m}}$$

4. Solving the Doppler formula for v gives

$$\frac{v}{c} = \frac{f^2 - f_0^2}{f^2 + f_0^2} = \frac{\lambda_0^2 - \lambda^2}{\lambda_0^2 + \lambda^2}$$

if λ and λ_0 are the wavelengths corresponding to f and f_0. Here we are given λ = 656.10 nm and λ_0 = 656.29 nm, which gives

$$v = (2.90 \times 10^{-4})(c) = 8.68 \times 10^4 \text{ m/sec}$$

If the period of the orbit is 9.06 days = 7.83×10^5 sec, its radius

$$r = \frac{(8.68 \times 10^4 \text{ m/sec})(7.83 \times 10^5 \text{ sec})}{2\pi} = \underline{1.08 \times 10^{10} \text{ m}}$$

5. There is nothing awfully subtle about this – you juggle equations
   around until all the variables but one have gone away. Writing
   the energy-momentum formula for each pion gives

$$E_1^2 = (p_1 c)^2 + (135 \text{ MeV})^2$$

$$(680 \text{ MeV} - E_1)^2 = (463 \text{ MeV} - p_1 c)^2 + (135 \text{ MeV})^2$$

Subtracting these two gives

$$E_1 = 0.681 p_1 c + 182.4 \text{ MeV}$$

If this is substituted back in the first of the two equations
above, to eliminate E_1, we get

$$(p_1 c)^2 - (463 \text{ MeV})(p_1 c) - 28,030 \text{ MeV}^2 = 0$$

The solutions of this quadratic are

$$p_1 = 517 \text{ MeV/c or} -54 \text{ MeV/c}$$

These are the momenta of the two pions. The corresponding kinetic
energies are

$$\underline{E_k = 399 \text{ MeV and } 11 \text{ MeV}}$$

DIGRESSION
Surface and Line Integrals

In the next several chapters, we shall encounter integrals of vector
fields. Some of the fundamental laws of electricity and magnetism
will have to be expressed in terms of such integrals. These tend
to look pretty formidable if they are new to you; but if we keep hold
of the essential idea of integration - that it is a means of adding
up the changing values of a continuous function - there is nothing
terribly mysterious about what surface and line integrals are.

Let $\vec{F}$ represent some vector field - that is, a vector function
which is defined at every point. $\vec{F}$ could be a force which depends
on position, like gravity, or a magnetic field, or the velocity of a
fluid at every point in some messy situation, or whatever you like.
And consider an arbitrary surface S, which can be either the surface
of some real physical object or just one which you imagine drawing
somewhere in space for convenience. At some particular point of
the surface, let $\hat{n}$ be a <u>unit vector perpendicular</u> to it. The quantity

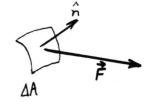

$$\vec{F} \cdot \hat{n} \; \Delta A$$

is the perpendicular component of $\vec{F}$ ($\hat{n}$ is a
unit vector, remember) multiplied by the area
of a little piece, ΔA, of the surface at that
point. Imagine, for instance, that $\vec{F}$ describes
the velocity of a fluid at every point, and ΔA
represents a hole in the wall of a container. Then you can see that
$\vec{F} \cdot \hat{n} \; \Delta A$ would be the rate at which fluid flows out the hole, because
only the outward component of velocity counts, in this case.

Now I imagine dividing the surface S up into lots of little ΔA's,
calculating $\vec{F} \cdot \hat{n} \; \Delta A$ on each one, and adding them all up. What I get
is a quantity representing this kind of "flow" of $\vec{F}$ through the whole
surface. Let the ΔA's become very small so the sum becomes an
integral. What we have calculated is the <u>surface integral</u> of $\vec{F}$ over
S. We write this

$$\int_S \vec{F} \cdot \hat{n} \; dA$$

To <u>evaluate</u> this, in a given situation, could be very easy or very
complicated. That would depend on what sort of information we have
about $\vec{F}$ and S. For instance, if we know, somehow, that $\vec{F}$ is constant
and is everywhere perpendcular to S, the surface integral would be
just $|\vec{F}|A$, where A is the whole surface area.

A very important special case is that of a <u>closed</u> surface - like
a balloon or some such. We denote this by putting a loop on the
integral sign:

$$\oint_S \vec{F} \cdot \hat{n} \, dA$$

The importance is this: suppose, again, that $\vec{F}$ represents the velocity of a fluid. Then the integral represents the net rate at which fluid flows out of the <u>closed</u> surface S. But in ordinary circumstances there wouldn't be any <u>net</u> outflow - as much would have to flow in as flowed out - unless there were some <u>source</u> of fluid within S. We say that the integral of a vector field $\vec{F}$ over a closed surface measures how much there is of whatever is the <u>source</u> of the field, <u>within</u> the surface. In Chapter 29, this is the form of Gauss' law; the source of the electric field $\vec{E}$ is electric charge.

The line integral, or path integral, is a similar construction. Here we imagine some curve, some path, in space. Let $\Delta\vec{s}$ be the length (with direction) of some little piece of the path C. The quantity $\vec{F} \cdot \Delta\vec{s}$ is the <u>component</u> of $\vec{F}$ <u>along the path</u> at that point, multiplied by the length of the piece $\Delta\vec{s}$. If $\vec{F}$ is a force, this is the way we defined the work which it does on a particle that undergoes displacement $\Delta\vec{s}$; the component of force perpendicular

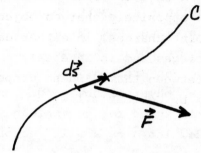

to the path does nothing to change the particle's kinetic energy, hence does no work on it.

To do this over an arbitrary finite path C, we calculate $\vec{F} \cdot \Delta\vec{s}$ on each little bit of the path and add them up. When the Δs's are very small, what we have is the <u>line integral</u> of $\vec{F}$ over C:

$$\int_C \vec{F} \cdot d\vec{s}$$

Again, evaluating this might be very simple or very messy, depending on what information we have about $\vec{F}$ and C.

Again, also, there is a special significance to the line integral around a <u>closed</u> path. We use the same notation:

$$\oint_C \vec{F} \cdot d\vec{s}$$

means that C is a closed path. If F is a force, that the line integral around a closed path be zero was our definition of a <u>conservative</u> force: one such that, if a particle moves around any closed path and comes back to its starting point, zero net work is done. In Chapter 37, we will encounter Ampère's law, which relates the line integral of the magnetic field around a closed path to the electric current which produces the field.

CHAPTER 29
The Electric Field

29.1 CHAPTER SUMMARY

A fundamental property of matter is electric charge. The amount of
charge on an object can be either positive or negative. Charge can
be transferred from one object to another, but not created or de-
stroyed - charge is conserved. Amounts of electric charge are quantized - they can be only multiples of a basic indivisible unit (e)
which is the charge of an electron.

Charged objects repel one another if their charges are of the
same sign; oppositely charged objects attract. The electric force
between point charges, in either case, is along the line joining
the two charges and is inversely proportional to the square of the
distance between them. These properties of electric forces are
summarized by Coulomb's law:

$$\vec{F}_{12} = k \, \frac{q_1 q_2}{r_{12}^2} \, \hat{r}_{12}$$

As for gravitational forces, we can describe electric forces in
terms of a field. If the force on a charge q_0, due to whatever other
charges may be around, is $\vec{F}$, the electric field $\vec{E}$ at the position of
q_0 is defined to be

$$\vec{E} = \frac{\vec{F}}{q_0}$$

Since $\vec{F}$ in any case is proportional to q_0, $\vec{E}$ is independent of q_0 and
is a property of whatever other charges exert forces on q_0. The force
on a charge at some point, in these terms, is due to there being an
electric field at that point, which in turn is produced by charges
elsewhere.

In many cases it is useful to map the electric field by drawing
lines of force. The direction of a force line at any point is that
of the field at that point; thus lines of force begin at positive
charges and end at negative charges. We can represent the magnitude
of the electric field, as well, on such a map by adopting the rule
that the number of lines drawn to or from a point charge is proportional to the magnitude of the charge; then the magnitude of $\vec{E}$ at
any point is represented by the density of lines (that is, the
number of lines crossing unit area perpendicular to the lines) at
that point. Lines-of-force maps for several simple cases are shown
in the text.

The electric flux through an area A is defined as

$$\Phi = E_n A$$

where E_n means the component of $\vec{E}$ normal to the surface A. The flux
is thus proportional to the number of lines of force crossing A.
If E_n is not constant over an extended surface, we define the flux
by adding it up over each infinitesimal element dA of the surface:

$$\Phi = \int E_n \, dA$$

Because of the way we draw lines of force, if we calculate the total
flux - the total number of lines - outward through a closed surface
surrounding charge Q, we must get a number proportional to Q. This
is Gauss' law,

$$\oint_S E_n \, dA = 4\pi kQ$$

where Q is the total charge inside the closed surface S. The result
is independent of the shape of the surface, the arrangement of Q
inside it, etc.

The force on a charge q in an electric field $\vec{E}$ is $q\vec{E}$. The motion
of charges in a uniform field, for instance, is thus a constant-
acceleration problem just like the projectile problem discussed in
Chapter 3.

An electric dipole is a pair of equal and opposite charges a
distance apart. Its dipole moment is

$$p = qL$$

where L is the vector from -q to +q. Since the net charge is zero,
there is no force on a dipole in a uniform electric field; but there
is a torque

$$\vec{\tau} = \vec{p} \times \vec{E}$$

tending to align the dipole with the field direction. Molecules,
while electrically neutral, interact as dipoles in many cases -
either because of a built-in dipole moment or one induced by an
external electric field.

29.2   CHECK LIST

coulomb (C)	test charge
ampere	action at a distance
$e = 1.60 \times 10^{-19}$ C	lines of force
$k = 1/4\pi\varepsilon_0 = 8.99 \times 10^9$ N-m^2/C^2	electric dipole
$\varepsilon_0 = 8.55 \times 10^{-12}$ C^2/N-m^2	dipole moment
electric force	electric flux
electric conduction	Gauss' law
electric charge	surface integral
conservation of charge	permittivity
quantization of charge	charge-to-mass ratio
electron	polar molecule
inverse-square force	induced dipole moment

29.3   TRUE OR FALSE?

____1. Franklin's observations led him to a "two-fluid" idea of the nature of electrification.

____2. "Conservation of charge" refers to the fact that electric charge exists only in multiples of an indivisible basic unit e.

____3. Coulomb's torsion-balance experiment demonstrated that the electric force varies inversely as the square of the distance between charges.

____4. The electric field was discovered by Coulomb.

____5. The unit of charge, the Coulomb, is defined fundamentally in terms of the behavior not of electric but of magnetic forces.

____6. The electric force, by Coulomb's law, depends on distance in just the same way as does the gravitational force.

____7. Two objects have equal charges q; it follows that the electric force on each is directed toward the other.

____8. The force exerted by a point charge on another is unchanged if a third point charge is brought near the first two.

____9. The gravitational force is ignored in analyzing atomic-scale problems, because electric and gravitational forces cannot act on the same object at once.

____10. A point charge q sets up an electric field $\vec{E}$ at the position of another charge q'; the force exerted by $\vec{E}$ on q' is independent of the magnitude of q'.

____11. Coulomb's law, as written, is automatically consistent with Newton's third law.

____12. The electric field can be defined only for point charges.

____13. An otherwise free point charge is in a region in which an electric field $\vec{E}$ exists; the acceleration of the charge is necessarily along the direction of $\vec{E}$.

____14. Electric force lines can cross only if several charges are present.

____15. In a system of charges which overall is electrically neutral, no lines of force exist.

____16. In a system of charges which overall is electrically neutral, no lines of force extend indefinitely far away from the charges.

____17. Lines of electric force begin on negative and end on positive charges.

____18. Lines of gravitational force begin on lesser and end on greater masses.

____19. The number of lines of force per unit area is proportional to the electric flux.

_____20. Gauss' law holds only because electric forces vary inversely as the square of the distance.

_____21. If the electric flux through a closed surface is zero, there can be no charged objects inside it.

_____22. If the electric flux through a closed surface is zero, there can be no electric field at any point on the surface.

_____23. If there is no electric field anywhere on a closed surface, the net charge inside the surface must be zero.

_____24. A charged object attracts bits of string, paper, etc., only if the materials involved consist of polar molecules.

_____25. Because the charges are equal and opposite, there is no force on an electric dipole in an electric field.

_____26. The torque on a dipole in an electric field tends to align the dipole across the field direction.

29.4 QUESTIONS

1. In the sketch, $\vec{F}_1$ is the force on a positive point charge q due to another charge q_1 and $\vec{F}_2$ the force on q due to a third charge q_2. The total force on q is $\vec{F} = \vec{F}_1 + \vec{F}_2$.
    (a) What is the sign of q_1?
    (b) Which (q_1 or q_2) is larger in magnitude?
    (c) If q_1 is doubled in magnitude, do the directions of F_1 and F_2 change? What about the direction of $\vec{F}$?

2. Why doesn't charge outside the surface of integration enter into Gauss' law?

3. $\vec{E}$ at point P in the sketch is found to be zero.
    (a) What can be said about the signs of q_1 and q_2?
    (b) What can be said about their magnitudes?

4. Consider making a lines-of-force map of the electric field due to the two point charges shown.
    (a) On which charge do field lines begin? On which do they end?
    (b) Suppose 30 lines are drawn terminating on the -3 C charge. How many terminate on the other? Do all lines that begin at one of the charges end on the other one?

5. A positively charged glass rod attracts a light object suspended by a thread. Does it follow that the object is negatively charged? If, instead, the glass rod repels it, does it follow that the suspended object is positively charged?

6. An electric field acts on an electric dipole as shown in the sketch.
    (a) The effect of $\vec{E}$ is to tend to rotate the dipole - which way?
    (b) If the dipole is free of any other forces except for the applied $\vec{E}$ field, describe its motion thereafter.

29.5 EXAMPLES

1. How far apart must two electrons be in order for the electric force which each exerts on the other to be equal to its weight?

2. Two objects, each positively charged, are 1.5 m apart and repel one another with a force of 0.02 N. If the total charge of the two objects is 6.0×10^{-6} C, how is the charge distributed between them?

3. An electron with an initial speed of 5.0×10^5 m/sec enters a region in which there is a uniform electric field directed along the electron's direction of motion. If the electron just reaches a point 5 cm from its initial position before being stopped, what is the strength of the electric field?

29.6 ANSWERS

True or False?

1. False - observation that the "two kinds" of electricity could cancel each other led Franklin to regard them as excess and deficiency of a single quality.

2. False - this is <u>quantization</u> of charge.

3. True.

4. False - the electric field is a defined, not a discovered, quantity.

5. True - the ampere is defined in terms of the magnetic forces between currents, and the coulomb as an ampere-second.

6. True - both inversely as the square of the distance.

7. False - the force on each is directed away from the other.

8. True - of course the total force on the first charge is different, but it is just the sum of the individual forces exerted by the other two.

9. False - it is ignored, but because it is enormously weaker than electric forces.

10. False - $\vec{E}$ is independent of q', but the force on q' is $q'\vec{E}$.

11. True - The force $\vec{F}_{21} = -\vec{F}_{12}$.

12. False - any charge exerts a force on another and hence sets up an electric field.

13. True - if no other force acts, $\vec{a} = \frac{q}{m}.\vec{F}$.

14. False - they can never cross; the force on a test charge at a particular point in space cannot have two different directions.

15. False - see the field map for a dipole.

16. True - the number of lines extending infinitely far away is proportional to the net charge of the system.

17. False - the other way around.

18. False - there is no negative mass; gravitational force lines extend from infinity, end on masses.

19. False - proportional to the electric-field strength.

20. True.

21. False - all you can say is that the <u>total</u> charge inside is zero.

22. False - if as many lines enter as go out, the net flux will still vanish.

23. True - in this case the flux must vanish; by Gauss' law this means no net charge inside.

24. False - they could be charged; even if not, the attraction is due to <u>induced</u> dipole moments in the bits, induced by the attracting charge.

25. False - this follows only if the field is <u>uniform</u>; otherwise the forces on the positive and negative poles are not necessarily equal and opposite.

26. False - tends to align it along the field direction.

Questions

1. (a) q_1 repels the positive q, must be positive.
   (b) From the diagram, q_1 is farther away, yet exerts more force on q - so q_1 must be bigger.
   (c) The directions of $\vec{F}_1$ and $\vec{F}_2$ don't change, as they depend only on the directions in which q_1 and q_2 lie from q, but the magnitude of $\vec{F}_1$ changes, so the direction of the total force $\vec{F} = \vec{F}_1 + \vec{F}_2$ will be different.

2. Lines of force from an external charge which enter the closed surface must leave it again, since lines from an isolated charge extend to infinity. But in adding up the total flux through the closed surface, we count outgoing flux lines as positive, incoming ones as negative - so the contributions from any external charge must cancel.

3. (a) Contributions to the field from the two point charges must cancel each other, so the contributions must have equal magnitude and opposite sign. Since P is in the same direction from both charges, the charges must have opposite signs.
   (b) q_1 is closer to P, so for the field contributions to have equal magnitude, q_2 must be larger than q_1.

4. (a) Lines of force begin on the positive charge and end on the negative charge.
   (b) By convention, the number of lines drawn terminating at each point charge is proportional to the magnitude of the charge. So if you draw 30 lines ending on the -3 C charge, you must draw 20 lines beginning on the +2 C one. The other 10 lines come in from indefinitely far away - corresponding to the fact that from very far away the system just looks like a -1 C charge.

5. In the first case, the object isn't necessarily charged at all; the charged rod will attract neutral bits by inducing dipole moments in them. But if the suspended object is repelled, it must be positively charged; the induced-dipole effect will always be attractive. Presumably this is why electrical attraction was known to the ancients, while repulsion wasn't.

6. (a) Clockwise - the force on the positive end is along $\vec{E}$, that on the negative end against $\vec{E}$.
   (b) If there are no other forces acting on it, the dipole will oscillate around the electric-field direction, since at any orientation there is a torque on it tending to align it with the electric field.

Examples

<u>Partial Solutions (1)</u>

1. The weight of an electron - or anything else - near the earth is the force exerted on it by the earth's gravity. The force either electron exerts on the other is given by Coulomb's law.

2. Again, the force that the two point charges exert on each other is given by Coulomb's law. In this case, we are also given the total charge of the two. This gives us two equations to be solved simultaneously for the two charges q_1 and q_2.

3. Because the electric field is constant, the acceleration of the electron is constant also. Thus finding the acceleration - and therefore the force exerted on it by the electric field - just reduces to a constant-acceleration problem out of Chapter 2. In this case, you know its initial speed and the distance it went before stopping. Find its acceleration.

<u>Partial Solutions (2)</u>

1. Its weight must equal the electrostatic force that the other exerts on it:

$$mg = \frac{kq_1q_2}{r^2} = \frac{ke^2}{r^2}$$

and just solve for r.

2. The force is
$$F = \frac{kq_1q_2}{r^2}$$

or

$$q_1q_2 = \frac{Fr^2}{k} = \frac{(0.02 \text{ N})(1.5 \text{ m})^2}{(8.99 \times 10^9 \text{ N-m}^2/\text{C}^2)}$$

$$= 5.0 \times 10^{-12} \text{ C}^2$$

and the total charge of the two is 6.0×10^{-6} C.

3. For this kind of problem, use
$$v^2 - v_0^2 = 2a(\Delta x)$$

Here the electron is brought to rest ($v = 0$) from an initial speed $v_0 = 5 \times 10^5$ m/sec after traveling a distance of 5×10^{-2} m. Find its acceleration and go on from there.

<u>Partial Solutions (3)</u>

1. Solve the equation above for the distance between the electrons:

$$r^2 = \frac{ke^2}{mg} = \frac{(8.99 \times 10^9 \text{ N-m}^2/\text{C}^2)(1.60 \times 10^{-19} \text{ C})^2}{(9.11 \times 10^{-31} \text{ kg})(9.80 \text{ m/sec}^2)}$$

$$= 25.8 \text{ m}^2$$

so <u>r = 5.08 m.</u>

2. Thus we have
$$q_1q_2 = 5.0 \times 10^{-12} \text{ C}^2$$

$$q_1 + q_2 = 6.0 \times 10^{-6} \text{ C}$$

Eliminating q_2 between these two equations gives
$$q_1\left[(6.0 \times 10^{-6} \text{ C}) - q_1\right] = 5.0 \times 10^{-12} \text{ C}^2$$

This is a quadratic expression for q_1. Solving by the binomial formula gives two possible values for either charge:

$$q_1 \text{ or } q_2 = \underline{1.0 \times 10^{-6} \text{ C}} \text{ or } \underline{5.0 \times 10^{-6} \text{ C}}$$

It doesn't matter which label goes on which value.

3. The acceleration

$$a = \frac{0 - (5.0 \times 10^5 \text{ m/sec})^2}{(2)(5.0 \times 10^{-2} \text{ m})} = -2.5 \times 10^{12} \text{ m/sec}^2$$

The force on the electron (charge $-e$) is $-eE$, so its acceleration is

$$a = \frac{F}{m} = -\frac{e}{m} E$$

so

$$E = -\frac{m}{e} a = -\frac{(9.11 \times 10^{-31} \text{ kg})(-2.5 \times 10^{12} \text{ m/sec}^2)}{(1.60 \times 10^{-19} \text{ C})}$$

$$= \underline{1.42 \times 10^1 \text{ N/C}}$$

CHAPTER 30
Calculation of the Electric Field

30.1 CHAPTER SUMMARY

The calculation of the electric field $\vec{E}$ produced by a given distribution of charge proceeds from Coulomb's law. The field at some point produced by point charge q_i is

$$\vec{E}_i = k \frac{q_i}{r_{i0}^2} \hat{r}_{i0}$$

where r_{i0} is the distance, and $\hat{r}_{i0}$ the unit vector, from q_i to the field point. The field from an assembly of point charges is the vector sum of the fields due to each. In many cases an assembly of many charges can be approximated as a continuous distribution of charge; in this case, the field is integrated over the distribution.

A method which is equivalent in principle is to use Gauss' law. Generally this is much more complicated, involving integrating the field over a closed surface. There are several cases, however, in which, from the symmetry of the charge distribution, a Gaussian surface over which $\vec{E}$ is constant can be found by inspection. In such cases it is much easier to use Gauss' law.

Several simple cases of importance are worked through in the text: the field of a dipole (on axis) is

$$E = \frac{2kp}{x^3}$$

where p is the dipole moment; from an infinitely long line of charge

$$E \frac{2k\lambda}{r}$$

where λ is the charge per unit length; from an infinite charged plane

$$E = 2\pi k\sigma$$

where σ is the charge per unit area. The field from a charged spherical shell, at a point outside, is the same as if all the charge were at the center; inside the shell, $E = 0$. In each of these cases, the direction of $\vec{E}$ is obvious from the symmetry of the situation.

Since Newton's law of gravitation has the same mathematical form as Coulomb's law, each of the above results applies also to the analogous gravitational field calculation.

30.2 CHECK LIST

$k = \dfrac{1}{4\pi\epsilon_0} = 8.99 \times 10^9$ N-m^2/C^2

electric field

Coulomb's law

surface charge density

linear charge density

Gauss' law

field point
test charge
continuous charge distribution
charge density

surface integral
dipole moment
gaussian surface
nonelectrostatic electric field

30.3 TRUE OR FALSE?

_____1. The field due to any assemblage of point charges can be found
         by adding vectorially the field due to each one.

_____2. The field due to a continuous charge distribution must be
         found from Gauss' law.

_____3. In general, Gauss' law is a more straightforward method of
         calculating the electric field than is direct application of
         Coulomb's law.

_____4. Gauss' law holds only for symmetric distributions of charge.

_____5. The field at the point directly between equal and opposite
         point charges is zero.

_____6. The field due to a plane disk of uniform charge density is
         uniform.

_____7. If the flux of the electric field over a given closed surface
         is zero, the surface can contain no charged objects.

_____8. The electric field outside any spherically symmetric charge
         distribution is the same as if all the charge were concentrated
         at the center.

_____9. Inside the surface of any spherically symmetric charge distribu-
         tion, the field is zero.

_____10. A gaussian surface is one on which, in a given situation, the
         electric field is everywhere the same.

_____11. Gauss' law and Coulomb's law are equivalent.

_____12. The shape of the electric field from a given distribution of
         static charge is the same as that of the gravitational field
         due to an analogous distribution of mass.

30.4 QUESTIONS

1. We found that the field due to a uniformly charged plane is uniform
    and proportional to the charge density. How does this square with
    the idea that, sufficiently far away, the field of any charge
    distribution must look like that from a point charge?

2. A tin can carries a uniform surface charge density. Could you
    conveniently use Gauss' law to calculate the electric field due
    to it?

3. You want to calculate the electric field due to two infinite parallel
    charged planes. Could you do this by considering it as a sheet
    of dipoles?

4. A spherical balloon is filled with a charged gas. If you blow it
    up further with neutral air, how does the field at the surface
    change? The field far away?

30.5 EXAMPLES

1. Find an expression for the field of an electric dipole at a point far away, in a direction making angle θ with the dipole moment vector.

2. Find the field, at a point on the median plane, due to an infinite charged strip of uniform surface charge density. If the strip is 10 cm wide, how far away must you be if approximating the strip as a line of charge is to be accurate within 0.5%? How close must you be if approximating it as an infinite sheet is to be accurate within 0.5%?

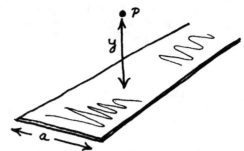

3. Use Gauss' law to find the field at points both inside and outside an infinite flat slab of thickness a, with a uniform charge density.

30.6 ANSWERS

True or False?

1. True - this is the property of superposition.

2. False - unless the distribution has high symmetry, Coulomb's law is more useful.

3. False - Gauss' law is more convenient only in a few cases where much about the field is obvious from the symmetry of the charge distribution.

4. False - it is true, but in general not useful for calculating the field, for any distribution of charge.

5. False - it is directed from the negative to the positive charge.

6. False - in general; sufficiently close to the disk, it looks like an infinite sheet, for which this would be true.

7. False - the total charge inside must be zero, but this isn't the same thing.

8. True.

9. False - the field looks like a point-charge field due to all the charge still closer to the center than the field point.

10. False - a gaussian surface is any surface you imagine drawing on which you apply Gauss' law.

11. True - either can be derived from the other.

12. True - if an analogous distribution of mass exists; there cannot be both positive and negative mass, however.

Questions

1. Sufficiently far away, the field of any <u>finite</u> distribution of charge looks like a point charge; but the field of a plane charge distribution is uniform only if the plane is infinite.

2. No; this charge distribution is not sufficiently symmetric that you know how to draw a gaussian surface over which the electric field is constant. We can use Gauss' law on a long cylindrical charge distribution, but not one with ends.

3. Yes; if the charge densities are equal and opposite. In that case you can call each element of area on one sheet, and an equal element just opposite it on the other sheet, a dipole with

$$p = \sigma a \, dS$$

and integrate over the sheets. If they are not equal and opposite, then the two planes are equivalent to a sheet of dipoles plus a sheet of charge.

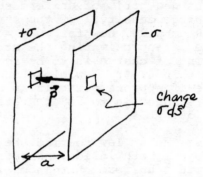

4. This amounts to a sphere of constant total charge, the volume increasing and the charge density decreasing as you blow it up. The field outside it is

$$E = \frac{kQ}{r^2}$$

if the charge density is spherically symmetric, as one would expect. Thus the field at the surface decreases but that at a given point far away is unaffected.

Examples

Partial Solutions (1)

1. The field is just the sum of the fields from the two point charges; the field due to a point charge is of course

$$\vec{E} = \frac{kq\vec{r}}{r^3}$$

where r is the vector from the charge to the field point.

2. See the diagram at right - the little slice at x, of width dx, can be considered as an infinite line charge with

$$d\lambda = \sigma \, dx$$

The field at distance r from a long line of charge is

$$dE = \frac{d\lambda}{2\pi\epsilon_0 r}$$

What is the direction of the field due to the whole strip?

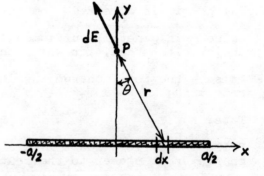

3. Remember that the surface over which you apply Gauss' law must be chosen to exploit the symmetry of the situation. What is the field outside the slab?

Partial Solutions (2)

1. Let the dipole lie in the positive x direction, as in the diagram. The field is

$$\vec{E} = -\frac{kq\vec{r}}{r^3} + \frac{kq\vec{r}'}{r'^3}$$

From the diagram, plainly

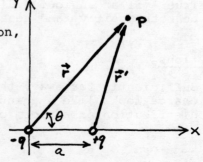

$$\vec{r}' = \vec{r} - \hat{i}a$$

so

$$\vec{E} = kq\left(-\frac{\vec{r}}{r^3} + \frac{\vec{r} - \hat{i}a}{|\vec{r} - \hat{i}a|^3}\right)$$

What you are asked for is a simplified version of this, assuming that r is very large compared to a. The approximation $(1 + \varepsilon)^n \sim 1 + n\varepsilon$, which holds for $\varepsilon \ll 1$, may be useful.

2. From the symmetry of the situation, plainly $\vec{E}$ is in the y direction. Thus we want only the y component

$$dE_y = dE \cos \theta = dE \frac{y}{r}$$

so

$$dE_y = \frac{\sigma\, dx}{2\pi\varepsilon_0 r} \frac{y}{r}$$

or

$$E_y = E = \int_{-a/2}^{a/2} dE_y = \frac{\sigma y}{2\pi\varepsilon_0} \int_{-a/2}^{a/2} \frac{dx}{x^2 + y^2}$$

For the comparison, the field due to a line charge of linear density $\lambda = \sigma a$ is

$$E_{line} = \frac{\sigma a}{2\pi\varepsilon_0 y}$$

and that due to an infinite sheet of surface density σ is

$$E_{plane} = \frac{\sigma}{2\varepsilon_0}$$

3. Since the field of an infinite plane of uniform charge is uniform, that - outside - due to the slab must be equivalent to a plane of surface charge density $\sigma = \rho a$. This is

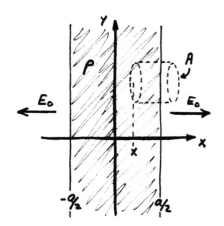

$$E_0 = \frac{\sigma}{2\varepsilon_0} = \frac{\rho a}{2\varepsilon_0}$$

Draw a gaussian surface as shown, from a point $x < a/2$ inside the slab to a point outside. There is no normal component of $\vec{E}$ along the sides of the surface, so only the ends contribute:

$$E_0 A - E(x)A = \frac{Q}{\varepsilon_0}$$

where Q is the charge contained in the surface.

Partial Solutions (3)

1. Expand

$$|\vec{r} - \hat{i}a|^{-3} = [y^2 + (x - a)^2]^{-3/2}$$

$$= (x^2 + y^2 - 2ax + a^2)^{-3/2} \simeq (x^2 + a^2 - 2ax)^{-3/2}$$

since a is much less than r. Then we have approximately

$$|\vec{r} - \hat{i}a|^{-3} \simeq (r^2 - 2ar \cos \theta)^{-3/2} \simeq r^{-3}\left(1 - \frac{2a}{r} \cos \theta\right)^{-3/2}$$

$$\simeq r^{-3}\left(1 + \frac{3a}{r} \cos \theta\right)$$

so in the equation above for $\vec{E}$,

$$\frac{\vec{r} - \hat{i}a}{|\vec{r} - \hat{i}a|^3} \simeq \frac{\vec{r}}{r^3} + \frac{3a\vec{r} \cos \theta}{r^4} - \frac{\hat{i}a}{r^3}$$

where a term proportional to a^2 has been dropped, again because a is small. So we get

$$\vec{E} \simeq \frac{kqa}{r^3}(3\hat{r}\cos\theta - \hat{i}) \qquad (r \gg a)$$

2. The field due to the strip is

$$E = \frac{\sigma}{2\pi\epsilon_0}\int_{-a/2y}^{a/2y}\frac{dt}{1+t^2} = \frac{\sigma}{\pi\epsilon_0}\tan^{-1}\frac{a}{2y}$$

If this is to be within 0.5% of the line-charge approximation, we must have

$$\frac{E}{E_{line}} = \frac{2y}{a}\tan^{-1}\frac{a}{2y} > 0.995$$

You solve this by trial and error, or from a graph, obtaining $a/2y < 0.123$, or y > 4.1a. If it is to be within 0.5% of the plane approximation, we require

$$\frac{E}{E_{plane}} = \frac{2}{\pi}\tan^{-1}\frac{a}{2y} > 0.995$$

which gives $a/2y > 126$ or y < 0.0039a.

3. The part of the gaussian cylinder drawn, that is inside the slab, has height $a/2 - x$, so the charge inside it is

$$\rho(\frac{a}{2} - x)A$$

Thus

$$E(x)A = E_0 A - \frac{Q}{\epsilon_0} = \frac{\rho a A}{2\epsilon_0} - \frac{\rho A}{\epsilon_0}(\frac{a}{2} - x)$$

or

$$E(x) = \frac{\rho x}{\epsilon_0}$$

CHAPTER 31
Conductors in Electrostatic Equilibrium

31.1 CHAPTER SUMMARY

It is well known that some materials conduct electric charge very
freely, while others do not. The difference is huge: a good conductor may have a conductivity 10^{15} times that of a good insulator.
A conductor is a material in which some of the electrons are free to
move through the whole body of the material, not bound to individual
atoms.

As there is charge free to move, the electric field within the
body of a conductor must be zero in electrostatic equilibrium. If
an external field is applied to the conductor, free charge within
rearranges itself to produce a canceling field. Consequently, by
Gauss' law, there is no <u>net</u> charge within the body of the conductor;
any net charge must reside on the surface. The electric field just
outside the surface, produced by this surface charge, is normal to
the surface and has magnitude

$$E = \frac{\sigma}{\varepsilon_0}$$

where σ is the surface charge density. Note that this is twice the
field produced by an infinite charged plane with charge density σ.
All these arguments hold for a conductor of arbitrary shape.

The free movement of charge within a conductor makes possible
charging by induction. If an external field is applied to two
conductors in contact, which are then separated, they will each be
charged.

31.2 CHECK LIST

conductor

insulator

conductivity

electrostatic equilibrium

surface charge density

free charge

electron

field emission

gaussian surface

charging by induction

grounding

polarization

31.3 TRUE OR FALSE?

_____ 1. The distinction between conductors and insulators was first
noticed as a distinction between materials which could readily
be electrified and those which could not.

_____ 2. A conductor is a material in which free charges exist.

_____3. Any excess charge on a conductor must be on the surface.

_____4. In a good conductor, such as most metals, the majority of the atomic electrons are free to move about as conduction electrons.

_____5. In an external electric field, free charge in a conductor rearranges itself so as to create an electric field canceling the external one.

_____6. At the surface of a conductor, the electric field has no component perpendicular to the surface.

_____7. The electric field just outside the surface of a conductor has magnitude σ/ε_0, where σ is the surface charge density.

_____8. An object can be charged by induction in the absence of any external electric field.

_____9. Insulators cannot be charged by induction.

31.4 QUESTIONS

1. Any free charge on a conductor must be on the outer surface. Does it follow that the field inside a hollow conductor must be zero?

2. Would the electrostatic field in the body of a conductor necessarily be zero if the exponent in Coulomb's law were not exactly 2?

3. Does it follow from Gauss' law that, in static equilibrium, all the conduction electrons in a metal must be on the surface?

4. We argued that the electric field must vanish everywhere in the body of a conductor. But there are certainly very strong electric fields in all materials, at points close to the atomic nuclei. Does this mean the argument was wrong?

5. A standard dodge in science-fiction stories is a "gravity screen" - and the analogy is often drawn with a metal box screening whatever is inside it from external electric fields. Comment on the analogy. Do the walls of the box really "stop" the external field?

31.5 EXAMPLES

1. A long conducting cylinder carries total charge $-2q$; it is surrounded by a coaxial conducting cylindrical shell of total charge $+3q$. Use Gauss' law to find (a) the field outside the outer shell, (b) the field between them, and (c) the charge distribution on the outer shell.

2. Suppose that each atom of some metal occupies a cube 2.2×10^{-10} m on a side. If each surface atom lost one electron, what would be the charge on, and the field at the surface of, a 10-cm sphere?

31.6 ANSWERS

True or False?

1. True - although of course it is possible to charge a conductor, provided that it is isolated from other conductors.

2. True.

3. True.

4. False - in most metals the number is on the order of 1 per atom.

5. True.

6. False - it has no component parallel to the surface.

7. True.

8. False - an external field is required to polarize the object.

9. True - charging by induction is a consequence of free charge.

Questions

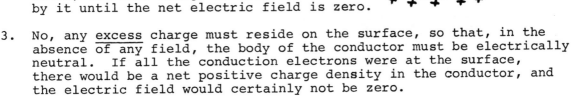

1. Yes; consider a gaussian surface drawn across the inner boundary, as sketched. It contains no charge because the charge is all on the outer surface, so the flux through the surface is zero. Of course, if there is charge inside, it is no longer true that the surface charge density on the inner boundary is zero.

2. Yes, this follows just from the fact that there is abundant free charge in the conductor. If there were an electric field, the free charge is shoved around by it until the net electric field is zero.

3. No, any *excess* charge must reside on the surface, so that, in the absence of any field, the body of the conductor must be electrically neutral. If all the conduction electrons were at the surface, there would be a net positive charge density in the conductor, and the electric field would certainly not be zero.

4. No, the argument is based on the approximation of a continuous charge density and is true in regions large enough to contain many atoms. The strong nuclear electric fields exist only in the interior parts of individual atoms.

5. The conducting box doesn't stop the external electric field, but simply provides free charge, which can rearrange itself so as to cancel the external field inside the box. But there is not, in ordinary solids, any analogous "free mass" - and, in any case, gravitational fields don't cancel one another in the same way, because all mass is of the same sign.

Examples

Partial Solutions (1)

1. We assume the cylinders are long enough so that we may neglect end effects. In this case, by symmetry alone, the charge distribution must be uniform along the length of the cylinders, and the field

must be radial. What is the convenient gaussian surface for this configuration?

2. At the surface of the conductor, the field is given by

$$E = \frac{\sigma}{\varepsilon_0}$$

Work out σ from the data given.

Partial Solutions (2)

1. The convenient gaussian surface is a cylindrical one, coaxial with the cylinders. From the symmetry of the situation, there is no contribution of $\oint E_n \, dA$ from the ends of the cylinder.

    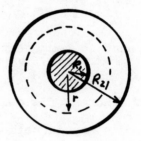

    If the length of the gaussian surface is ℓ, and the total length of the conductors is L, the charge within the surface is

    $$\frac{\ell}{L} Q(r)$$

    where $Q(r)$ is the charge <u>inside</u> radius r. Find the electric field.

2. The surface charge density, on the assumptions given, is one electron charge per atom-area, or

$$\sigma = \frac{(1.60 \times 10^{-19} \text{ C})}{(2.2 \times 10^{-10} \text{ m})^2} = 3.31 \text{ C/m}^2$$

The total charge on a known area, and the field at the surface of the conductor, follow directly from this.

Partial Solutions (3)

1. (a) For $r > R_2$, that is, outside the outer cylinder, $Q(r) = -2q + 3q = q$, so

$$2\pi r\ell E = \frac{\ell q}{\varepsilon_0 L} \qquad \text{or} \qquad E = \frac{q}{2\pi \varepsilon_0 RL}$$

(b) Between the cylinders, for $R_1 < r < R_2$, $Q(r) = -2q$, and

$$E = -\frac{q}{\pi \varepsilon_0 rL}$$

The minus sign just means the field points radially inward.

(c) Just outside R_2, the field is

$$E_{out} = \frac{q}{2\pi \varepsilon_0 R_2 L}$$

so the charge density on the outer surface of the outer cylinder is

$$\sigma_{out} = \varepsilon_0 E_{out} = \frac{q}{2\pi R_2 L}$$

Likewise, the charge density on the inner surface is

$$\sigma_{in} = \frac{q}{\pi R_2 L}$$

2. The field is

$$E = \frac{\sigma}{\varepsilon_0} = \frac{3.31 \text{ C/m}^2}{8.85 \times 10^{-12} \text{ C}^2/\text{N-m}^2} = \underline{3.74 \times 10^{11} \text{N/C}}$$

The assumptions made yield a huge electric field. The total charge on an 0.1-m sphere with this surface charge density is

$$Q = (3.31 \text{ C/m}^2)(4\pi)(0.1 \text{ m})^2 = \underline{0.416 \text{ C}}$$

CHAPTER 32
Electric Potential

32.1 CHAPTER SUMMARY

The electrostatic force is conservative; therefore a corresponding
potential-energy function exists. The force on a charge q_0 is
always proportional to q_0, and thus so are potential-energy differences; we define the electric-potential difference as

$$\Delta V \equiv \frac{\Delta U}{q_0}$$

Since the electric field is defined as the force on a unit charge, we
have also

$$V_b - V_a = -\int_a^b \vec{E} \cdot d\vec{s}$$

We may also say that $V_b - V_a$ is the work which an external force must
do in order to move a unit test charge from a to b at constant speed.
The dimensions of V are plainly those of energy per unit charge. We
define potential difference; the point at which the potential function
is zero is, as for a potential-energy function, always arbitrary.
The potential bears the same relation to the electric field as does
any potential-energy function to the corresponding force.

Given the potential function, the electric field may be determined.
In general, $\vec{E}$ is the gradient of V; that is, -dV/ds with ds taken in
the direction of maximum change, which is the field direction. A
component is

$$E_x = - \frac{\partial V}{\partial x}$$

(the ∂ indicates a partial derivative).

From the Coulomb's law field, the potential due to a point charge
q is

$$V = \frac{kq}{r}$$

(Here - as is usually convenient for any finite charge distribution -
we take V = 0 infinitely far away.) For an arbitrary charge distribution, the electric potential may be determined by integrating $\vec{E}$,
if the field is already known; for instance, zero field means
constant V. Alternatively the potential may be calculated by summing
(or, for a continuous distribution, integrating) the potential from
each point charge in a finite assembly of charges. Sufficiently far
away, any finite distribution approaches the 1/r potential of a point
charge.

An equipotential surface is one over which, in a given case, the
potential is everywhere constant. By definition, then, there is no
component of E in such a surface; the lines of electric force are

therefore normal to the equipotential surface at every point. The entire volume of a conductor in electrostatic equilibrium is an equipotential.

If two conductors are brought into contact, the charge on them, if any, redistributes so that they are at the same potential. For instance, if a charged conductor is brought into contact with an uncharged identical conductor, half the charge ends up on each. If a charged conductor contacts the <u>inside</u> of a hollow conductor, <u>all</u> the charge is transferred to the outside of the outer one; by this means a hollow conductor may be charged to very high potential, as in a Van de Graaff accelerator. (Note that this whole argument depends on the inverse-square form of Coulomb's law, which can therefore be very sensitively tested by this experiment.)

32.2 CHECK LIST

volt	test charge
central force	field point
electrostatic force	continuous charge distribution
Coulomb's law	equipotential surface
conservative force	lines of force
potential difference	charge sharing
electric potential	Van de Graaff accelerator
gradient	dielectric breakdown
	partial derivative

32.2 TRUE OR FALSE?

_____1. The electrostatic force is conservative.

_____2. The work which must be done to move a unit charge from point A to point B is defined as the difference of electrostatic potential between the two points.

_____3. The potential is the electrostatic potential energy per unit charge.

_____4. The electrostatic potential is a vector function of position.

_____5. If the difference in potential between two points is zero, the electric field in the region between the two points must be zero.

_____6. If a charge distribution has spherical symmetry, the potential due to it depends only on the distance from the center.

_____7. In order to calculate the potential due to an arbitrary charge distribution, the electric field due to it must be known.

_____8. The potential due to an arbitrary assemblage of charges is simply the sum, at the same point, of the potential due to each one.

_____9. The electric potential due to an infinite line of charge is directed radially outward.

_____10. The potential inside a uniformly charged spherical shell is constant.

_____11. The surface of a conductor in static equilibrium is an equipotential surface.

_____12. At every point, in a given situation, lines of force lie parallel to equipotential surfaces.

_____13. Two conductors in contact with one another share their total charge equally.

32.4 QUESTIONS

1. Imagine an electron which is moved in a direction opposite to that of the local electric field. Does its potential increase or decrease? What about its potential energy?

2. Lines of force for a system of two point charges are sketched at the right. Draw on the sketch what you think a few equipotentials for this system would look like.

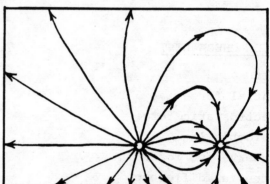

3. If the potential at a point is known, can the electric field at that point be calculated? If so, how? If not, what further information would you need?

4. Suppose that the earth has a nonzero net charge. Is it still possible to use it as a reference point for potential - that is, to call its potential zero?

5. A square metal plate carrying a net positive charge is isolated - hung from a fine insulating thread, say. Sketch what you think equipotentials and lines of force would look like, in the plane of the plate.

6. We saw in Chapter 16 that the gravitational field is zero inside a spherical shell of matter. The electric field is zero inside a conductor of arbitrary shape. Does the analogy hold - that is, would the gravitational field vanish inside a rectangular box of matter, say?

32.5 EXAMPLES

1. Given that the electrostatic potential due to some collection of charges is

$$V(\vec{r}) = \frac{kq}{r}(1 + \frac{a}{r} \cos \theta)$$

where θ is the angle between the position vector $\vec{r}$ and the x axis, and a is a constant. Find an expression for the electric field E in the xy plane.

2. Suppose that an iron atom is approximated by a sphere of negative charge -26e and uniform charge density, 2.5×10^{-10} m in diameter with a positive point charge +26e at its center. Find the potential and potential energy of an electron at a distance 2×10^{-12} m from the center. (This is the approximate size of the innermost electron orbits in iron.)

3. The high-voltage parts of a Van de Graaff accelerator are usually operated in a high-pressure gas to reduce breakdown and sparking. Approximate the high-voltage terminal and the pressure tank of a Van de Graaff as concentric conducting spheres of radius 0.4 and 1.1 m, respectively. If the gas in the tank is nitrogen at 5 atm, which has a dielectric strength of about 2.5×10^7 V/m, what is the maximum voltage that can be placed on the terminal relative to the (grounded) pressure tank?

4. Two infinitely long parallel lines of charge have equal and opposite linear charge densities. Find an expression for the potential at a point between them, in their common plane.

32.6 ANSWERS

True or False?

1. True.

2. True - since the statement doesn't make clear the question of signs; the work which must be done <u>on</u> a unit charge in order to move it is the potential increase.

3. True.

4. False - it is scalar.

5. False - $\int_a^b \vec{E} \cdot d\vec{l}$ is zero, but it doesn't follow that $\vec{E}$ is everywhere zero.

6. True - in this case, the potential outside just looks like that of a point charge.

7. False - the potential can be calculated directly from the superposition of point-charge potentials.

8. True - this is the superposition property.

9. False - the electric potential isn't a vector, doesn't have a direction.

10. True - the electric field is zero.

11. True - since there can be no electric field in the conductor, it must be at a uniform potential.

12. False - force lines are everywhere perpendicular to equipotentials.

13. False - unless the conductors are identical, in which case you can argue this from symmetry alone.

Questions

1. The force on an electron, since it is negatively charged, is opposite E, so if it is moved opposite E work is done on it by the field and its potential <u>energy</u> decreases. Since the charge is negative, therefore, its electrostatic potential - its potential energy per unit charge - increases.

2. The equipotentials must be everywhere perpendicular to the lines of force; thus they'll look something like what is sketched at right.

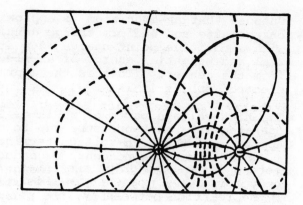

3. Knowing the potential at a point is not enough to give you the field there. The field is the potential <u>gradient</u>, its rate of change. Thus if you know the potential everywhere in a small region around the point, you could calculate the field.

4. Certainly; the earth is a pretty fair conductor and can be considered a huge equipotential, regardless of whether or not there is a net charge on it. In fact, since the earth is constantly bombarded with charged particles from space, its net charge probably is nonzero.

5. This is a case in which it's easier to draw the equipotentials. Since the conducting square is itself an equipotential, the equipotentials <u>near</u> it, in its own plane, must be nearly square. The farther away you get, the more they must look like circles just due to the "point" total charge.

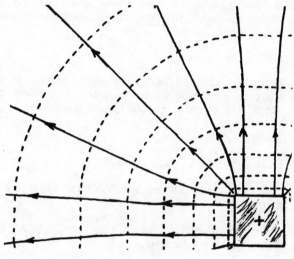

Given the equipotentials you know that the lines of force must be everywhere perpendicular. You get something like what is sketched at the right. Notice that, due to the equipotential surfaces' curvature, the field lines must concentrate near the corners of the square.

6. No, it would not. There is no analog in matter of the <u>free</u> charge on a conductor, which redistributes itself to cancel any field inside, and there is no analog of positive <u>and negative</u> charge.

Examples

Partial Solutions (1)

1. Write out the given potential in terms of x and y. In the xy plane

$$x = r \cos \theta$$
$$y = r \sin \theta$$

The x component of the electric field is

$$E_x = -\frac{\partial V}{\partial x}$$

where the partial-derivative sign means differentiate with respect to x as if y were constant.

2. The most convenient way to find the potential in this case is from the electric field. Since the problem has spherical symmetry, $\vec{E}$ is radial and

$$E = \frac{kQ(r)}{r^2}$$

where $Q(r)$ is the total charge <u>inside</u> radius r. What is an expression for $Q(r)$?

3. Again, we have a problem with spherical symmetry. In the region between the two spheres,

$$E = \frac{kQ}{r^2}$$

where Q is the charge on the inner conductor. What you want in this case is the relation between ΔV, the potential difference between the two conductors, and the field E_1 <u>at</u> the inner one.

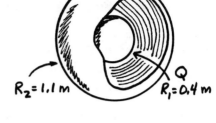

4. The field due to a single line charge, at distance r, is

$$E = \frac{\lambda}{2\pi\varepsilon_0 r}$$

In the plane of the two, what field is produced by the <u>two</u> line charges shown?

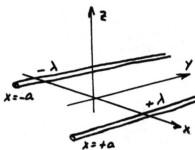

Partial Solutions (2)

1. The potential given is

$$V = \frac{kq}{r} + \frac{kqa \cos\theta}{r^2} = \frac{kq}{(x^2 + y^2)^{\frac{1}{2}}} + \frac{kqax}{(x^2 + y^2)^{3/2}}$$

so the x component of the field is

$$E_x = -\frac{\partial V}{\partial x} = kqx(x^2 + y^2)^{-3/2} - kqa(x^2 + y^2)^{-3/2}$$
$$+ 3kqax^2(x^2 + y^2)^{-5/2}$$

$$= \frac{kq}{(x^2 + y^2)^{5/2}}\left[x(x^2 + y^2) - a(x^2 + y^2) + 3ax^2\right]$$

$$= \frac{kqx}{r^3} + \frac{kqa}{r^5}(2x^2 - y^2)$$

The y component is to be found in the same way.

2. If the electron "cloud" is uniform, the charge within a sphere of radius r is

$$Q(r) = 26e\left(1 - \frac{r^3}{R^3}\right)$$

where R is the outer radius of the cloud and $-26e$ its given total charge. Thus

$$E = \frac{26ke}{r^2}\left(1 - \frac{r^3}{R^3}\right)$$

Outside radius R, the atom is a neutral object; thus $V(R) = V(\infty)$ and it is convenient to take $V(R) = 0$. Thus

$$V(r) = \int_r^R E(r)\ dr$$

and you can work out the potential.

3. The potential difference is

$$\Delta V = \int_{R_1}^{R_2} \frac{kQ}{r^2}\ dr = kQ\left(\frac{1}{R_1} - \frac{1}{R_2}\right)$$

and

$$E_1 = E(R_1) = \frac{kQ}{R_1^2}$$

so

$$\Delta V = E_1 R_1 \left(1 - \frac{R_1}{R_2}\right)$$

4. At a point x we have a line charge $-\lambda$, a distance $a + x$ away and another $+\lambda$ at a distance $a - x$. Thus

$$E = \frac{-\lambda}{2\pi\varepsilon_0 (a + x)} + \frac{\lambda}{2\pi\varepsilon_0 (a - x)} = \frac{-a\lambda}{\pi\varepsilon_0 (a^2 - x^2)}$$

the negative sign because $\vec{E}$ points in the $-x$ direction. In the xy plane the field depends only on x, so

$$\Delta V = -\int E \, dx$$

gives the potential.

Partial Solutions (3)

1. In the same way, we get for the y component

$$E_y = -\frac{\partial V}{\partial y} = \frac{kqy}{r^3} + \frac{kqa}{r^5}(3xy)$$

The two together give the field

$$\vec{E} = \frac{kq}{r^3}(\hat{i}x + \hat{j}y) + \frac{kqa}{r^5}[\hat{i}(2x^2 - y^2) + \hat{j}(3xy)]$$

and, substituting x and y in terms of r and θ again, we can write this

$$\vec{E} = \frac{kq\vec{r}}{r^3} + \frac{kqa}{r^3}(3\hat{r}\cos\theta - \hat{i})$$

From the form of the field, the given potential is that due to a point charge q and a dipole qa, together.

2. The potential at a distance r from the nucleus is

$$V(r) = 26ke \int_r^R \left(\frac{1}{r^2} - \frac{r}{R^3}\right) dr$$

$$= \frac{26ke}{r}\left(1 - \frac{3}{2}\frac{r}{R} + \frac{1}{2}\frac{r^3}{R^3}\right)$$

In this case,

$$\frac{r}{R} = \frac{2.0 \times 10^{-12} \text{ m}}{2.5 \times 10^{-10} \text{ m}} = 0.008$$

so

$$V(r) = \frac{(26)(8.99 \times 10^9 \text{ N-m}^2/\text{C}^2)(1.6 \times 10^{-19} \text{ C})}{2.0 \times 10^{-12} \text{ m}}(0.988)$$

$$= \underline{1.85 \times 10^4 \text{ V}}$$

and the potential energy is

$$-eV = \underline{-2.96 \times 10^{-15} \text{ J}}$$

3. We are given that the maximum field allowable is 2.5×10^7 V/m; thus

$$\Delta V < (2.5 \times 10^7 \text{ V/m})(0.4 \text{ m})(1 - 0.364)$$

$$= \underline{6.36 \times 10^6 \text{ V}}$$

Even though the geometry is a lot less simple than this, the answer is of the right order of magnitude - 8 or 10 million volts is about all you can put on a Van de Graaff terminal, in practice.

4. You can't call the potential zero at $r = \infty$ in this case, because it's not a bounded charge distribution. The potential difference from $x = 0$ is

$$V(x) - V(0) = \frac{a\lambda}{\pi\epsilon_0} \int_0^x \frac{dx}{a^2 - x^2} = \frac{\lambda}{\pi\epsilon_0} \int_0^{x/a} \frac{dt}{1 - t^2}$$

The integral is done simply by partial fractions, but you might rather just look it up in a table. Either way, you end up with

$$V(x) = V_0 + \frac{\lambda}{2\pi\epsilon_0} \ln\left(\frac{a + x}{a - x}\right)$$

CHAPTER 33
Capacitance, Electrostatic Energy, and Dielectrics

33.1 CHAPTER SUMMARY

The potential of an arbitrary isolated conductor, relative to $V = 0$ at infinity, is proportional to the charge on it. We define the capacitance as

$$C \equiv \frac{Q}{V}$$

where C is a factor determined just by the geometry of the conductor. A capacitor is a system of two conductors carrying equal and opposite net charge Q; its capacitance is given by the same expression, if V is understood as the potential difference between the two elements.

To calculate the capacitance of a given system, we need only calculate the potential difference between the conductors for a given charge. For some important simple geometries (assuming in each case that the conductors are large enough so that edge effects are unimportant), the results are

Parallel plates (area A, separation d) $C = \frac{\varepsilon_0 A}{d}$

Concentric cylinders (radii a, b; length L) $C = \frac{2\pi\varepsilon_0 L}{\ln b/a}$

Concentric spheres (radii R_1, R_2) $C = 4\pi\varepsilon_0 \frac{R_1 R_2}{R_2 - R_1}$

If two capacitors are connected in parallel, the effective capacitance of the combination is just their sum; in series,

$$C_{eff} = \frac{C_1 C_2}{C_1 + C_2}$$

that is, 1/C adds.

Work must be done to charge a capacitor; some or all of it is stored as electrostatic potential energy. The stored energy in a capacitor C charged to a potential difference V_0 is $\frac{1}{2}CV_0^2$, regardless of geometry. We may equally well regard this energy as an attribute of the electric field which has been set up in the capacitor; the energy density in the electric field is therefore

$$\frac{U}{vol} = \frac{1}{2}\varepsilon_0 E^2$$

This holds for any electric field.

In practical capacitors, an insulating material is often inserted between the conducting elements. One effect of this is to increase the capacitance by a factor (the dielectric constant) which is characteristic of the insulating material. For a given charge on the capacitor, the dielectric material decreases the field between the plates. The reason is that the field in the capacitor polarizes the dielectric; a bound charge density is induced on the surfaces of the dielectric which partially cancels the effect of the free charge on the conductors. This can be related to molecular properties of the dielectric: if an applied field $\vec{E}$ induces a molecular dipole moment $\vec{p} = \alpha\vec{E}$, the dielectric constant K and the polarizibility α are related by

$$\alpha \simeq \frac{\varepsilon_0}{n}(K - 1)$$

where n is the number of molecules per unit volume. The size of induced dipole moments can be estimated, for example, from the Bohr model of the hydrogen atom; they are very small.

33.2 CHECK LIST

farad	dielectric material
capacitance	dielectric constant
capacitor	polarization of a dielectric
condenser	induced dipole moment
edge effects	permanent dipole moment
parallel combination	polar molecule
series combination	bound charge
stored energy	dielectric strength
electrostatic field energy	molecular polarizibility
energy density	Bohr atom

33.3 TRUE OR FALSE?

_____ 1. The potential - relative to V = 0 at infinity - of an isolated conductor is proportional to the net charge on it.

_____ 2. The capacitance of an isolated conductor is defined as the potential required to store unit charge on it.

_____ 3. A capacitor is any system of two conductors carrying equal and opposite charges.

_____ 4. The capacitance of a system depends only on the geometry of the conductors.

_____ 5. Neglecting edge effects, the capacitance of parallel plates is proportional to the volume Ad between the plates.

_____ 6. Two capacitors connected in series have an effective capacitance which is the sum of the individual capacitances.

_____ 7. Two capacitors connected in parallel have an effective capacitance which is the sum of the individual capacitances.

_____ 8. Charging a capacitor requires no work provided that the charges placed on the two elements are equal and opposite.

_____ 9. The work required to charge a capacitor of arbitrary shape may be written $\frac{1}{2}CV^2$.

_____10. If the space between the elements of a capacitor is filled with an insulating material, the capacitance is increased.

_____11. If the space between the elements of a capacitor is filled with a conducting material, the capacitance is decreased.

_____12. An insulating material between the plates of a capacitor increases its capacitance only if the material possesses a permanent electric dipole moment.

_____13. The effect of a dielectric between the elements of a capacitor is to weaken the electric field originally present.

_____14. The net effect of an electric field on a dielectric material is to produce a <u>surface</u> charge density.

_____15. The surface charge on a dielectric in a capacitor augments the charge on the capacitor plates and thus increases the capacitance.

_____16. The magnitude of the bound-surface-charge density on a dielectric in a capacitor is always less than the free-surface-charge density on the plates.

_____17. The dielectric constant of a material is directly related to the polarizibility of its molecules.

_____18. The molecular polarizibility α is defined as the average molecular dipole moment induced per unit electric field.

33.4 QUESTIONS

1. The plates of a parallel-plate capacitor are pressed together until the spacing between the plates is halved. While this takes place the plates are isolated from any electrical contact with anything else. What has happened to the magnitude of: the capacitance, the potential difference, the charge on each plate, the energy stored in the electric field?

2. Repeat Question 1 if, while the capacitor is compressed, a battery is connected across it.

3. A dielectric slab is half in and half out of a parallel-plate capacitor. Is there a force on it? Why? Does the force tend to draw it in or spit it out?

4. A metal plate, isolated, is between the plates of a capacitor. How is the capacitance affected? Does your answer depend on the thickness of the plate? Neglect edge effects.

5. How would you expect the dielectric constant of a gas to depend on temperature and pressure?

6. The bound surface charge on the dielectric in a capacitor is always less, although perhaps only slightly less, than the free charge density on the plates. Why?

7. In Questions 1 and 2 above, the energy stored in the capacitor changed when the plates were moved closer together. Where did the energy go (or come from)?

33.5 EXAMPLES

1. Find the capacitance of coaxial cylinders 30 cm long and with radii
    1.0 and 1.18 cm. How much does it differ from that of a parallel-
    plate capacitor whose elements have the same area and spacing?

2. The dielectric strength of air is about 3×10^6 V/m, that of
    polyethelene about 5×10^7 V/m; the dielectric constant of poly-
    ethelene is 2.3. With two plane conductors of area 500 cm^2, for
    a potential difference of 600 V, what is the largest capacitance you
    can make with air as the dielectric? With polyethelene?

3. You have enough dielectric material to fill half the volume between
    the plates of a capacitor. Where should you put it - that is, how
    much area should you fill, and to what thickness - to maximize the
    capacitance?

4. Helium gas at 20°C and 1 atm pressure has a dielectric constant of
    1.000065. What is its molecular polarizibility? If you imagine the
    molecular polarization to be due to a simple displacement of the
    center of negative charge of the helium atom from the nucleus, how
    much must the separation be in a field of 1000 V/m?

33.6 ANSWERS

True or False?

1. True.

2. False - as the charge that it can store per unit potential.

3. True.

4. True.

5. False - to the ratio A/d.

6. False - 1/C adds for capacitors in series.

7. True.

8. False - work must be done to separate the positive and negative charge.

9. True - this is general, although it's only derived in the text for the
    case of parallel plates.

10. True.

11. False - if the space were filled with conductor, no potential differ-
    ence could be maintained across it - you wouldn't have a capacitor
    any more.

12. False - if there is no permanent dipole moment, there is one induced
    by the field.

13. True.

14. True.

15. False - it is in the opposite sense and so decreases the field between
    the plates.

16. True.

17. True.

18. True.

Questions

1. If the elements are isolated, the charge on them doesn't change. By halving the distance between the plates, you have doubled the capacitance, so the potential difference Q/C is halved and so is the stored energy $CV^2/2$.

2. If a battery holds the plates at constant potential difference and the capacitance - which depends only on geometry - is doubled, the charge $Q = CV$ is doubled and so is the stored energy.

3. There is a force drawing it in because the charge density on each plate attracts the opposite charge density induced on the surfaces of the dielectric. Another way to say it is that inserting the dielectric decreases the stored energy $CV^2/2$ because it decreases the capacitance.

4. The capacitor with an isolated plate between the plates is equivalent to two capacitors, each with half the distance between plates, connected in series(see sketch at right). The capacitance of each is 2C, since the spacing is half; thus the combination is

$$\frac{(2C)(2C)}{2C + 2C} = C$$

The capacitance is unchanged. If the plate has finite thickness, however, the spacing of "each capacitor" will be less than d/2 and the effective capacitance of the whole thing will be bigger than C.

5. The dielectric constant can be written

$$K = 1 + \frac{n\alpha}{\varepsilon_0}$$

where the polarization α is a molecular property and n is the number of molecules per unit volume. For an ideal gas

$$n = \frac{P}{kT}$$

so, other things being equal, the dielectric constant increases with pressure and decreases with temperature.

6. Because the difference between free and bound surface charges is what produces the (net) electric field in the dielectric, which causes the polarization of the material.

7. From (or to) whoever or whatever pushed the plates together, and, in Question 2, some was supplied by the battery.

Examples

Partial Solutions (1)

1. The capacitance of long concentric cylinders is

$$C = \frac{2\pi\varepsilon_0 \ell}{\ln b/a}$$

where a and b are the inner and outer radii. What is the area for the equivalent parallel-plate capacitor?

2. Write the capacitance so that it depends explicitly on E_{max}, the dielectric strength of the dielectric.

3. Suppose you fill area A of the plates (total area A_0) with a thickness t of the dielectric. You are given that

$$At = \frac{1}{2}A_0 d$$

You can regard this as two capacitors in parallel: one with area $A_0 - A$, spacing d, and no dielectric, the other with area A and <u>partly</u> filled with a dielectric. Find the capacitance of the combination. For what value of t is it maximum?

4. The polarizibility is

$$\alpha \simeq \frac{\varepsilon_0 (K - 1)}{n}$$

What is n - the number of molecules per unit volume - for an ideal gas?

Partial Solutions (2)

1. The areas of inner and outer cylinders are not the same; let the "equivalent" parallel plates have the area of a cylinder halfway between:

$$A = 2\pi \left(\frac{a + b}{2}\right) \ell$$

and the same spacing b - a. Then their capacitance is

$$C_{11} = \frac{\varepsilon_0 A}{d} = \frac{\pi \varepsilon_0 \ell (b + a)}{b - a}$$

How does this compare with that of the cylinders?

2. If the capacitance is to operate with 600 V across it, without breakdown, we require

$$\left(E = \frac{600 \text{ V}}{d}\right) < E_{max} \quad \text{so} \quad d > \frac{600 \text{ V}}{E_{max}}$$

Find the corresponding capacitance.

3. Let t = xd and $A = A_0/2x$. The capacitance - call it C_1 - of the part that is partly filled with dielectric takes a little thought. In the empty part the field is

$$E = \frac{\sigma}{\varepsilon_0} = \frac{Q}{\varepsilon_0 A}$$

and in the part containing the dielectric it is

$$E' = \frac{E}{K} = \frac{Q}{\varepsilon_0 A K}$$

so the potential difference between the plates is

$$\Delta V = \frac{Q}{\varepsilon_0 A}(d - t) + \frac{Q}{\varepsilon_0 A K}(t) = \frac{Q}{\varepsilon_0 A}\left[d - \left(\frac{K - 1}{K}\right)t\right]$$

and thus

$$C_1 = \frac{\varepsilon_0 A}{d - [(K - 1)/K]t} = \frac{\varepsilon_0 A_0/d}{2x\left[1 - (K - 1)/K\right]x}$$

What is the total capacitance of the "parallel combination"?

4. For an ideal gas

$$n = \frac{P}{kT}$$

so

$$\alpha \simeq \frac{kT\varepsilon_0(K - 1)}{P}$$

Given the polarizibility, what dipole moment is induced in a molecule?

Partial Solutions (3)

1. The capacitance of the cylinders is

$$C = \frac{(2\pi)(8.85 \times 10^{-12} \text{ F/m})(0.3 \text{ m})}{\ln 1.18} = \underline{1.01 \times 10^{-10} \text{ F}}$$

and the ratio of this to the capacitance of the parallel plates is

$$\frac{C}{C_{11}} = \frac{2(b - a)}{(b + a) \ln b/a}$$

For $a = 1.0$ cm, $b = 1.18$ cm, this is

$$\frac{(2)(0.18)}{(2.18) \ln 1.18} = 0.998$$

In other words, the capacitance of closely spaced plates is not affected very much if you roll them in a circle.

2. We have

$$C = \frac{\varepsilon_0 KA}{d} < \frac{\varepsilon_0 KAE_{max}}{\Delta V}$$

$$= (7.38 \times 10^{-16} \text{ F-m/V})(KE_{max})$$

for the parameters given. For air ($K = 1$; $E_{max} = 3 \times 10^6$ V/m), $C < 2.2 \times 10^{-9}$ F and for polyethelene ($K = 2.3$; $E_{max} = 5 \times 10^7$ V/m), $\underline{C < 8.5 \times 10^{-8} \text{ F}}$.

3. The capacitance of the other part - no dielectric - is

$$C_2 = \varepsilon_0 \frac{A_0 - A}{d} = \frac{\varepsilon_0 A_0}{d}(\frac{2x - 1}{2x})$$

and parallel capacitors just add, so

$$C = C_1 + C_2 = \frac{C_0}{2x[1 - (K - 1)/K]x} + \frac{C_0(2x - 1)}{2x}$$

where $C_0 = \varepsilon_0 A_0/d$ is the capacitance of the plates with no dielectric. After a little juggling this boils down to

$$C = C_0\left[1 + \frac{1}{2(\frac{K}{K - 1} - x)}\right]$$

where x, again, is the fractional thickness t/d of the dielectric. Plainly, from the form of this expression, C increases monotonically with increasing x; thus the maximum capacitance is obtained with

$$\underline{t = d} \qquad \text{and} \qquad \underline{A = A_0/2}$$

4. The polarizibility is

$$\alpha = \frac{(1.38 \times 10^{-23} \text{ J/K})(293 \text{ K})(8.85 \times 10^{-12} \text{ C}^2/\text{N-m}^2)(1.000065 - 1)}{1.01 \times 10^5 \text{ N/m}^2}$$

$$= \underline{2.29 \times 10^{-41} \text{ C}^2\text{-m/N}}$$

If a is the effective separation of positive and negative charge in the He atom, then

$$p = (2e)a = \alpha E$$

and so

$$a = \frac{\alpha E}{2e} = \frac{(2.29 \times 10^{-41} \text{C}^2\text{-m/N})(10^3 \text{ N/C})}{(2)(1.60 \times 10^{-19} \text{ C})} = \underline{7.17 \times 10^{-20} \text{ m}}$$

which is very small compared to the size of the atom.

CHAPTER 34
Electric Current

An electric current is a flow of charge. This may take place in a conducting medium, but need not. Current is the rate of flow of charge:

$$I \equiv \frac{\Delta Q}{\Delta t}$$

conventionally positive in the sense of flow of positive charge, regardless of the actual sign of charge carriers. If in some situation there are n charge carriers per unit volume, with average velocity $\vec{v}_d$ and charge q, the current density is $\vec{J} = nq\vec{v}_d$ and the current through area A is $I = J_n A$. Typical values of v_d in conductors are very small.

A current flows in response to an electric field in a conductor. Empirically

$$\vec{J} = \sigma E$$

in many materials; this is Ohm's law. A material which obeys it is called "ohmic." The conductivity σ is a constant characteristic of the material; the resistivity is $\rho = 1/\sigma$. In a conductor, ρ is typically found to increase more or less linearly with the temperature. If a potential difference V is applied to a piece in an ohmic material of length ℓ and cross-sectional area A, Ohm's law becomes

$$V = \frac{\rho \ell}{A} I = RI$$

R is called the resistance of the piece. For many materials, resistance disappears altogether below some critical temperature; this phenomenon is called superconductivity.

The classical model of conduction in metals predicts the form of Ohm's law. Free electrons in the metal have large random velocities due to thermal agitation; an applied field superimposes an average drift velocity in the field direction, which is much smaller. On each collision with an ion of the metal, all sense of the direction of the drift of the electron is lost; consequently the energy given it by the applied field contributes to the random thermal motions, and a steady average drift speed is imparted to the electrons, given by

$$v_d = \frac{1}{2} \frac{q}{m} E t_c \qquad \text{so that} \qquad \rho = \frac{2m}{nq^2 t_c}$$

where t_c is the average time between collisions. As $v_d \ll \bar{v}$, t_c is essentially independent of the applied field, so that ρ is a constant, as required. However, the model fails quantitatively; if the thermal velocities of free electrons are estimated from the equipartition theorem, predicted conductivities are off by a factor of 10 or more, and the predicted temperature dependence is not linear.

Properly to treat the motion of free electrons in metals requires quantum mechanics. The equipartition theorem does not hold. Further, the scattering of the electrons is a wave phenomenon; in a perfectly regular periodic crystal lattice there would be no collisions. Collisions result only from irregularities in the metal crystal; at normal temperatures the most important irregularities arise from thermal vibrations of the metal ions. This argument leads to the observed linear temperature dependence. The availability of free electrons, which is the crucial difference between a conductor and an insulator, is also treated by the quantum theory of solids. In this theory, the energy of an electron can lie only within certain allowed bands of discrete energy levels. If there are available empty states at nearly the same energy as the states of the outermost electrons, an applied field can accelerate the electrons easily; such a material conducts. If there is an energy gap between the outer electron states and the conduction band, the material is an insulator. (A semiconductor is a material in which the energy gap is very small, so that some electrons are in the conduction band due to thermal agitation. The number of free charge carriers in a semiconductor may also be controlled by adding traces of various impurities to the material; this is the basis of electronic applications of semiconductors.)

Conservation of charge requires that the change of the net charge within any region be accounted for by whatever current flows in or out; this is the continuity equation

$$\oint J_n \, dA = - \frac{dQ}{dt}$$

This allows us to calculate the rate at which any free charge in a conductor comes to static equilibrium; the time is of the order ε_0/σ, which for a good conductor is very small.

When a current flows in a conductor, energy is dissipated as heat; the rate of this energy loss is $P = IV = I^2 R$. Some source of electrical energy is thus required to drive a steady current flow. A device which converts mechanical or chemical energy to electrical energy is called a seat of electromotive force (EMF). Such a device acts effectively as a pump; charge flows from low to high potential within the seat of EMF, from high to low potential in the external circuit.

34.2 CHECK LIST

ampere	equipartition theorem
ohm	insulator
electric current	semiconductor
conductor	energy quantization
ion	Bohr atom
electrolysis	Pauli exclusion principle

current density

drift velocity

Ohm's law

resistance

conductivity

ohmic and nonohmic materials

resistivity

temperature coefficient of resistivity

wire gauge

superconductivity

critical temperature

classical model of conduction

free electron

collision time

thermal velocity

mean free path

energy level

conduction band

valence band

energy gap

hole

doped semiconductor

n-type and p-type semiconductors

conservation of charge

electrostatic equilibrium

positron

continuity equation

power loss

Joule heating

battery

generator

seat of EMF

34.3   TRUE OR FALSE?

_____1.   Any flow of electric charge constitutes a current.

_____2.   The direction of current flow is taken always as that in which actual charged particles are moving.

_____3.   A conductor is a material which contains free electrons.

_____4.   The "drift velocity" of electrons in a conductor refers to the average thermal velocity in the absence of an applied electric field.

_____5.   The drift velocity of electrons in a metal is typically very small.

_____6.   The drift velocity of electrons in an ohmic material is proportional to the electric field in the material.

_____7.   An ohmic material is one in which the conductivity is independent of electric field over a wide range.

_____8.   The resistance of a given piece of an ohmic material is proportional to the potential difference across it.

_____9.   For most conductors under ordinary conditions, the resistivity is inversely proportional to the temperature.

_____10. Superconductivity occurs for many metals at high temperatures.

_____11. The drift velocity of an electron is the average velocity it gains from the electric field between successive collisions.

_____12. The classical model of electric conduction fails to predict the correct temperature dependence of the resistivity.

_____13. One fundamental reason for the failure of the classical model of conduction is the fact that the equipartition theorem does not hold for conduction electrons.

_____14. If a sample of a metal consisted of a perfect crystal lattice, with no defects or impurities, its resistivity would be infinite.

_____15. The factor mainly responsible for the enormous variation in the conductivity of different materials is the density of charge carriers n.

_____16. It is characteristic of semiconductors, unlike conductors, that their conductivity increases with increasing temperature.

_____17. Holes, as well as electrons, are important as free charge carriers in conductors.

_____18. It is characteristic of semiconductors that small traces of impurities can have a very strong effect on the conductivity.

_____19. In a n-type semiconductor, conduction is primarily not by electrons but by holes.

_____20. Electric charge is conserved.

_____21. The conservation of charge means that the net current into any closed surface must be zero.

_____22. In a good conductor, the time required for charge to come to static equilibrium is typically of the order of 10^{-3} or 10^{-4} sec.

_____23. Electrons in a conductor flow from high to low potential.

_____24. In a conductor of given resistance, the power loss is directly proportional to the potential difference applied.

_____25. A device which mechanically, chemically, or otherwise produces a potential difference is called a seat of electromotive force.

34.4 QUESTIONS

1. A piece of wire has resistance R. If it is stretched to 1.2 times its original length, assuming its volume doesn't change, what happens to its resistance?

2. We justified a number of electrostatic phenomena with the argument that there can be no potential difference or electric field in the body of a conductor. Now we say that for most conducting materials the field is proportional to the current density. Is there a contradiction here?

3. The average drift velocity of electrons in a current-carrying wire is constant. But the electric field in the wire does work on the electrons; where is the energy going?

4. We make analogies between electrical conduction and the flow of water in a pipe - the drift velocity is the flow velocity and so forth. What quantity is the "plumbing" analog of the potential difference?

5. Comment on the difficulties one might encounter in trying to test whether or not the filament of a light bulb is ohmic.

6. Under ordinary conditions, the drift velocity of electrons in a metal is around 10^{-3} cm/sec. Then how is it that when you turn on your electric shaver, you don't have to wait half an hour for the motor to start?

7. In a certain material the energy gap between valence and conduction bands is 3.7 eV. Is it a conductor, an insulator, or a semiconductor?

1. In the theory of conduction, the electron mobility μ is defined by $v_d = \mu E$. A length of copper wire 0.5 mm in diameter and 25 m long has a resistance of 2.16 Ω. The density of copper is 8.9 gm/cm^3, and its atomic weight is 63.5. Assuming 1.0 conduction electron per copper atom, find the mobility.

2. The melting point of copper is 1083°C. If a potential difference of 6 V is applied to the piece of wire in Example 1, assuming no heat losses, how long will it take before the wire starts to melt? Neglect the temperature dependence of the resistance. The specific heat of copper is 0.092 cal/gm-°C.

3. The temperature coefficient of resistivity of copper is 3.9 x 10^{-3} °C^{-1}, and that of carbon -5.0 x 10^{-4} °C^{-1}, at 20°C. You want to make a resistor consisting of a piece of carbon and a piece of copper in contact, whose "effective temperature coefficient"

$$\chi = \frac{1}{R}\frac{dR}{dT}$$

is zero near 20°C. The conductivities of copper and carbon at 20°C are 5.9 x 10^7 (Ω-m)$^{-1}$ and 2.8 x 10^4 (Ω-m)$^{-1}$, respectively. (a) Assuming equal cross-sectional areas, what must be the ratio of lengths? (b) What will be the effective temperature coefficient of your resistor at 50°C?

4. A particle accelerator takes electrons with kinetic energy 100 eV and accelerates them to a kinetic energy of 10^7 eV. If the beam current is 10^{-6} A and the cross-sectional area of the beam is 0.35 cm^2, find the density of charge carriers at the beginning and end of the acceleration process.

34.6 ANSWERS

True or False?

1. True.

2. False - by convention, it is usually taken as in the direction of flow of positive charge, regardless of the actual sign of charge carriers.

3. True - although it would be possible to call a solution in electrolysis, in which the charge carriers are positive and negative ions, a "conductor."

4. False - it is the average directed velocity caused by the electric field.

5. True.

6. True.

7. True.

8. False - the conductivity is a property of the material, independent of the potential difference in an ohmic material.

9. False - typically it increases with increasing temperature.

10. False - it is a low-temperature phenomenon.

11. True.

12. True - it predicts a decrease of resistivity with increasing temperature.

13. True.

14. True.

15. True.

16. True - increased thermal agitation means a higher probability of electrons in conduction-band states.

17. False - holes are important only in semiconductors.

18. True.

19. False - this defines a p-type semiconductor.

20. True.

21. False - consider a closed surface which contains one element of a capacitor.

22. False - they are many orders of magnitude smaller than this.

23. False - from low to high potential, since they are negatively charged; current flows always from high to low potential.

24. False - it is proportional to the square of the potential difference.

25. True.

Questions

1. If the volume doesn't change and the length increases by 20%, the cross-sectional area must decrease to 0.833 of its original value. Thus its resistance becomes

$$R' = \frac{\rho \ell'}{A'} = \frac{(\rho)(1.2\ell)}{0.833\ A} = 1.44\ \frac{\rho \ell}{A} = 1.44R$$

2. No, the electric field must be zero in a conductor if it is in electrostatic equilibrium. One carrying a current is not.

3. A basic idea of the model is that whenever an electron collides with something, its motion preferentially in the field direction is lost, since the random undirected thermal velocities of electrons and lattice ions are so much larger than the drift velocity. As far as accelerating along the field direction is concerned, it starts over again after each collision. Thus the extra kinetic energy it gains from the field becomes a contribution, through collisions, to the random, disorganized motions of the material; in other words, the conducting material is heated.

4. The pressure difference between ends of a pipe; this is the "driving force" for fluid flow, as the potential difference is for current flow.

5. As it stands, the resistance of the filament depends on the voltage across it. However, this is because the filament is designed to heat up to a very high temperature - several thousand degrees centigrade. If you took the light bulb apart and measured the resistance of the filament while at a constant temperature, you would find the resistance to be more or less constant.

6. The electric field, which is what sets the electrons drifting, is set up along the whole length of the wire essentially instantaneously.

7. This energy gap is very much larger than kT, which is on the order
    of 0.02 eV. Thus the material is an insulator.

Examples

Partial Solutions (1)

1. The current is

    $$I = nv_d eA$$

    where n is the number of charge carriers per unit volume. Since we
    assume 1.0 conduction electron per atom, n is just the number of atoms
    per unit volume. Given n, you can relate v_d and I. What is the
    electric field in the wire?

2. This is really a calorimetry problem from Chapter 18, slightly dis-
    guised. The source of the energy that heats the wire is the electri-
    cal (Joule) heating. At what rate is this delivering energy?

3. The two pieces are "in series" - their resistances add. Thus the
    resistance of the combination is

    $$R = \frac{\rho_1 \ell_1}{A} + \frac{\rho_2 \ell_2}{A}$$

    where subscript 1 refers to copper, subscript 2 to carbon. Under
    what circumstances will this expression be temperature-independent?
    For part (b), assume you've made the above expression temperature-
    independent at 20°C. Will it still be so at 50°C? Why or why not?

4. This is very straightforward - the only possible pitfall is that you
    must not forget that a 10-MeV electron is highly "relativistic" -
    $m_0 c^2 = 0.511$ MeV for an electron.

Partial Solutions (2)

1. Avogadro's number of copper atoms mass 63.5 gm; thus

    $$n = \frac{(6.02 \times 10^{23})(8.9 \text{ gm/cm}^3)}{63.5 \text{ gm}} = 8.44 \times 10^{22} \text{ cm}^{-3}$$

    $$= 8.44 \times 10^{28} \text{ m}^{-3}$$

    is the number of atoms, and conduction electrons, per unit volume.
    Find the current.

    As for the electric field, if the wire is uniform, it is just

    $$E = \frac{\Delta V}{25 \text{ m}} = \frac{IR}{25 \text{ m}}$$

2. The rate at which Joule heating dissipates energy in the wire is

    $$P = \frac{V^2}{R} = \frac{(6V)^2}{2.16 \ \Omega} = 16.7 \text{ W} = 16.7 \text{ J/sec}$$

    Assuming you start with it at room temperature - 20°C, say - how much
    heat does it take to bring the wire to the melting point?

3. We get

    $$\frac{dR}{dT} = \frac{\ell_1}{A} \frac{d\rho_1}{dT} + \frac{\ell_2}{A} \frac{d\rho_2}{dT}$$

    $$= \frac{\ell_1 \alpha_1 \rho_1}{A} + \frac{\ell_2 \alpha_2 \rho_2}{A} \qquad \text{if } \alpha \equiv \frac{1}{\rho} \frac{d\rho}{dT}$$

    and want this to vanish, for the resistance to be temperature-indepen-
    dent. But the resistivities depend on temperature - that's the point;

thus if we choose things so that dR/dT vanishes at one temperature, it won't be zero, in general, at another.

4. The kinetic energy is

$$E_k = (\gamma - 1)m_0 c^2$$

with

$$\gamma = (1 - \frac{v^2}{c^2})^{-\frac{1}{2}}$$

This gives you the volocity, if you know the kinetic energy. The current is

$$I = nevA$$

Here, given velocity of charge carriers and current, solve for n.

Partial Solutions (3)

1. The drift velocity is

$$v_d = \frac{I}{neA} = \frac{I}{ne\pi r^2}$$

and therefore

$$\frac{v_d}{E} = \mu = \frac{25\ m}{ne\pi r^2 R}$$

is the mobility. With the numbers given

$$\mu = \frac{25\ m}{(8.44 \times 10^{28}\ m^{-3})(1.60 \times 10^{-19}\ C)(\pi)(2.5 \times 10^{-4}\ m)^2(2.16\ \Omega)}$$

$$= \underline{4.37 \times 10^{-3}\ m^2/C\text{-sec}}$$

2. The heat required is

$$Q = cm\ \Delta T$$

The mass of the piece of wire is

$$(8.9\ gm/cm^3)(\pi)(2.5 \times 10^{-2}\ cm)^2(2.5 \times 10^3\ cm) = 43.6\ gm$$

Thus

$$Q = (0.092\ cal/gm\text{-}^{O}C)(43.6\ gm)(1083^{O}C - 20^{O}C) = 4264\ cal = 1.78 \times 10^4\ J$$

The time required to delvier this much heat energy is

$$\frac{1.78 \times 10^4\ J}{1.67 \times 10^1\ J/sec} = 1.07 \times 10^3\ sec$$

about 18 min.

3. For the first question, dR/dT plainly vanishes if the lengths are in the ratio

$$\frac{\ell_2}{\ell_1} = -\frac{\rho_1 \alpha_1}{\rho_2 \alpha_2} = -\frac{\sigma_2 \alpha_1}{\sigma_1 \alpha_2} = -\frac{(3.9 \times 10^{-3})(2.8 \times 10^4)}{(5.0 \times 10^{-4})(5.9 \times 10^7)}$$

$$= \underline{3.7 \times 10^{-3}}$$

that is, 3.7 mm of carbon for every meter of copper.
Let ρ' be the resistivity at $50^{O}C$. Then

$$\rho' = \rho(1 + 30\alpha) = \frac{1 + 30\alpha}{\sigma}$$

The resistance at $50^{O}C$ is

$$R' = \frac{\rho_1' \ell_1 + \rho_2' \ell_2}{A}$$

and

$$\frac{dR'}{dT} = \frac{\alpha_1 \rho_1' \ell_1 + \alpha_2 \rho_2' \ell_2}{A}$$

For copper and carbon, respectively, with the numbers given,

$$\rho_1' = 1.89 \times 10^{-8} \ \Omega\text{-m} \qquad \text{and} \qquad \rho_2' = 3.52 \times 10^{-5} \ \Omega\text{-m}$$

Putting all the numbers together gives

$$\chi = \frac{1}{R}\frac{dR}{dT} = \underline{5.82 \times 10^{-5} \ {}^{\circ}C^{-1}}$$

at $50^{\circ}C$.

4. For a 10-MeV electron

$$\gamma - 1 = \frac{10}{0.511} = 20.6$$

which gives v = 0.999c = 2.99×10^8 m/sec. The area of the beam is $3.5 \times 10^{-5} m^2$ and the current 10^{-6} A. So

$$n = \frac{10^{-6} \ A}{(2.99 \times 10^8 \ \text{m/sec})(1.60 \times 10^{-19} \ C)(3.5 \times 10^{-5} \ m^2)}$$

$$= \underline{5.96 \times 10^8 \ m^{-3}}$$

In the same way, for a 100-eV electron we get v = 5.93×10^6 m/sec and

$$n = \underline{3.01 \times 10^{10} \ m^{-3}}$$

CHAPTER 35
Direct-Current Circuits

35.1 CHAPTER SUMMARY

Simple direct-current circuits consisting of batteries, resistors, etc., may be analyzed by Kirchhoff's rules:

1. The sum of the potential drops around any closed loop must equal the the sum of the potential increases.
2. At every junction, the sum of the currents into the junction must equal the sum of the currents out of it.

The first follows from conservation of energy, the second from conservation of charge. Several examples are worked through in the text. Resistors connected in series simply add; for parallel connection,

$$R_{eff} = \frac{R_1 R_2}{R_1 + R_2}$$

Note that a battery is not a pure seat of EMF but has some effective internal resistance. There is thus Joule heating loss whether the battery is being charged or discharged; it is an irreversible device. Maximum power is drawn from the battery if the external load resistance matches the internal resistance.

The current in a circuit containing a capacitor is not constant but varies as the capacitor is charged or discharged. Charging or discharging a capacitor C through a resistance R proceeds exponentially with a characteristic time constant

$$t_c = RC$$

If a capacitor is charged through a resistance R, half the energy put out by the battery is dissipated as heat in the resistor and only half is stored in the capacitor.

Various devices exist for measuring electrical quantities. The most usual ones are based on the d'Arsonval galvanometer, in which a suspended coil rotates in a magnetic field by an amount proportional to the current in the coil; in appropriate circuit combinations this can be used as voltmeter, ammeter, or ohmmeter. One wants the measuring device to have as little effect on the circuit being measured as possible; thus an ammeter should have a very low, and a voltmeter a very high, internal resistance.

A much more accurate circuit for resistance measurements is the Wheatstone bridge, in which an unknown resistance is balanced against standard resistors. A potentiometer is a similar circuit which measures an unknown potential difference without drawing any current from it.

35.2 CHECK LIST

dc circuits	seat of EMF
battery	terminal voltage
resistor	internal resistance
capacitor	Joule heating
Kirchhoff's rules	impedance matching
conservation of energy	series and parallel combination
conservation of charge	grounding
potential drop	time constant
loop	d'Arsonval galvanometer
junction	Wheatstone bridge
	potentiometer

35.3 TRUE OR FALSE?

_____1. Kirchhoff's rules for circuit analysis follow directly from fundamental conservation laws.

_____2. Kirchhoff's rules apply only to circuits containing ohmic devices only.

_____3. A dry battery is a pure seat of EMF.

_____4. The power delivered by a given source of EMF to a load resistance is maximum when the resistance of the load matches the internal resistance of the EMF.

_____5. If in some situation current flows backward through a seat of EMF, Kirchhoff's voltage rule does not apply.

_____6. Two or more resistors connected in such a way that the same potential difference must appear across each are said to be connected in series.

_____7. The effective resistance of a combination of resistors in series is just the sum of the individual resistances.

_____8. To ground a point in a circuit means to fix its potential by connecting it electrically to the earth.

_____9. The current in either of two resistors connected in parallel is inversely proportional to its resistance.

_____10. Kirchhoff's junction rule does not apply as such to circuits containing capacitors.

_____11. If an EMF is applied to a circuit containing both resistance and capacitance in series, the current which flows initially is just $\mathcal{E}/R$.

_____12. The time required for a capacitance C to discharge through a resistance R is on the order of R/C.

_____13. The effective resistance of resistors combined in parallel is always less than either resistance alone.

_____14. If a battery charges a capacitor through a resistor, the energy stored in the charged capacitor is just half that supplied by the battery, regardless of the resistance.

_____15. When current is drawn from a battery, part of the energy supplied goes into heating the battery itself.

_____16. An ideal ammeter has a very large internal resistance.

_____17. An ideal voltmeter has a very large internal resistance.

_____18. A D'Arsonval galvanometer is a voltmeter applied to the measurement of very small voltage.

_____19. A Wheatstone bridge is a circuit designed to measure potential differences by balancing them against a standard.

_____20. It is possible to measure the EMF of a source without drawing any current from it.

35.4 QUESTIONS

1. Does the time to charge a capacitor through a given resistance depend on the applied EMF?

2. Measuring very large resistances - 10^8 Ω or more - by ordinary methods becomes difficult. Why? How might a very large resistance be measured using a voltage source, a capacitor, and a galvanometer? What would be the limitation on this method?

3. In the circuit sketched at right, let I_1 be the current in resistor R_1. If resistor R_3 is removed, does I_1 change? Explain.

4. In many applications, a battery can be regarded as essentially a pure voltage source. Can you think of some things that act as a nearly pure <u>current</u> source?

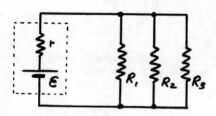

5. Commercial voltmeters will often be specified as "20,000 ohms per volt full scale," or "1,000 ohms per volt," or whatever. What does this mean? Which of the two voltmeters just mentioned is "better"?

6. You have resistors of 20, 60, and 120 Ω. Which of the following effective resistance values can be made by series and parallel combinations involving all three: 13.3, 42, 60 Ω?

35.5 EXAMPLES

1. Derive the rule for combination of resistances in parallel by calculating the power dissipation in each resistance.

2. A galvanometer has an internal resistance of 27 Ω, and the current required for full scale deflection is 15 μA. Use it to design (a) an ammeter to read 0.1 A full scale and (b) a voltmeter to read 3.0 V full scale.

3. Find the effective time constant of the circuit sketched at the right.

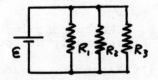

4. Use Kirchhoff's rules to solve for the currents in the circuit sketched at the top of the next page.

5. In the circuit sketched on the top of the next page, find an expression for the current in R.

282

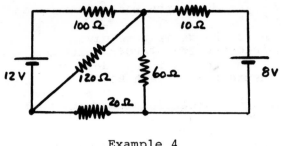
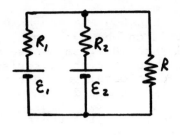

Example 4   Example 5

35.6 ANSWERS

True or False?

1. True - from conservation of energy and conservation of charge.

2. False - they are more general than this.

3. False - any real seat of EMF contains some internal resistance.

4. True.

5. False.

6. False - in a series connection the current through each is the same.

7. True.

8. True.

9. True.

10. False - at least, it applies everywhere except at one of the elements of the capacitor, where charge is accumulating.

11. True.

12. False - the time constant is RC.

13. True.

14. True.

15. True - this is the I^2R loss in the internal resistance of the battery.

16. False - it should have as small an internal resistance as possible.

17. True - the ideal voltmeter would draw no current.

18. False - it is the moving-coil galvanometer.

19. False - it is a circuit used for measuring resistance.

20. True - this is the purpose of a potentiometer circuit.

Questions

1. This depends on what you mean. The time to charge it to a given potential – to 10 V, say – is certainly shorter if a larger voltage is applied, but the characteristic time constant is independent of the applied voltage, so the time, for instance, to reach 90% of full charge does not depend on the EMF.

2. A basic idea, of which there could be several variations, is to measure R by measuring an RC time constant. If RC is made long enough – a few seconds or more – measuring the rate at which the discharge current falls off with time will determine the time constant. In any case, the basic limitation on this method is the leakage of the capacitor; its effective leakage resistance is in parallel with the resistance you are trying to measure.

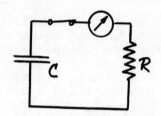

3. If the voltage source had no internal resistance, then I_1 would not change because the voltage drop in R_1 would be exactly $\mathcal{E}$, with or without R_3. But as it is, removing R_3 will decrease the current being drawn from the battery and so increase I_1.

4. A pure current source would be something that would supply a current whose value is independent of the load. One good approximation is just a high-voltage source of EMF in series with a very large resistor. In the circuit at right,

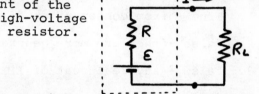

$$I = \frac{\mathcal{E}}{R + R_L} \simeq \frac{\mathcal{E}}{R} \text{ if } R >> R_L$$

is essentially independent of the load. A particle-accelerator beam is nearly a pure current source, also.

5. A voltmeter specified as 1000 Ω/V is one which is drawing 0.001 A when the meter is reading full scale. A good voltmeter should draw as little current, so have as high a resistance rating, as possible – 20,000 Ω/V is better.

6. All of them can be made.

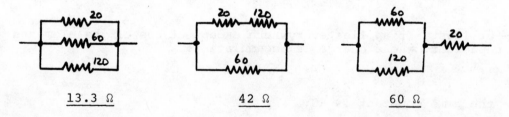

$$\underline{13.3\ \Omega} \qquad\qquad \underline{42\ \Omega} \qquad\qquad \underline{60\ \Omega}$$

Examples

Partial Solutions (1)

1. By the "effective resistance of the combination," in this context, we mean the resistance that, connected to the same power source, would dissipate the same power.

2. For an 0.1 ammeter, make a parallel combination – a current divider – such that, when 0.1 A flows in the whole combination, 1.5×10^{-5} A flows in the meter branch. How do you make a voltmeter?

3. By analogy with the discussion in the text, the time constant is the value τ in the equation

$$-\frac{dI_3}{dt} = \frac{I_3}{\tau}$$

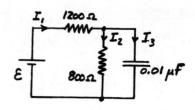

where I_3 is the current in the capacitor branch. To set this up, use Kirchhoff's rules just as you would for a circuit containing resistance only; but, what is the relation between current and voltage in the branch containing the capacitor?

4. There are five current-carrying branches, so you need to derive five equations from Kirchhoff's rules, relating them. You get two equations from the junction rule - the circuit has three junctions, but the third one is redundant - so you need three from the loop rule. There are several ways to pick three closed paths in this circuit; one is shown on the diagram.

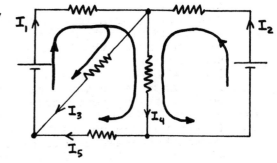

5. Again, you get three equations for the three unknown currents from Kirchhoff's rules - in this case, one junction and two loops.

Partial Solutions (2)

1. A parallel combination is one such that the potential difference is the same across each branch. Thus the power being dissipated in the circuit is

$$P = P_1 + P_2 + P_3 = \frac{\mathcal{E}^2}{R_1} + \frac{\mathcal{E}^2}{R_2} + \frac{\mathcal{E}^2}{R_3}$$

2. For the ammeter, use the circuit sketched at right; $r = 27\ \Omega$ is the galvanometer resistance. In order to have 0.1 A in the combination when there is 1.5×10^{-5} A in the meter branch,

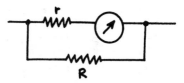

$$(10^{-1}\ \text{A})\,(\frac{rR}{r + R}) = (1.5 \times 10^{-5}\ \text{A})\,(r)$$

Solve for R. For the voltmeter, you want a series combination such that a potential difference of 3.0 V produces a current of 1.5×10^{-5} A.

3. In the branch containing the capacitor,

$$I = \frac{dQ}{dt} = \frac{1}{C}\frac{d\mathcal{E}c}{dt}$$

Kirchhoff's rules on this circuit give

$$\mathcal{E}_1 = I_1\,(1200\ \Omega) + I_2\,(800\ \Omega)$$

$$\mathcal{E}_2 = I_1\,(1200\ \Omega) + \mathcal{E}_C$$

$$I_1 = I_2 + I_3$$

Eliminate I_1 and I_2 and find an equation for I_3.

4. The Kirchhoff equations for this circuit are

$$12\ \text{V} = (100\ \Omega)I_1 + (120\ \Omega)I_3$$

$$12\ \text{V} = (100\ \Omega)I_1 + (60\ \Omega)I_4 + (20\ \Omega)I_5$$

$$8\ \text{V} = (10\ \Omega)I_2 + (60\ \Omega)I_4$$

$$I_1 + I_2 = I_3 + I_4$$

$$I_4 = I_2 + I_5$$

and you have to solve for the five currents. Direct substitution is easier than determinants.

5. Kirchhoff's rules give

$$\mathcal{E}_1 = I_1 R_1 + IR$$

$$\mathcal{E}_2 = I_2 R_2 + IR$$

$$I = I_1 + I_2$$

Solve for I.

Partial Solutions (3)

1. By definition of R_{eff} the total power being dissipated in the circuit is

$$P = \frac{\mathcal{E}^2}{R_{eff}}$$

thus

$$R_{eff} = \frac{1}{1/R_1 + 1/R_2 + 1/R_3}$$

is the effective resistance of the combination.

2. Solving for R, in the ammeter case, gives

$$\frac{R}{R + 27\ \Omega} = 1.5 \times 10^{-4}$$

which gives

$$R = \underline{4.05 \times 10^{-3}\ \Omega}$$

In the voltmeter case, at the right, we get

$$(R + 27\ \Omega)(1.5 \times 10^{-4}\ A) = 3.0\ V$$

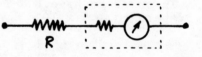

or

$$R = \underline{2.0 \times 10^5\ \Omega}$$

3. Use the third equation to eliminate I_1; then

$$\mathcal{E} - I_2(2000\ \Omega) - I_3(1200\ \Omega) = 0$$

$$\mathcal{E} - I_2(1200\ \Omega) - I_3(800\ \Omega) = \mathcal{E}_C$$

and eliminate I_2 between these two to give

$$(0.40)\mathcal{E} - (480\ \Omega)I_3 = \mathcal{E}_C$$

Differentiate this with respect to time ($\mathcal{E}$ is constant):

$$-(480\ \Omega)\left(\frac{dI_3}{dt}\right) = \frac{d\mathcal{E}_C}{dt} = \frac{I_3}{C} = \frac{I_3}{1.0 \times 10^{-8}\ F}$$

or

$$-\frac{dI_3}{dt} = \frac{I_3}{4.8 \times 10^{-6}\ sec}$$

so

$$\underline{\tau = 4.8 \times 10^{-6}\ sec}$$

Note τ is just $R_{||}C$.

4. Use the current equations to substitute for I_4 and I_5 in the loop equations, and divide out common factors to give

$$5I_1 + 6I_3 = 0.6 \text{ A}$$

$$9I_1 + 3I_2 - 4I_3 = 0.6 \text{ A}$$

$$6I_1 + 7I_2 - 6I_3 = 0.8 \text{ A}$$

Eliminating I_3 from the first of these leaves

$$12.33I_1 + 3I_2 = 1.0 \text{ A}$$

$$11I_1 + 7I_2 = 1.4 \text{ A}$$

which are satisfied by

$$\underline{I_1 = 0.0525 \text{ A}} \qquad \underline{I_2 = 0.1175 \text{ A}}$$

These, in turn, give for the other currents

$$\underline{I_3 = 0.0562 \text{ A}} \qquad \underline{I_4 = 0.1138 \text{ A}} \qquad \underline{I_5 = 0.0038 \text{ A}}$$

5. From the first two equations

$$I_1 = \frac{\mathcal{E}_1}{R_1} - \frac{R}{R_1}I$$

$$I_2 = \frac{\mathcal{E}_2}{R_2} - \frac{R}{R_2}I$$

so

$$I = \frac{\mathcal{E}_1}{R_1} - \frac{R}{R_1}I + \frac{\mathcal{E}_2}{R_2} - \frac{R}{R_2}I$$

or

$$\underline{I = \frac{\mathcal{E}_1 R_2 + \mathcal{E}_2 R_1}{RR_1 + RR_2 + R_1 R_2}}$$

CHAPTER 36
The Magnetic Field

Natural magnetic attraction was known to the ancients. Every magnet has
two poles - points at which its attraction is strongest - one called a
north and the other called a south pole bacause of a magnet's tendency
to align with the earth's magnetism. Poles always come in inseparable
pairs. Like poles repel each other, unlike poles attract. Magnetism
is an effect of electric currents; Ampère explained natural magnetism in
terms of persistent microscopic currents within the magnetic material.
Electric and magnetic forces are related, but magnetism is a distinct
force which acts between moving charges.

As we did with electrostatic interactions, it is useful to describe
the magnetic force in terms of a field. From the behavior of nonelectrostatic force on a moving charge, we can define the field $\vec{B}$ by

$$\vec{F} = q\vec{v} \times \vec{B}$$

or, equivalently, by the force on a current element of length $\vec{dl}$:

$$\vec{dF} = I \, \vec{dl} \times \vec{B}$$

For the force on a complete current-carrying circuit we integrate $\vec{dF}$ over
the circuit. The force is at right angles both to $\vec{B}$ and to the motion
of charge.

A magnet in a magnetic field tends to align itself with the field.
We may define the pole strength q* by

$$\vec{F} = q*\vec{B}$$

(A magnet is two equal and opposite poles - a dipole. If its length is
$\vec{l}$, we define the magnetic dipole moment $\vec{m} \equiv q*\vec{l}$; in a magnetic field there
is then a torque $\tau = \vec{m} \times \vec{B}$ on the magnet, analogous to the torque on an
electric dipole in an $\vec{E}$ field.) We can thus map lines of $\vec{B}$ with a
compass needle, for instance.

If a current loop is placed in a magnetic field, it behaves like a
dipole; there is no net force on it (if the field is uniform), but there
is a torque tending to align the loop axis with the field. If the loop
has area A and its axis in the direction of a unit vector $\hat{n}$, its magnetic
moment $\vec{m} = IA\hat{n}$. The field generated by the loop will also turn out to be
the same as that of the equivalent dipole. An important application of
the torque on a current loop is the moving-coil galvanometer, a basic
device for electrical measurements.

A point charge moving in a uniform magnetic field experiences a force
which is always perpendicular to $\vec{v}$. The magnetic force therefore does no
work on the charge but deflects it without changing its speed. A particle
moving perpendicular to $\vec{B}$ moves in a circle around the field direction;

288

if it has any velocity component along the direction of $\vec{B}$, its path becomes a helix. The angular frequency of this revolution for a particle of mass m is

$$\omega = \frac{qB}{m}$$

This is called the cyclotron frequency; note that it is independent of v, the radius of the orbit, etc.

Among the devices which are based on the circular path of a charged particle in a magnetic field are the cyclotron and the mass spectrometer. Crossed $\vec{E}$ and $\vec{B}$ fields exert no net force on a particle moving perpendicular to the fields with a speed $v = E/B$ – this has various applications as a velocity selector. Thomson's identification of the electron as a fundamental particle was based on the deflection of cathode rays in magnetic fields.

The motion of charged particles in a nonuniform magnetic field is generally quite complicated. Particular field configurations act as magnetic "bottles" to trap and contain charged particles in some applications.

The force on a current-carrying wire in a magnetic field is actually a force on charge carriers moving in the wire. A consequence is that a potential difference is generated laterally across the conductor due to the lateral deflection of the charge carriers. This is the Hall effect; the EMF generated is

$$\mathcal{E}_H = v_d Bw$$

if w is the width of the conductor. The Hall effect can be used to measure a magnetic field, or to determine v_d in a given conductor.

36.2   CHECK LIST

tesla

gauss

weber

magnetism

poles

ferromagnet

intrinsic electron spin

magnetic field

magnetic induction

magnetic flux density

magnetic-field intensity

current element

pole strength

magnetic moment

Hall effect

couple

d'Arsonval galvanometer

cyclotron frequency

cyclotron

mass spectrograph

helix

velocity selector

magnetic bottle

van Allen belts

cathode rays

electron

current loop

36.3 TRUE OR FALSE?

____1. Natural magnetism was discovered in the 13th century.

____2. Every natural magnet possesses two poles – points at which its attraction is strongest.

____3. The north geographic pole of the earth is a south magnetic pole.

____4. It is impossible, so far as is known, to isolate a single magnetic pole.

____5. A charge in motion exerts both electric and magnetic forces on another charge at rest.

____6. The magnetic force on a charge is directly proportional to the magnitude of the charge.

____7. The magnetic force on a moving charge is in the direction of its velocity.

____8. In any situation where there exists a magnetic force on a particle, there is one direction in space such that there is no force on a particle moving in that direction.

____9. A gauss and a weber per square meter are the same unit.

____10. The earth possesses a permanent magnetic field whose magnitude at the earth's surface is of the order of 1 G.

____11. For a given current, the magnetic force on a current-carrying wire is independent of the charge and drift velocity of charge carriers in the wire.

____12. A permanent magnet in a magnetic field tends to align itself along the field, with the south pole pointing in the field direction.

____13. There is no net force on a magnetic dipole in a uniform magnetic field.

____14. Magnetic "lines of force" are drawn so that at any point their direction would be that in which a small magnetic dipole would tend to line up.

____15. Lines of force outside a natural magnet run from the south to the north pole.

____16. A small loop of current, of arbitrary shape, enclosing area A, has a magnetic dipole moment IA.

____17. The magnetic moment of an elementary current loop is directed perpendicular to the plane of the loop.

____18. The magnetic force does no work on a moving charge.

____19. A charged particle moving in the direction of a uniform magnetic field travels in a circular path.

____20. The radius of the circular path of a charged particle in a uniform magnetic field is independent of its velocity.

____21. $\vec{E}$ and $\vec{B}$ fields are so arranged as to exert zero total force on a moving charged particle; the particle's velocity must be perpendicular to both $\vec{E}$ and $\vec{B}$.

____22. The $\vec{E}$ and $\vec{B}$ fields required to exert zero total force on a charge do not depend on the charge.

_____23. A mass spectograph is a device for measuring many optical spectra simultaneously.

_____24. The Van Allen radiation belts consist of charged particles trapped in the earth's magnetic field.

_____25. The accuracy of a mass spectrograph is limited, in practice, by the fact that most natural elements are mixtures of isotopes.

_____26. Neutrons cannot be accelerated in a cyclotron.

_____27. The Hall effect is a transverse EMF due to magnetic force on charge carriers moving in a conductor.

_____28. For given current, the Hall EMF is independent of the drift velocity of charge carriers in a conductor.

36.4 QUESTIONS

1. If a natural magnet is the analog of an electric dipole, what is the magnetic analog of a point charge?

2. A charged particle moves through a region of space in which a magnetic field, but no electric field, is known to exist. If there is no force on the particle, what can you say about the magnitude and direction of the field? What if both electric and magnetic fields are present?

3. We draw lines of force for the electric field such that the direction of the line at any point is the direction of the force on a point charge at that point. There is an obvious visual convenience to this rule; why are lines of force for the magnetic field not mapped in the same way?

4. There is no force on a magnetic dipole in a uniform field. If the magnetic field is nonuniform, however - if it varies from point to point - there is a net force on the dipole. Why?

5. If no work is done by the magnetic force on a moving charge, how are charged particles accelerated in a cyclotron?

6. Thomson's apparatus, in which he measured e/m for electrons, employed both electric and magnetic fields. Could the experiment have been done with one kind of field only? Discuss.

7. If a current-carrying wire has no net charge, how is it that there is a force on it in a magnetic field?

8. A high-energy proton from an accelerator moves through matter, gradually losing kinetic energy due to collisions with atomic electrons. There is a magnetic field directed perpendicular to its velocity. What does its path look like?

36.5 EXAMPLES

1. A small permanent magnet is suspended as a compass needle. It is 2 cm long and has a cross-sectional area of 0.1 cm^2. The local magnetic field of the earth is 0.6 G, directed 70° from the horizontal. If the maximum torque on the needle, when it is horizontal, is 6 x 10^{-5} N-m, what is its magnetic moment? If this moment were due to a current loop of the same area as the magnet's cross section, what current would have to be flowing in it?

2. A cylinder 10 cm long and 5 cm in diameter rests on a 30° incline, in a magnetic field, directed vertically, of magnitude 0.08 T. The mass of the cylinder is 0.5 kg. A coil of 100 turns of fine wire is wrapped about the cylinder as sketched. If the cylinder is in static equilibrium when the coil is in a vertical plane, what must be the current in the coil? Is the equilibrium stable?

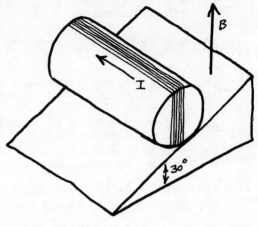

3. The Bohr model of the normal state of the hydrogen atom has the electron in a circular orbit of radius 5.29×10^{-11} m. If a magnetic field of 1.8 T is applied perpendicular to the plane of the electron orbit, by how much is the orbital frequency changed?

4. The magnetic field in a cyclotron is 15,000 G. If the cyclotron is to be used to accelerate protons to a kinetic energy of 10 MeV, what must be the radius of the region in which this magnetic field exists? If the accelerating voltage between "dees" has a peak value of 75,000 V, how many turns do the protons make on the way out?

5. In a magnetic field of 1.0 T, the Hall EMF developed across a strip of copper is found to be 1.1×10^{-6} V. The strip is 10 cm wide and 1 mm thick and carries a current of 15 A. The density of copper is 8.71 gm/cm^3 and its atomic weight is 63.54. From these data, infer the number of free conduction electrons per atom in copper.

36.6 ANSWERS

True or False?

1. False - it was known to the ancients.

2. True.

3. True - the "north" pole of a compass needle is so called because it is attracted to the north geographic pole.

4. True.

5. False - there is no magnetic force on a charge at rest.

6. True.

7. False - always perpendicular to the velocity.

8. True - this is what we define as the direction of the magnetic field.

9. False - a tesla is a weber per square meter; either is 10,000 G.

10. True.

11. True.

12. False - the north pole points in the field direction.

13. True - if you imagine them as isolated entities, the forces on equal and opposite poles cancel.

14. True - in fact, this is why iron filings tend to line up along field lines.

15. False - from the north to the south pole.

16. True.

17. True.

18. True.

19. False - a charge moving in the field direction experiences no force.

20. False - it's the frequency that is independent of the velocity.

21. True.

22. True - the force that <u>either</u> field exerts is proportional to the charge.

23. False - it's a device for measuring atomic masses.

24. True.

25. False - this is no limitation on its accuracy.

26. True - you can't grab something with a magnetic field if it has no charge.

27. True.

28. False - although the statement would be true the other way around.

Questions

1. An isolated magnetic pole - although there doesn't seem to be any such thing.

2. If there is no force on the particle in a magnetic field alone, it must be moving along the field direction. If both $\vec{E}$ and $\vec{B}$ fields are known to be nonzero, the electric and magnetic forces must cancel, because an $\vec{E}$ field always exerts a force on a charge. For this to be the case, $\vec{E}$ and $\vec{B}$ must be perpendicular to each other, and $\vec{E}$ must be perpendicular to the velocity of the charge.

3. Lines of the magnetic force <u>are</u> mapped this way, if we mean the force on an isolated magnetic pole; but this isn't very useful, if there is no such thing. There <u>is</u> no single direction for the force on a <u>charge</u> in a given magnetic field - the force depends on the direction of motion.

4. Think of the dipole as two opposite poles of equal strength. If the field is non-uniform, then in general it will be of different strength at the locations of the two poles, and

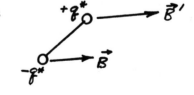

$$\vec{F} = q*\vec{B}' - q*\vec{B} \neq 0$$

5. The magnetic field in a cyclotron just serves to hold particles in a circular orbit so that the <u>electric</u> field between the dees can accelerate them repeatedly.

6. The Thomson experiment measured the deflection of a beam of electrons. The deflection due to either an electric or a magnetic field alone depends on the velocity of the charged particles, as well as the charge-to-mass ratio. In Thomson's experiment, crossed $\vec{E}$ and $\vec{B}$ fields were used to measure the velocity independently. With only one kind

of field, unless the charge of the particles were known independently, you can't do this.

7. Because, if the wire carries current, the total charge-times-velocity doesn't add up to zero, even though the net charge does - and this is what determines the force in a magnetic field. That is, a neutral current-carrying wire consists of positive charge at rest and negative charge in motion.

8. If the proton moved at constant speed, its path would be a circle of radius

$$R = \frac{mv}{eB}$$

Since, in this case, its kinetic energy and thus its speed are gradually decreasing, so is the radius of its circular path - thus it spirals inward.

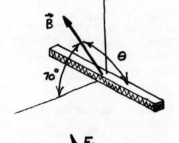

Examples

Partial Solutions (1)

1. The situation is sketched at the right. If the permanent magnet is in the horizontal plane, under what circumstances is the torque on it <u>maximum</u>?

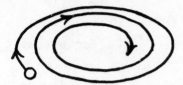

2. A free-body diagram for the cylinder is sketched at the right. F_i is the force of the incline on it, F that of the magnetic field on the coils. The force due to the magnetic field on the top and bottom of the coil constitutes a <u>couple</u>. What is the torque of a couple? Under what conditions will the cylinder be in static equilibrium?

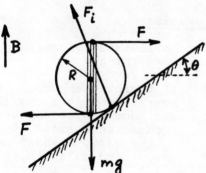

3. Write out the net force on the electron in this case, including that of the magnetic field. If the orbit is circular, this must equal the appropriate centripetal force.

4. The angular velocity of a circular orbit in a uniform magnetic field is

$$\omega = \frac{qB}{m}$$

If you know both this and the speed of the orbiting particle, plainly you can find the radius of the orbit. To relate the speed and kinetic energy of a 10-MeV proton, do you need to worry about relativistic effects?

5. If the width of the strip is w, the Hall EMF developed across it is

$$\mathcal{E}_H = wBv_d$$

which gives you the drift velocity. How do you relate this to the number of conduction electrons per unit volume?

Partial Solutions (2)

1. The magnitude of the torque on a magnetic dipole is

$$|\vec{\tau}| = |\vec{m} \times \vec{B}| = mB \sin \theta$$

if $\vec{m}$ is its magnetic moment. From the diagram given above, plainly θ is always greater than 70° if the magnet is in the horizontal plane; the torque has its maximum value if $\theta = 90°$.

2. If the distance between equal and opposite forces is d, the torque of a couple is just Fd – about any axis. Thus the torque on the cylinder, due to the magnetic forces on the coil, is

$$\tau_{mag} = nI\ell dB = nI\ell(2R)B$$

where ℓ is the length of the cylinder, I the current in the coil, n the number of windings of the coil, and B the magnetic field. If the cylinder is in static equilibrium, the net force on it and the net torque on it must both be zero. The first condition tells us nothing, since the net force due to the magnetic field is zero. What other torques are there?

3. In the sketch at right, the magnetic field is directed into the plane of the paper. The net force on the electron is

$$F = |\vec{F}_e| - |\vec{F}_m| = \frac{ke^2}{R^2} - evB$$

thus

$$\frac{mv^2}{R} = \frac{ke^2}{R^2} - evB$$

if the electron is in a circular orbit. Put this in terms of the angular frequency and solve.

4. The radius of the orbit is

$$R = \frac{v}{\omega} = \frac{mv}{eB}$$

The rest energy of a proton is around 10^9 eV, and the given kinetic energy is 0.01 times that; thus no consequential error will be made if you use the nonrelativistic kinetic-energy equation. As for how many turns it must make – how much energy does it gain on each full turn?

5. The current is

$$I = neAv_d$$

if A is the cross-sectional area of the conductor and n is the number of charge carriers per unit volume. Let

$$n = \chi n_0$$

where n_0 is the number of copper atoms per unit volume and χ is the number of conduction electrons per atom. Thus if the thickness of the strip is t,

$$I = \chi n_0 e(wt)v_d$$

Partial Solutions (3)

1. The maximum torque

$$m = \frac{\tau_{max}}{B} = \frac{6.0 \times 10^{-5} \text{ N-m}}{6.0 \times 10^{-5} \text{ T}} = \underline{1.0 \text{ A-m}^2}$$

If this moment were due to a current loop of the same cross section 0.1 cm, the current would have to be

$$I = \frac{m}{A} = \frac{1.0 \text{ A-m}^2}{10^{-5} \text{ m}} = \underline{10^5 \text{ A}}$$

2. Take torques about the point of contact between the cylinder and incline – this avoids a lot of messing around finding the force due to the incline. Then, for equilibrium,

$$\tau_{mag} = \tau_{grav} = (mg \sin \theta)R$$

so

$$2nI\ell RB = mgR \sin \theta$$

Thus

$$I = \frac{mg \sin \theta}{2n\ell B} = \frac{(0.5 \text{ kg})(9.8 \text{ m/sec}^2)(\sin 30^\circ)}{(2)(100)(0.1 \text{ m})(0.8 \text{ T})} = \underline{1.53 \text{ A}}$$

flowing in the coil will keep it in equilibrium. If the coil rolls in either direction, the magnetic torque will be decreased and there will be a net torque on it tending to roll it downhill; so the equilibrium is unstable with respect to deviations downhill, stable with respect to uphill.

3. Put $\omega = v/R$; then the force equation becomes

$$\omega^2 + 2\left(\frac{eB}{2m}\right)\omega - \frac{ke^2}{mR^3} = 0$$

The solutions of this are

$$\omega = -\frac{eB}{2m} \pm \sqrt{\frac{ke^2}{mR^2} + \left(\frac{eB}{2m}\right)^2}$$

The second term under the radical sign is very much larger than the first, for any possible value of B. Thus one of the solutions for ω is negative; all this means is that the orbital velocity and the magnetic force are in directions opposite those assumed. Thus

$$|\omega| = \sqrt{\frac{ke^2}{mR^3}} \pm \frac{eB}{2m}$$

The first term is the orbital frequency in zero magnetic field:

$$\omega_0 = \sqrt{\frac{ke^2}{mR^3}} = \underline{4.14 \times 10^{16} \text{ sec}^{-1}}$$

and the second is the change in (angular) frequency due to the field:

$$\delta\omega = \frac{eB}{2m} = \underline{1.58 \times 10^{11} \text{ sec}^{-1}}$$

for the numbers given.

4. The mass of a proton is 1.67×10^{-27} kg; thus

$$E_k = 10^7 \text{ eV} = 1.60 \times 10^{-12} \text{ J} = \tfrac{1}{2}(1.67 \times 10^{-27} \text{ kg})(v^2)$$

or

$$v = 4.38 \times 10^7 \text{ m/sec}$$

thus

$$R = \frac{mv}{eB} = \frac{(1.67 \times 10^{-27} \text{ kg})(4.38 \times 10^7 \text{ m/sec})}{(1.60 \times 10^{-19} \text{ C})(1.5 \text{ T})} = \underline{0.304 \text{ m}}$$

The magnetic field must be just about 2 ft in diameter.

Each time the proton comes around it is accelerated by the potential difference between the dees, twice - that is, it gains 150 keV. Thus the number of turns it makes is

$$\frac{10^7 \text{ eV}}{1.5 \times 10^5 \text{ eV}} = \underline{67}$$

5. Putting together the equations for $\mathcal{E}_H$ and I we get

$$\chi = \frac{IB}{n_0 e \mathcal{E}_H t}$$

n_0 is the number of copper atoms per unit volume. From the data given, Avogadro's number of atoms occupies a volume of $(63.54/8.71)$ cm^3, so

$$n_0 = \frac{6.02 \times 10^{23}}{7.30 \times 10^{-6} \text{ m}^3} = 8.25 \times 10^{28} \text{ m}^{-3}.$$

thus

$$\chi = \frac{(15 \text{ A})(1.0 \text{ T})}{(8.25 \times 10^{28} \text{ m}^{-3})(1.60 \times 10^{-19} \text{ C})(1.1 \times 10^{-6} \text{ V})(10^{-3} \text{ m})}$$

$\chi = \underline{1.03}$ conduction electrons per atom

CHAPTER 37
Sources of the Magnetic Field

37.1 CHAPTER SUMMARY

The fundamental source of the magnetic field is electric current. Magnetized materials natural and otherwise, are understood in terms of microscopic current loops in the material. These "amperean currents," however, arise from the motions of atomic electrons and cannot be described classically. The field arising from a current element $I \, d\vec{l}$ at distance r is given by the Biot-Savart law,

$$d\vec{B} = k_m I \, \frac{d\vec{l} \times \hat{r}}{r^2}$$

where $\hat{r}$ is the unit vector to the field point and k_m is a constant. The field from an extended current is found by integrating $d\vec{B}$ over all current elements. The Biot-Savart law is analogous to Coulomb's law in that it expresses the fundamental source-field relationship, but the directional dependence is entirely different.

The unit of current, the ampere, is <u>defined</u> by letting $k_m \equiv 10^{-7}$ N/A^2 exactly. We sometimes instead use a constant $\mu_0 = 4\pi k_m$ called the permeability of free space. The ratio of electric and magnetic force constants, $k/k_m = 1/\varepsilon_0\mu_0$, has a value equal to the square of the speed of light; this clue led to the identification of light as an electromagnetic wave.

The force on a current element $I_2 \, d\vec{l}_2$ due to the field of another, $I_1 \, d\vec{l}_1$, is

$$d\vec{F} = k_m I_1 I_2 \frac{d\vec{l}_2 \times (d\vec{l}_1 \times \hat{r})}{r^2}$$

It should be noted that Newton's third law does not, in general, hold for this force; however, conservation of momentum is not violated if the momentum of the electromagnetic fields themselves, as well as that of the current elements, is accounted for. The force between complete circuits does obey Newton's third law.

The magnetic field produced by a long, straight wire carrying current I is found from the Biot-Savart law to be

$$B = \frac{\mu_0}{2} \frac{I}{r}$$

at a distance r. The force on a second, parallel, wire per unit length is

$$\frac{F}{L} = \frac{\mu_0 I I'}{2\pi r}$$

(It is this expression that relates the definition of the ampere to a mechanical measurement.) The field from a current loop with magnetic moment m is

$$B = \frac{2k_m m}{r^3}$$

298

on the loop axis. Notice the analogy to the $\vec{E}$ field of an electric dipole.

The magnetic force on a moving charge can be shown to be a necessary addition to the electrostatic force in the context of the special theory of relativity, when the interaction of a current and a point charge is examined in different reference frames.

The lines of $\vec{B}$, from the Biot-Savart law, from a long, straight current are circles around the current direction. In general, the line integral of $\vec{B}$ around a closed curve is not zero:

$$\oint_C \vec{B} \cdot d\vec{l} = \mu_0 I$$

where I is the current through a surface bounded by the closed curve – this is Ampère's law. Like Gauss' law for the electric field, it facilitates calculation of the field in a few highly symmetric cases. For instance, the field inside a long solenoid (n turns per unit length) is found from Ampère's law to be

$$B = \mu_0 n I$$

Outside the solenoid, its field looks like that of a bar magnet with the same shape and with dipole moment m = nIAL. The resemblance is significant; inside a bar of magnetized material, the amperean currents cancel and their resultant is an effective current around the surface of the bar. The "surface current" per unit length, analogous to nI for the solenoid, is called the magnetization $\vec{M}$ of the bar; $\vec{M}$ is also the magnetic moment per unit volume of the material. The pole strength of a bar magnet of cross-sectional area A is q* = MA.

The flux of the magnetic field through a surface is defined as

$$\Phi_m \equiv \int \vec{B} \cdot \hat{n}\ dA$$

where $\hat{n}$ is the normal to the surface at every point. In general, two current-carrying circuits interact magnetically so as to try to increase the total flux through them. Note that, since the lines of $\vec{B}$ are endless – there are no isolated magnetic poles – the flux through any closed surface is zero.

Ampère's law, above, is valid only for steady currents. It can be generalized, however, by adding to the real, macroscopic, conduction current a "displacement current"

$$I_d = \varepsilon_0 \frac{d\Phi_e}{dt}$$

where Φ_e is the flux of the electric field. This says that a time-varying electric field (as well as real current) is a source of the magnetic field.

37.2 CHECK LIST

$k_m = \mu_0/4\pi = 10^{-7}\ N/A^2$

weber

magnetic field

natural magnet

ampere

coulomb

Ampère's law

line integral

amperean current
ferromagnetism
permeability
electromagnetic radiation
lines of $\vec{B}$
magnetic induction
current balance
speed of light
special relativity
Lorentz contraction
charge invariance

solenoid
pole strength
magnetic dipole moment
bar magnet
magnetization
surface pole density
magnetic flux
flux density
displacement current
generalized current
Faraday's law

37.3 TRUE OR FALSE?

_____1. The source of the magnetic field is electric current.

_____2. The force exerted on one current element by another is given by Ampère's law.

_____3. The magnetic field due to a current element varies inversely as the square of the distance from it.

_____4. The force of one current element on another, deduced from the law of Biot and Savart, is not consistent with all of Newton's laws.

_____5. Because of this, the momentum of a system containing magnetic forces between current-carrying circuits is not necessarily conserved.

_____6. The apparent violation of Newton's third law by magnetic forces is not real.

_____7. The lines of the magnetic field due to a long straight wire are circles around the wire.

_____8. An elementary current loop acts as a magnetic dipole, both in the magnetic field which it produces and in its response to an external magnetic field.

_____9. The fact that the ratio of the electric and magnetic force-law constants is the square of the speed of light is a numerical coincidence only.

_____10. In the special theory of relativity, magnetic forces are a derivable consequence of Coulomb's law of electrostatic force.

_____11. It follows from the principle of charge invariance that the current in a conductor is the same in all frames of reference.

_____12. The fact that $\oint \vec{B} \cdot d\vec{l}$ around a closed path is not necessarily zero means that the magnetic force is nonconservative.

_____13. In a situation involving only steady currents, Ampère's law is valid.

_____14. Ampère's law is valid only in situations of sufficient symmetry that the direction of the magnetic field is readily apparent.

_____15. The Biot-Savart law can be derived by applying Ampère's law to a current element.

_____16. Ampère's law and the law of Biot and Savart are not equivalent, because Ampère's law holds only for steady currents.

_____17. The lines of $\vec{B}$ inside a long solenoid are circles coaxial with the solenoid.

_____18. The magnitude of the field inside a long, tightly wound solenoid is essentially uniform.

_____19. The field outside a long solenoid is equivalent to that of a bar magnet.

_____20. For a given current and total number of turns, the magnetic field of a solenoid is independent of its geometry.

_____21. The net effect of aligned microscopic current elements in a permanent magnet is equivalent to a current flowing around its surface.

_____22. The pole strength of a bar magnet can be written as its magnetization multiplied by its length.

_____23. In general, the magnetic force or torque on a current-carrying circuit is in such a direction as to increase the magnetic flux through the circuit.

_____24. The net magnetic flux through any closed surface is always zero.

_____25. The situations in which Ampère's law fails are those in which the flux through all surfaces bounded by a given closed curve is not the same.

_____26. Including, in appropriate situations, the "displacement" current with the real conduction current makes Ampère's law generally valid.

_____27. A displacement current, as well as a real conduction current, is a source of the magnetic field.

37.4 QUESTIONS

1. Two flat, square current-carrying loops in the plane of the paper are sketched. In terms of these, relate the following two statements about magnetic forces: (a) like poles repel, opposite poles attract, (b) parallel currents attract, antiparallel currents repel.

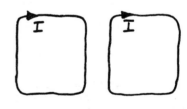

2. Consider Ampère's law applied to a complex communications cable which carries many currents, not all with the same magnitude or direction. What is the "current through the surface" in this case?

3. A current flows in a hollow conductor such as a long, straight pipe. Is there a magnetic field inside the pipe? What about outside it?

4. Would the magnetic field inside a long solenoid depend on the cross-sectional shape of the solenoid?

5. In the sketch at the top of the next page, a mass hangs in equilibrium on the end of a spring. If a current is passed through the spring, which way does the mass move? Will its motion, while the current is flowing, be a simple harmonic motion?

6. Consider the field due to two long, straight wires carrying parallel currents. Is the field at a point between them, in their mutual plane, weaker or stronger than that due to one of the wires alone? What if the currents are in opposite directions?

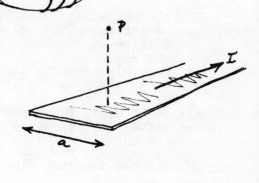

7. A toroid is a coil wound around a doughnut shape; think of it as a solenoid bent into a circle. From Ampère's law, what is the field outside the toroid?

37.5 EXAMPLES

1. Find an expression for the field due to a long, flat strip of conducting material carrying a current I, on a point in its median plane. For a given current, how far away from the strip must one be if the field is within 0.1% of that due to a straight wire?

2. A flat, rectangular coil of wire measures 5 by 15 cm and has 120 turns. If the coil carries a current of 0.66 A, what is the magnetic field at its geometrical center?

3. A long, straight coaxial cable carries a current of 2.5 A. If the radii of the cable are 0.2 and 0.5 cm, find the magnetic field at a point which is (a) 0.1 cm, (b) 0.3 cm from the axis.

4. A bar magnet 12 cm long and with a cross-sectional area of 1 cm^2, in a magnetic field of 0.22 T, experiences a torque of 0.54 N-m. Find the magnetization and the equivalent amperean surface current.

5. A parallel-plate capacitor is being charged at a rate of 1.2×10^{-3} A. Neglecting edge effects, what is the displacement current in the region between the plates?

37.6 ANSWERS

True or False?

1. True.

2. False - the law of Biot and Savart.

3. True.

4. True - the force between current <u>elements</u> violates Newton's third law.

5. False - although current elements violate Newton's third law, the law holds for the force integrated over entire closed circuits.

6. False - it is real. For instance, the third law is violated by bursts

of charge which are accelerated and then stopped; in order for momentum conservation to hold for this kind of case, the momentum of electromagnetic radiation must be included.

7. True.

8. True.

9. False - this result is derivable from the theory of electromagnetic waves.

10. True.

11. False - charge may be moving in one frame and at rest (no current) in another.

12. False - the force is nonconservative, because it depends on velocity; but $\oint \vec{B} \cdot d\vec{l}$ is not the work done around the path, because $\vec{B}$ isn't the force on anything.

13. True.

14. False - if there are steady currents, it is valid regardless of the geometry of the situation.

15. False - Ampère's law doesn't work for isolated current elements.

16. True.

17. False - they are along the axis.

18. True.

19. True.

20. False - the field depends on the number of turns <u>per unit length</u>.

21. True - this is the basis of the equivalence of a bar magnet and a solenoid.

22. False - this is its magnetization times its cross-sectional area.

23. True.

24. True.

25. False - those in which the <u>current</u> through all such surfaces is not the same.

26. True.

27. False - this is pretty picky, but the source of a magnetic field is a real current somewhere; see the law of Biot and Savart. A displacement current is a time-varying electric field, but if the electric field at this point is changing, it's because charge is being moved around somewhere else.

Questions

1. Since the currents are in the same sense, the magnetic moments are in the same direction. If we think of these as little bar magnets, they are lined up north to north and south to south and so they repel. In terms of the currents, the <u>strongest</u> force is that between the two anti-parallel currents which are closest together, so they repel.

303

2. The <u>net</u> current is the sum (with sign, if they aren't all in the same direction) of all the individual currents.

3. Draw any contour you like in the region <u>inside</u> the hollow pipe; there is no current through it, so the line integral of B vanishes by Ampère's law. Thus there is no field inside.

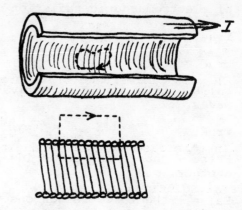

4. Yes, it would, although not terribly strongly if the shape isn't too strange. The point is that only for a circular cross section can you be sure, by symmetry, that the field everywhere inside is along the axis. If it is not, there may be a contribution to the Ampère's law integral from the ends of the path sketched.

5. There will be an attractive magnetic force between every coil of the spring and every other, which will contract the spring and the mass will move upward. The force gets stronger as the coils get closer together, so the motion - without trying to describe it - is certainly not simple harmonic. This effect can be quite strong, and high-field laboratory solenoids have to be constructed very ruggedly to prevent them from imploding.

6. The field between is weakened if the currents are parallel, because the fields tend to cancel. If the currents are in opposite directions, their fields add in the region between them.

7. Consider Ampère's law around the contour shown. If there is a field, the geometry of the situation is such that you would expect it to be along this curve. But the <u>net</u> current flowing through the page is zero, since just as much flows out as in. Thus the field outside is zero.

Examples

Partial Solutions (1)

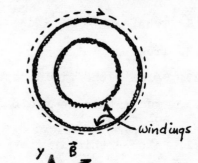

1. The geometry of the situation is shown in the diagram at right. The little slice of the strip, of width dx, is equivalent to a long straight wire carrying current

$$dI = I\frac{dx}{a}$$

What is the direction of the magnetic field due to the entire strip?

2. The field due to a straight length of current-carrying wire is found in the text to be

$$B = \frac{\mu_0 I}{4\pi r} (\sin \theta_1 + \sin \theta_2)$$

where θ_1 and θ_2 are the angles subtended at the field point by the ends of the wire. You can consider each side of the rectangular coil as n straight wires, each carrying current I.

3. Assume that the cable is long enough so that end effects are negligible. Then from the symmetry of the situation, the lines of B are circles around the axis of the cylinder. The convenient contour on which to apply Ampère's law is a circle around the axis, of the desired radius.

4. Since the torque depends on the angle between the magnetic moment and $\vec{B}$, assume the given value is the maximum torque. This is

$$\tau_{max} = mB$$

This gives us the magnetic moment vector $\vec{m}$. From this, how do you find the magnetization?

5. The displacement current through a surface S depends just on the rate of change of the flux of the electric field through the surface:

$$I_d = \varepsilon_0 \frac{d}{dt} \int_S \vec{E} \cdot \hat{n} \, dA$$

In this case, what is changing?

Partial Solutions (2)

1. Just by symmetry, the field in the median plane must be parallel to the plane of the strip. In the diagram, you can see that the perpendicular components of the field due to x and -x will cancel out. The field due to the slice at dx is

$$dB_x = dB \cos \theta$$

$$= \frac{\mu_0 dI}{2\pi r} \frac{y}{r} = \frac{\mu_0 Iy \, dx}{2\pi a (x^2 + y^2)}$$

Integrate over the wire to find B.

2. For the field due to one of the short sides put

$$r = \frac{b}{2}$$

$$\sin \theta_1 = \sin \theta_2 = \frac{a/2}{\sqrt{(a/2)^2 + (b/2)^2}}$$

So the field is

$$B = \frac{\mu_0 nI}{4\pi (b/2)} \frac{2a}{\sqrt{a^2 + b^2}} = \frac{\mu_0 nIa}{\pi b \sqrt{a^2 + b^2}}$$

What is the field due to one of the long sides?

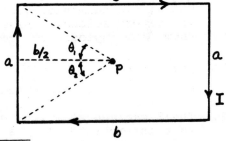

3. Ampère's law gives

$$\oint \vec{B} \cdot d\vec{s} = 2\pi r B = \mu_0 I(r)$$

where $I(r)$ is the net current through a circle or radius r. Thus

$$B = \frac{\mu_0 I(r)}{2\pi r}$$

At the two radii given, what is $I(r)$?

4. The magnetization is the magnetic dipole moment per unit volume. Thus if the bar magnet has cross-sectional area A and length L,

$$M = \frac{m}{AL}$$

What is the relation of the magnetization to the amperean surface current?

5. If the capacitor is charging, the electric field inside is changing. Assume the capacitor is large enough so that edge effects are negligible. Then through a contour surrounding the plates,

$$\frac{d}{dt} \int \vec{E} \cdot \hat{n} \, dA = A \frac{dE}{dt}$$

since $\vec{E}$ is uniform over the area A of the capacitor plates. You aren't given the physical dimensions of the capacitor plates. To get a numerical result for the displacement current, are you going to need them?

Partial Solutions (3)

1. The field of the strip is

$$B = \int_{-a/2}^{a/2} \frac{\mu_0 I y \, dx}{2\pi a (x^2 + y^2)} = \frac{\mu_0 I}{2\pi a} \int_{-a/2y}^{a/2y} \frac{dt}{1 + t^2}$$

or

$$B = \frac{\mu_0 I}{\pi a} \tan^{-1}\left(\frac{a}{2y}\right)$$

If the strip were replaced by a wire carrying the same current, the field at the same point would be

$$B_{wire} = \frac{\mu_0 I}{2\pi y}$$

For this to differ by less than 0.1% from the field of the strip, we must have

$$\frac{B}{B_{wire}} = \frac{2y}{a} \tan^{-1} \frac{a}{2y} > 0.999$$

which gives

$$\frac{a}{2y} < 0.0548 \quad \text{or} \quad \underline{v > 9.1\,a}$$

2. The field due to a long side can be found in just the same way - or just interchange b and a in the formula for that of one of the short sides. The whole field of the coil at its center is thus

$$B = \frac{2\mu_0 n I}{\pi\sqrt{a^2 + b^2}} \left(\frac{a}{b} + \frac{b}{a}\right) = \frac{2\mu_0 n I \sqrt{a^2 + b^2}}{\pi a b}$$

giving

$$B = \frac{(2)(4\pi \times 10^{-7}\ N/A^2)(120)(0.66\ A)(\sqrt{0.05^2 + 0.15^2}\ m)}{(\pi)(0.05\ m)(0.15\ m)} = \underline{1.34 \times 10^{-3}\ T}$$

or 13.4 G.

3. If r is larger than the radius of the inner conductor, then I(r) is the current in the inner conductor, which is 2.5 A. To find the field at a point within the inner conductor, however, we must assume that the current density is uniform, in which case

$$I(r) = \frac{r^2}{R_1^2} I \qquad \text{if } r < R_1$$

Thus for r = 0.3 cm,

$$B(0.3\ cm) = \frac{(4\pi \times 10^{-7}\ N/A^2)(2.5\ A)}{(2\pi)(3 \times 10^{-3}\ m)} = \underline{1.67 \times 10^{-4}\ T}$$

and for r = 0.1 cm,

$$I(r) = \frac{1}{4} I \quad \text{and} \quad B(0.1\ cm) = \underline{1.25 \times 10^{-4}\ T}$$

4. We have

$$M = \frac{\tau_{max}}{ALB} = \frac{0.54\ N\text{-}m}{(10^{-4}\ m^2)(0.12\ m)(0.22\ T)} = \underline{2.05 \times 10^5\ A/m}$$

for the magnetization, which is the surface current per unit length for a straight bar magnet. Thus the equivalent surface current is

$$I = (2.05 \times 10^5\ A/m)(0.12\ m) = \underline{2.45 \times 10^4\ A}$$

5. The field in the capacitor has magnitude

$$E = \frac{V}{d}$$

Thus

$$I_d = \frac{\varepsilon_0 A}{d} \frac{dV}{dt} = C \frac{dV}{dt} = \frac{dQ}{dt}$$

where Q is the charge on the capacitor plates. But this is the rate at which the capacitor is being charged. Thus

$$\underline{I_d = 1.2 \times 10^{-3} \ A}$$

CHAPTER 38
Faraday's Law

38.1 CHAPTER SUMMARY

If the magnetic flux through a circuit changes in time, an electromotive
force is induced in the circuit, given by Faraday's law:

$$\mathcal{E} = - \frac{d\Phi_m}{dt}$$

The EMF is distributed throughout the circuit; we may write it in terms
of the nonelectrostatic $\vec{E}$ field induced by the changing magnetic flux:

$$\oint_C \vec{E} \cdot d\vec{l} = - \frac{d\Phi_m}{dt}$$

Φ_m can change in various ways; if by physical motion of conductors in a
$\vec{B}$ field, we understand the induced EMF in terms of magnetic forces on
charges in the conductor. If a wire is moved transversely through a
uniform $\vec{B}$ field, the induced EMF $\mathcal{E} = vBl$ is the result of the $\vec{v} \times \vec{B}$
force on electrons in the wire. However, a changing flux arises also
when the magnetic field changes in the neighborhood of a circuit at rest.
Faraday's law gives the induced EMF in either case.

The induced EMF is always in such a sense as to oppose whatever
change induced it. This is Lenz's law; it is required by conservation
of energy. In the case of the moving wire, current flows (if the circuit
is closed) in the direction such that the magnetic force on it opposes
the wire's motion. Notice that, if the current in a circuit changes, an
EMF is induced in the circuit itself opposing the change; thus the
current in a circuit cannot be changed instantaneously.

Faraday's law applies to any closed path - not only to a real
physical circuit. Thus if the magnetic field in a bulk material is
changed, current loops called "eddy currents" are induced in the material.
In many situations this is undesirable because of I^2R power losses.

The betatron is an electron accelerator based on Faraday's law.
Electrons move in circular orbits in a magnetic field which changes in
time, producing an EMF around the orbit which accelerates the electrons.
A properly nonuniform B field is required to serve both functions at once.

The property of a circuit which expresses its Faraday's-law effect
on itself and other circuits near it is called inductance. If two
circuits are near each other, and no other sources of magnetic field are
around, the flux through one is

$$\Phi_{2m} = L_2 I_2 + M_{12} I_1$$

defining the self-inductance (L) and the mutual inductance (M). (Mutual
inductance is reciprocal: $M_{21} = M_{12}$.) If one or the other current changes,
Faraday's law gives

$$\mathcal{E}_2 = -L_2 \frac{dI_2}{dt} - M_{12} \frac{dI_1}{dt}$$

for the induced EMF in one of the circuits.

Calculation of L or M is simple in principle; for given circuits and given currents one simply calculates the field and integrates to find the flux. In practice this is usually complicated. An important simple case is a solenoid:

$$L = \mu_0 n^2 A \ell$$

where ℓ is the length and n the number of turns per unit length. Inductance is always, as here, a purely geometric property.

Inductance in a circuit, as already argued, prevents instantaneous change of the current. If an EMF $\mathcal{E}_0$ is applied to a circuit consisting of a resistor and an inductor in series, the current increases to its steady value $\mathcal{E}_0/R$ as an exponential with a time constant L/R. In this situation, some of the work done by the battery goes to setting up the magnetic field in the inductor; energy required to establish a current I is $\frac{1}{2}LI^2$. We can regard this energy as an attribute of the field itself, ascribing to a magnetic field B an energy density

$$\frac{U_m}{vol} = \frac{B^2}{2\mu_0}$$

If a circuit contains both inductance and capacitance, it tends to oscillate: charge, current, and energy slosh back and forth between L and C with an angular frequency $\omega = (LC)^{-\frac{1}{2}}$. If there is resistance in the circuit, the oscillations die out with time as energy is dissipated by I^2R heating.

38.2 CHECK LIST

henry

Faraday's law

EMF

nonelectrostatic electric field

Lenz's law

motional EMF

Hall effect

induced magnetic moment

back EMF

self-induction

eddy currents

betatron

inductance

mutual inductance

magnetic flux

solenoid

inductor

LR circuit

time constant

magnetic field energy

LC circuit

LRC circuit

simple harmonic motion

angular frequency

phase constant

damped harmonic oscillator

critical damping

38.3 TRUE OR FALSE?

_____1. If the magnetic flux through a circuit changes with time in any way, there is an EMF induced in the circuit.

_____2. The nonelectrostatic electric field induced by a changing magnetic flux is conservative.

_____3. The origin of the Faraday's-law EMF can in all cases be attributed to $\vec{v} \times \vec{B}$ forces on charge carriers in the circuit.

_____4. Lenz's law says that the direction of the induced EMF is always opposite to that of the magnetic field which induced it.

_____5. Lenz's law says that the direction of the induced EMF is always such as to oppose whatever change induced it.

_____6. An EMF induced in a direction opposite that given by Lenz's law would violate conservation of energy.

_____7. Two circuits are close to one another but not in electrical contact; a change in the current in one will induce an EMF in the other.

_____8. An isolated circuit carrying a steady current induces a back EMF in itself tending to oppose the current.

_____9. The currents caused by back EMF generated in a circuit by itself are called eddy currents.

_____10. Betatron operation requires a magnetic field which is stronger at the electron orbit than it is, on the average, inside the orbit.

_____11. The self-inductance of a circuit is a geometric property measuring the magnetic effect of the circuit on itself.

_____12. The mutual inductance of two circuits is determined entirely by the geometry of each circuit individually.

_____13. The self-inductance of a circuit is the proportionality constant between the flux and the magnetic field at the circuit.

_____14. For a given total number of turns, the self-inductance of a solenoid is directly proportional to its length.

_____15. The current in a circuit containing inductance cannot change instantaneously.

_____16. If an EMF is applied to a circuit containing both resistance and inductance, the current rises to its steady-state value in a time of the order LR.

_____17. The time constant of an LR circuit is the time which the current would take to rise to its steady-state value, at the initial rate of increase.

_____18. In a pure inductor with zero resistance, no energy is required to set a current flowing.

_____19. In a pure inductor with zero resistance, no energy is required to keep a constant current flowing.

_____20. The energy of the magnetic field set up by the current in a given circuit is directly proportional to the current.

_____21. Current in a circuit containing both inductance and capacitance tends to oscillate back and forth with an (angular) frequency given by $1/\sqrt{LC}$.

22. As the current oscillates in an LC circuit containing no resistance, the sum of the energy stored in the electric field of the capacitor, and that in the magnetic field in the inductor, remains constant.

23. If the circuit contains resistance as well as inductance and capacitance, the oscillations die out with time.

38.4   QUESTIONS

1. A given length of wire is wound into a solenoid. If it is rewound into another (a) of twice the length or (b) of twice the diameter, how does its inductance compare to the original value?

2. A thin sheet of metal, suspended as a pendulum, is allowed to swing into the region between the poles of a strong magnet. You observe that it slows down or, if the magnetic field is strong enough, even stops. What is happening?

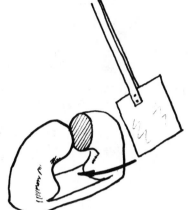

3. Electrons can be accelerated in a betatron only during one quarter of each cycle of the alternating current in the magnet coils. Explain why.

4. A cyclotron is a resonance accelerator, in the sense that - for a given magnetic field - it has a characteristic frequency at which the particles circulate. Is a betatron a resonance device, in the same sense?

5. A bar magnet is projected at some initial velocity down the inside of a long, horizontal, frictionless conducting pipe. Describe its subsequent motion.

6. An earth satellite travels at high speed through the earth's magnetic field. What do you think of the possibility of using induced EMF to power its instruments?

7. Imagine a small bar magnet moving around inside a toroidal - that is, doughnut-shaped - coil. Is there any net EMF induced in the coil? Would there be any EMF if it were an isolated magnetic pole moving in the toroid?

8. Two coils are connected in series. Does their equivalent total inductance depend on their geometrical relation to one another?

38.5   EXAMPLES

1. You use a small search coil (20 turns, 3 cm square, resistance 216 Ω) to measure the magnetic field between the poles of a magnet. If, while you withdraw it from the field at a speed of 1.5 m/sec, a current of 0.15 A flows in the coil, what was the strength of the magnetic field?

2. A conducting rod rolls without friction down two conducting rails which complete a circuit, as sketched. The resistance of the circuit is 0.32 Ω and there is a uniform magnetic field, directed vertically, of 0.86 T in the region of the circuit. If the rod is 25 cm long and of mass 40 gm, what terminal velocity does it reach?

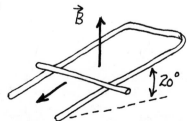

3. You have an 0.1-μF capacitor and 100 ft of very fine wire. How would you make a solenoid which, in circuit with the capacitor, would resonate at 10^4 Hz?

4. In the circuit sketched at right, at the instant at which half the power being supplied by the battery is being dissipated in the resistor, what is the current? How fast is it increasing?

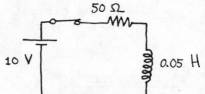

38.6 ANSWERS

True or False?

1. True - this is Faraday's law.

2. False - a conservative field does no net work around a closed path, so there would be no EMF.

3. False - this doesn't explain, for example, the case of a circuit at rest in a time-varying magnetic field.

4. False - see the next question.

5. True.

6. True.

7. True - the current in each sets up a magnetic field which contributes to the flux through the other.

8. False - if the current is steady, its magnetic flux through itself is not changing in time.

9. False - eddy currents are current loops induced in conductors moved through a magnetic field.

10. False - the field at the orbit must be half the average field inside.

11. True.

12. False - their position relative to one another also matters.

13. False - between the flux and the current in the circuit.

14. False - this would be true for a given number of turns per unit length.

15. True - and every circuit contains some inductance.

16. False - the time constant is L/R.

17. True.

18. False - there is energy "stored" in the magnetic field in the inductor, which must be supplied to set the current flowing.

19. True - a pure inductor would be a nondissipative element.

20. False - the energy is $\frac{1}{2}LI^2$ in an inductor.

21. True.

22. True - energy is traded back and forth between magnetic and electric fields but is not dissipated unless there is resistance.

23. True.

1. The inductance of a solenoid is given by

$$L = \mu_0 n^2 A \ell$$

where n is the number of turns per unit length. If the length is doubled, ℓ is doubled but $n^2 \ell$ is halved, so the inductance is reduced by half. If the diameter is doubled, A is quadrupled but n^2 goes down by a factor of 4, since each turn takes twice as much wire. Thus $n^2 A$ is unchanged and so is L.

2. As the sheet swings through the magnetic field, eddy currents are induced in it. By Lenz's law the eddy currents must be in a direction such that the net force on them retards the motion of the pendulum. Another way to say the same thing is that the kinetic energy of the swinging sheet is dissipated as $I^2 R$ losses by the eddy currents.

3. Because, for a given direction of the electron orbit, one direction of B is necessary, and for electron acceleration, the proper sign of dB/dt is necessary. If B varies sinusoidally with the time, this restricts operation to one quarter of the cycle.

4. Not really - the electrons in a betatron circulate in a fixed orbit, their frequency increasing as their speed increases. The only characteristic frequency of the device is that of the magnet current, which governs only the repetition rate of bursts of electrons from the machine.

5. As the magnet moves down the wire, it sets up currents flowing around the walls of the pipe, by electromagnetic induction. By Lenz's law, these currents are in a direction such as to retard its motion. Since, as the question was stated, there are no other forces on the magnet, it will eventually slow down and stop.

6. Since the field is both very weak and nearly constant around the satellite orbit, the induced EMF would be too small to do anything with. There would be a little variation in B going around a polar orbit, but the EMF's induced would still be in the microvolt range.

7. If the toroidal coil is uniformly wound, the little bar magnet - a dipole - will produce no signal. Whatever change in flux occurs due to the motion of one pole will be opposed by an equal change in flux due to the other. A single isolated pole, however, would cause a signal; in fact, this is one kind of experiment that can be done to search for magnetic monopoles.

8. Yes, because their equivalent total inductance includes their mutual inductance. That is, the flux in one due to the field of the other plainly depends, for instance, on how far apart they are.

Examples

Partial Solutions (1)

1. Assume, for simplicity, that the field due to the magnet drops sharply to zero at the edge of the pole. In the sketch, the distance that the leading edge of the coil has moved out of the field is x. What is the flux through the coil?

2. The flux through the circuit is

$$\Phi_B = \vec{B} \cdot \hat{n} \, A = BA \cos \theta$$

where A is the area of the circuit and θ is the angle it makes with the horizontal. Thus the EMF induced is

$$\mathcal{E} = \frac{d\Phi}{dt} = B(\cos\theta)\frac{dA}{dt}$$

(We can ignore signs because we know, from Lenz's law, which way the force acts and so need only the magnitude of the induced EMF.) What is dA/dt?

3. The inductance of a solenoid is

$$L = \mu_0 n^2 \ell A = \frac{\mu_0 N^2 A}{\ell}$$

if N is the total number of turns. Make the solenoid of circular cross section with radius r. Then

$$A = \pi r^2$$

What is N?

4. The power being supplied by the battery is $\mathcal{E}I$. How much is being dissipated in the resistor?

Partial Solutions (2)

1. If the side of the square search coil is a, the flux through it at the instant shown is

$$\Phi_B = nBa(a - x)$$

and the EMF induced is (ignoring signs)

$$\mathcal{E} = \frac{d\Phi}{dt} = nBa\frac{dx}{dt} = nBav$$

From this, relate B to the current that flows in the coil.

2. If the velocity at which the rod rolls down is v, then dA/dt = ℓv, where the length of the rod is ℓ. The current is

$$I = \frac{\mathcal{E}}{R} = \frac{B\ell v}{R}\cos\theta$$

and the power being dissipated in the resistance of the circuit is

$$P = I^2 R = (B\ell v)^2 R \cos^2\theta$$

Where is this energy coming from?

3. If the total length of wire available is s, the number of turns

$$N = \frac{s}{2\pi r}$$

and the inductance of the solenoid can be written

$$L = \frac{\mu_0 (s/2\pi r)^2 (\pi r^2)}{\ell} = \frac{\mu_0 s^2}{4\pi\ell}$$

What inductance is required to give a resonance frequency of 10^4 Hz?

4. The power going to Joule heating in the resistor is $I^2 R$. Thus

$$I^2 R = \frac{1}{2}\mathcal{E}I \qquad \text{or} \qquad I = \frac{\mathcal{E}}{2R}$$

Partial Solutions (3)

1. From the expression found for $\mathcal{E}$, the magnetic field is

$$B = \frac{\mathcal{E}}{nav} = \frac{IR}{nav}$$

$$= \frac{(0.15 \text{ A})(2.60 \text{ }\Omega)}{(20)(0.03 \text{ m})(1.5 \text{ m/sec})}$$

$$= \underline{0.433 \text{ T}}$$

2. If the rod rolls down at a constant terminal speed v, the energy being dissipated in the resistance must come from the decrease in the rod's gravitational potential energy. This is

$$\frac{d(mgh)}{dt} = mg \frac{dh}{dt} = mgv \sin \theta$$

since the incline is at an angle θ to the horizontal. Thus from conservation of energy

$$mgv \sin \theta = (B\ell v)^2 R \cos^2 \theta$$

or

$$v = \frac{mg \sin \theta}{B^2 \ell^2 R \cos^2 \theta}$$

$$= \frac{(0.04 \text{ kg})(9.80 \text{ m/sec}^2)(\sin 20^\circ)}{(0.86 \text{ T})^2 (0.25 \text{ m})^2 (0.32 \text{ }\Omega)(\cos^2 20^\circ)}$$

$$= \underline{10.3 \text{ m/sec}}$$

The rails would have to be rather long for the rod to reach terminal speed.

3. The resonance frequency is

$$f_0 = \frac{\omega_0}{2\pi} = \frac{1}{2\pi\sqrt{LC}}$$

so

$$L = \frac{1}{4\pi^2 f_0^2 C} = 2.53 \times 10^{-3} \text{ H}$$

for this case. The length of the solenoid has to be

$$\ell = \frac{\mu_0 s^2}{4\pi L} = \frac{(4\pi \times 10^{-7} \text{ N/A}^2)(30.5 \text{ m})^2}{(4\pi)(2.53 \times 10^{-3} \text{ H})} = \underline{3.67 \times 10^{-2} \text{ m}}$$

The diameter is not determined, except that to apply the formula for a solenoid the diameter must be small compared to the length of 3.67 cm; other than this, any coil of this length will resonate at the required frequency.

4. The current is

$$I = \frac{\mathcal{E}}{2R} = \frac{10 \text{ V}}{100 \text{ }\Omega} = \underline{0.10 \text{ A}}$$

Thus

$$\mathcal{E}_R = IR = (0.1 \text{ A})(50 \text{ }\Omega) = 5 \text{ V}$$

and so

$$\mathcal{E}_L = 10 \text{ V} - 5 \text{ V} = 5 \text{ V}$$

and

$$\frac{dI}{dt} = \frac{\mathcal{E}_L}{L} = \frac{5 \text{ V}}{0.05 \text{ H}} = \underline{100 \text{ A/sec}}$$

CHAPTER 39
Magnetism in Matter

39.1 CHAPTER SUMMARY

Electric fields in matter are affected by the induced polarization of the material. Similar, but more complicated, effects occur for magnetic fields. The permanent molecular magnetic moments tend to align so as to augment an applied magnetic field (paramagnetism); the <u>induced</u> magnetic moments oppose the inducing field (diamagnetism).

The magnetization $\vec{M}$ is defined as the magnetic moment per unit volume of a material. $\vec{M}$ results from the $\vec{B}$ field; but, in turn, the $\vec{B}$ field results from $\vec{M}$, as well as from real external conduction currents. We define

$$\vec{H} \equiv \frac{\vec{B}}{\mu_0} - \vec{M}$$

as a field arising from real conduction currents <u>only</u> (provided effects at the ends of magnetic materials are negligible); Ampère's law and the law of Biot and Savart apply to $\vec{H}$ using real macroscopic conduction currents only. Near the ends of a piece of magnetized material there are poles; these also contribute to $\vec{H}$:

$$\oint \vec{H} \cdot \hat{n} \ dA = q^*$$

From the resemblance to Gauss' law we infer that the $\vec{H}$ field due to a pole falls off as $1/r^2$.

Except in a ferromagnet, the magnetization is proportional to the applied field; we define the magnetic susceptibility χ_m of a material by $\vec{M} \equiv \chi_m \vec{H}$. It follows that

$$\vec{B} = \mu_0 (1 + \chi_m) \vec{H} \equiv \mu \vec{H}$$

where μ is the permeability. The permeability of a <u>ferromagnetic</u> material is not a simple quantity: it depends on the past state of magnetization as well as the applied field.

Permanent magnetic moments of atoms are of the order of the Bohr magneton, m_B. If all were aligned in a given material, the resulting magnetic field would be of the order of 1 T, which agrees with the saturation field of ferromagnetic materials. For most materials, the degree of alignment is much less, because the interaction energy $\vec{m} \cdot \vec{B}$ between a molecular magnetic moment and the magnetic field is much less than the thermal energy of a molecule. As a result, the susceptibility is inversely proportional to temperature for a paramagnetic material.

Whether or not a given material has a permanent molecular moment, an applied field induces a magnetic moment, due to the magnetic force on atomic electrons, which opposes the field. We may estimate the size of the effect from the Bohr model of the atom. It is very small. However, the effect is temperature-independent, so that at high enough temperature, everything is diamagnetic.

Certain materials are ferromagnetic. This means that there is a high degree of alignment of magnetic moments in the material, even in a fairly small applied field: the susceptibility is much larger than 1. There are <u>domains</u> in the material which are completely aligned; the applied field changes and aligns these domains. If such a material is magnetized, the magnetization does not disappear when the external field is removed; a reverse H must be applied to demagnetize it. (This effect is the origin of permanent magnets.) This "hysteresis" is illustrated at right. The area within the hysteresis curve measures the irreversible energy loss in going through one complete cycle of magnetization.

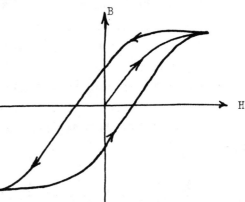

39.2 CHECK LIST

Bohr magneton, $m_B = 9.27 \times 10^{-24}$ A-m^2
Planck's constant, $h = 6.63 \times 10^{-34}$ J-sec
electric dipole
polar and nonpolar molecules
magnetic dipole moment
paramagnetism
diamagnetism
ferromagnetism
magnetization vector
magnetic susceptibility
permeability
Bohr theory of the atom
angular momentum
quantization of angular momentum
saturation magnetization
Curie's law

amperean current
magnetic-field intensity
toroid
Ampère's law
Biot-Savart law
macroscopic conduction current
pole strength
Curie temperature
atomic number
magnetic domain
hysteresis
magnetically hard and soft materials
remanent field
coercive force

39.3 TRUE OR FALSE?

_____ 1. Like that of the electric field, the behavior of the magnetic field in material media is affected by the presence of electric dipoles in matter.

_____ 2. In general, the presence of matter in a magnetic field tends to weaken the field.

_____ 3. The alignment of a magnetic dipole along an external magnetic field tends to increase the applied field.

_____ 4. Materials whose molecules have permanent magnetic dipole moments are called diamagnetic.

317

____5. Ferromagnetic materials are paramagnetic materials in which a high degree of alignment of molecular dipoles with an external magnetic field can be achieved.

____6. In a paramagnetic material the magnetization $\vec{M}$, in the absence of any external magnetic field, is zero.

____7. In a situation involving magnetic fields in material media, we define the magnetic intensity $\vec{H}$ as that part of the total field $\vec{B}$ which is due to the medium.

____8. The units of $\vec{H}$ are amperes per meter.

____9. In cases where Ampère's law or the law of Biot and Savart can be written in terms of $\vec{H}$, the current involved is the real macroscopic conduction current only.

____10. The $\vec{H}$ field due to a magnetic pole decreases with distance as $1/r^2$.

____11. For a given material, the proporionality constant between the magnetization $\vec{M}$ and the magnetic induction $\vec{B}$ is called the magnetic susceptibility.

____12. The susceptibility χ_m is negative for a diamagnetic material.

____13. The susceptibility of a ferromagnetic material is a constant usually large compared to 1.

____14. The magnetization of a ferromagnetic material depends not only on the applied field, but on what has happened to the material previously.

____15. The magnetic moment vector of an electron is parallel to its angular momentum.

____16. Atomic magnetic moments are on the order of 1 m_B.

____17. The saturation magnetization of ferromagnetic materials is of the order of magnitude of that which would result from complete alignment of molecular magnetic moments.

____18. The susceptibility of a paramagnetic material increases with the temperature.

____19. A strongly diamagnetic material is repelled by either pole of a magnet.

____20. At sufficiently high temperatures, all materials are diamagnetic.

____21. The molecular magnetic moment induced by a reasonably strong laboratory magnetic field is of the order of 1 m_B.

____22. A given ferromagnetic material has a critical temperature above which ferromagnetism disappears.

____23. An external magnetic field is applied to a bar of iron and then removed; the magnetization of the iron returns to zero.

____24. As the external field applied to a bar of iron is increased, the magnetization of the iron increases without limit.

____25. The area bounded by a hysteresis loop measures the energy required to magnetize the material to its saturation value.

39.4 QUESTIONS

1. Sketch the magnetic field of a current loop and the electric field of an electric dipole, and comment on the similarities and differences in the fields.

2. In estimating atomic magnetic moments, we neglected the contribution of the atomic nucleus, which is also a rotating charged object. Why?

3. The hysteresis curve of a sample of some magnetic material is shown at right. Identify on it the saturation magnetic field, the remanent field, and the coercive force.

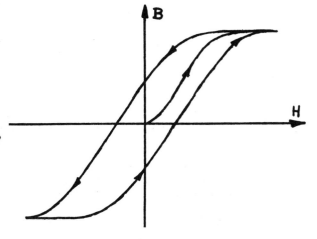

4. An unmagnetized iron bar is placed in a uniform magnetic field. Is there any force on it? Any torque? Explain why or why not.

5. The neutron, which has no charge, has a nonzero magnetic moment. Can you explain how this might be, or must it be a completely nonclassical effect?

6. Explain why it is that a magnet will pick up an unmagnetized iron nail but not an identical aluminum nail.

39.5 EXAMPLES

1. A 10-gm cube of aluminum (density 2.70 gm/cm^3) is in a nonuniform magnetic field, in a region where B is 18,000 G and the <u>gradient</u> (dB/dx) of the field is 1100 G/cm. If the force on the <u>sample is</u> found to be 2.4 x 10^{-4} N, calculate the susceptibility of aluminum.

2. A "Rowland ring" is a system for studying the magnetic properties of ferromagnetic materials. A toroidal coil is wound around a ring-shaped sample of the material, and a separate pickup coil surrounds it. In this case the inner and outer radii of the torus are 10 and 11 cm, and it is wound with 600 turns. The sample inside has a cross-section diameter of 0.8 cm, and the pickup coil has a resistance of 8 Ω and 50 turns. When a current of 1.4 A is turned on in the torus, a total charge of 3.3 x 10^{-4} C flows in the pickup coil. Find B and H in the sample.

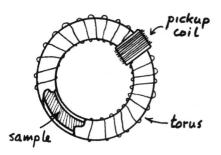

3. If the sample in the previous problem was a piece of iron, compare the magnetization of the sample to that expected for total alignment of the atomic magnetic moments. The atomic weight of iron is 55.85, its density 7.86 gm/cm^3. Take the intrinsic atomic moment to be 2.17 m$_B$.

4. The hysteresis curve at the top of the next page is that of 3.5 kg of iron which is being used as the core of a power transformer operated on the 60-Hz power line. What is the power loss in the transformer?

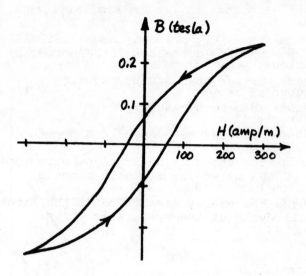

39.6 ANSWERS

True or False?

1. False - <u>magnetic</u> dipoles, intrinsic or induced, affect the magnetic
   field.

2. False - it may either augment or cancel the external field.

3. True.

4. False - diamagnetism is the result of induced magnetic moments.

5. True.

6. True - the magnetization is proportional to the applied field.

7. False - in many cases $\vec{H}$ measures that part of $\vec{B}$ due to real external
   conduction currents only.

8. True - one sometimes says ampere-turns per meter.

9. True - this is the point of introducing $\vec{H}$.

10. True - or would, if there were such a thing as an isolated magnetic
    pole.

11. False - χ is the proportionality constant between $\vec{H}$ and $\vec{M}$.

12. True.

13. False - it is generally large compared to 1, but is not a constant;
    it depends on the magnetization, both past and present.

14. True.

15. False - it is in the opposite direction, because the electron charge
    is negative.

16. True.

17. True.

18. False - it decreases with increasing temperature, as thermal agitation tends to destroy the alignment of the molecular magnetic moments.

19. True.

20. True - diamagnetism is weakly present in all materials, and the paramagnetic susceptibility decreases with increasing temperature.

21. False - it is much smaller than a Bohr magneton.

22. True - this is the Curie temperature.

23. False - this is more or less how you make a permanent magnet.

24. False - there is a saturation magnetization corresponding to near-total alignment of the molecular magnetic moments.

25. False - it measures the energy dissipated in the material in taking it around one full cycle of the hysteresis curve.

Questions

1. These should look something like what is sketched below. The fields far away are identical. The main difference is that the field "inside" - between the poles - is oppositely directed.

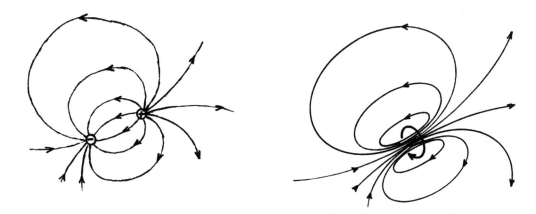

2. The magnetic moment of the nucleus, relative to a given spin angular momentum, is much smaller because of the much larger mass of the nucleus.

3. The saturation field is the limiting value at which B levels off. The remanent field is the magnitude of the $\vec{B}$ field left when $\vec{H}$ is returned to zero. The coercive force is the magnitude of $\vec{H}$ required to return $\vec{B}$ to zero. These are identified on the sketch as B_s, B_r, and H_c, respectively.

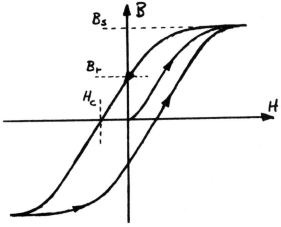

4. There is no force and no torque. The external field induces a magnetic moment in the bar, but there is no force on a dipole in a uniform field and the induced moment is along the field, so there is no torque ($\vec{m} \times \vec{B}$).

5. All that this means is that the neutron must have an internal structure involving both positive and negative charge, even though the total charge is zero.

6. Simply because the magnetic dipole moment induced in the iron nail is many orders of magnitude larger than that induced in the aluminum nail; the force of the nonuniform magnetic field of the magnet on the induced dipole moment is correspondingly very much stronger.

Examples

Partial Solutions (1)

1. There is no force on a dipole in a <u>uniform</u> magnetic field, but in a nonuniform field there is a force

$$F = m \frac{dB}{dx}$$

in the direction of the field gradient. If you think of the dipole as two magnetic poles, and remember that q*B is the force on an isolated pole, this should be clear. This gives you the magnetic moment induced in the sample; what is the magnetization?

2. The magnetic intensity inside a torus of N turns and mean radius r is

$$H = \frac{NI}{2\pi r}$$

Think of it as a solenoid of length $2\pi r$ bent into a circle. There are no end effects, since there are no ends; so H is unaffected by the sample in the torus. You get B from Faraday's law applied to the pickup coil. Note that Φ_B is almost entirely due to the magnetic induction in the <u>sample</u>. Why?

3. The magnetization produced in the sample you get from

$$M = \frac{B}{\mu_0} - H$$

which is the definition of the magnetic intensity. To predict the magnetization due to complete alignment, you need the number of iron atoms per unit volume.

4. The energy per unit volume required to take the core through one full cycle is the area bounded by the hysteresis loop, so you need to measure or estimate or cut it out and weigh it, or something.

Partial Solutions (2)

1. We are given the force and the field gradient; thus the induced dipole moment is

$$m = \frac{F}{dB/dx} = \frac{2.4 \times 10^{-4} \text{ N}}{11.0 \text{ T/m}} = 2.18 \times 10^{-5} \text{ J/T}$$

(Before the units get away from you, note that a joule/tesla is the same as an ampere-meter^2.) The susceptibility χ is defined by

$$\vec{M} \equiv \chi\vec{H}$$

and the magnetization $\vec{M}$ is the magnetic moment per unit volume. What is the volume of the sample?

2. The flux through the pickup coil is almost entirely due to the sample, just because $\vec{B}$ in the sample is very large. The current that flows in the pickup coil, by Faraday's law, is

$$I = \frac{\mathcal{E}}{R} = \frac{1}{R}\frac{d}{dt}(nB_sA_s)$$

where A_s is the area of the core sample and n is the number of turns in the pickup coil. What total charge flows in the coil?

3. The number of atoms per unit volume is

$$\frac{(7.86 \text{ gm/cm}^3)(6.02 \times 10^{23} \text{ mole}^{-1})}{(55.86 \text{ gm/mole})} = 8.47 \times 10^{22} \text{cm}^{-3} = 8.47 \times 10^{28} \text{ m}^{-3}$$

This times the intrinsic magnetic moment of an atom should give the saturation magnetization. What was the magnetization M actually produced in the sample?

4. My estimate of the area bounded by the loop is

$$36 \, (\text{T}) \, (\text{A/m}) = 36 \text{ J/m}^3$$

What is the volume of the core? If this much energy is dissipated per cycle, what is the power loss?

Partial Solutions (3)

1. The volume is

$$\frac{10 \text{ gm}}{2.7 \text{ gm/cm}^3} = 3.70 \text{ cm}^3 = 3.70 \times 10^{-6} \text{ m}^3$$

So the magnetization is

$$M = \frac{m}{v} = \frac{2.18 \times 10^{-5} \text{ A-m}^2}{3.70 \times 10^{-6} \text{ m}} = 5.87 \text{ A/m}$$

and the magnetic intensity is

$$H = \frac{B}{\mu_0} = \frac{1.8 \text{ T}}{4\pi \times 10^{-7} \text{ N/A}^2} = 1.43 \times 10^6 \text{ A/m}$$

so the magnetic susceptibility is

$$\chi = \frac{M}{H} = \frac{5.87 \text{ A/m}}{1.43 \times 10^6 \text{ A/m}} = \underline{4.10 \times 10^{-6}}$$

2. The charge that flows in the coil is

$$Q = \int I \, dt = \frac{nBA}{R}$$

so

$$B = \frac{QR}{nA} = \frac{(3.3 \times 10^{-4} \text{ C})(8 \, \Omega)}{(50)(\pi)(4 \times 10^{-3} \text{ cm})^2} = \underline{1.05 \text{ T}}$$

and we had already

$$H = \frac{NI}{2\pi r} = \frac{(600)(1.4 \text{ A})}{(2)(\pi)(10.5 \times 10^{-2} \text{ m})} = \underline{1270 \text{ A/m}}$$

3. We thus expect

$$M_{\text{sat}} = (8.47 \times 10^{28} \text{ m}^{-3})(2.17)(m_B = 9.27 \times 10^{-24} \text{ A-m}^2)$$

$$= \underline{1.70 \times 10^6 \text{ A/m}}$$

whereas the magnetization actually produced was

$$M = \frac{B}{\mu_0} - H$$

$$= \frac{1.05 \text{ T}}{4\pi \times 10^{-7} \text{ N/A}^2} - 1270 \text{ A/m}$$

$$= \underline{8.34 \times 10^5 \text{ A/m}}$$

or about half the saturation value.

4. The volume is

$$\frac{3500 \text{ gm}}{7.9 \text{ gm/cm}^3} = 443 \text{ cm}^3$$

So the power loss is

$$(36 \text{ J/m}^3)(4.43 \times 10^{-4} \text{ m}^3)(60 \text{ Hz}) = \underline{0.96 \text{ W}}$$

CHAPTER 40
Alternating-Current Circuits

40.1 CHAPTER SUMMARY

We have seen already a little of the behavior of resistance, capacitance,
and inductance in electric circuits; we now consider their properties
in circuits driven by an ac voltage. Fundamentally, an **ac** generator is
a coil rotated in a magnetic field. If a coil of N turns and area A is
rotated at angular velocity ω, Faraday's law gives the induced EMF:

$$\mathcal{E}(t) = \omega BNA \sin \omega t = \mathcal{E}_m \sin \omega t$$

If a current flows, mechanical work must be done to turn it against the
magnetic force; the generator converts mechanical into electrical energy.

A sinusoidal voltage applied to any one of the three circuit elements
produces a sinusoidal response. From Kirchhoff's voltage rule,

$$\text{Resistor} \qquad I(t) = \left(\frac{\mathcal{E}_m}{R}\right) \sin \omega t$$

$$\text{Capacitor} \qquad I(t) = \left(\frac{\mathcal{E}_m}{X_C}\right) \cos \omega t \qquad \text{with } X_C = \frac{1}{\omega C}$$

$$\text{Inductor} \qquad I(t) = -\left(\frac{\mathcal{E}_m}{X_L}\right) \cos \omega t \qquad \text{with } X_L = \omega L$$

The first amounts to Ohm's law. The other two expressions have similar
form, but note the reactances X_C and X_L are frequency-dependent, and the
current, although with the same frequency as the driving voltage, is
90^0 out of phase with it.

Now if the same voltage is applied to a circuit with R, C, and L in
series, the current has the same frequency:

$$I(t) = \frac{\mathcal{E}_m}{Z} \sin (\omega t + \phi)$$

where

$$Z = \sqrt{(X_C - X_L)^2 + R^2} \qquad \text{and} \qquad \tan \phi = \frac{X_C - X_L}{R}$$

Z is called the impedance of the combination. Plainly it has a minimum,
and the current in the circuit a maximum, when $X_C = X_L$; this occurs at a
frequency

$$\omega_0 = \frac{1}{\sqrt{LC}}$$

This "natural frequency" is that at which the circuit tends to oscillate
in the absence of the ac driving voltage. The relation of impedance and
phase to the individual reactances and resistance in the circuit can be
illustrated by means of a phasor diagram, the voltage across each element
being represented by a vector with the proper phase difference from the
current.

The resonance at the natural frequency is narrower and stronger as
the resistance in the circuit decreases; the "quality factor" $Q = \omega_0 L/R$

is an index of the sharpness of resonance. This resonance phenomenon has applications in circuits, as in a radio receiver, where a single frequency is to be selected from a complex signal.

The power delivered to the circuit by the generator, averaged over a full cycle, is

$$P = \frac{1}{2} \left(\frac{\mathcal{E}_m^2}{Z} \right) \cos \phi$$

This is maximum at the resonance frequency, when the driving voltage and the current in the circuit are in phase.

A pair of circuits inductively coupled so as to change the level of an ac signal is called a transformer. An ideal transformer is one in which there are no power losses - from eddy currents, hysteresis, or whatever - and in which all the flux produced by one circuit also links the other. In an ideal transformer, the amplitude of the voltage and current in the secondary coil are N_2/N_1 and N_1/N_2 times, respectively, those in the primary coil. (N_1 and N_2 are the number of turns in primary and secondary coils.)

40.2   CHECK LIST

alternating current
generator
Fourier analysis
Faraday's law
capacitative reactance
inductive reactance
transient current
steady-state current
resonance

natural frequency
impedance
phasor diagram
quality factor
power factor
RMS voltage and current
transformer
primary and secondary coils
impedance transformation

40.3   TRUE OR FALSE?

_____1. Practical ac generators ordinarily supply an EMF that varies sinusoidally with time.

_____2. A sinusoidal EMF applied to a resistor, capacitor, or inductor produces a sinusoidal current.

_____3. If a coil rotating in a magnetic field is used as an ac generator, the maximum value of the EMF produced is independent of the frequency.

_____4. The ac current in a pure resistance is 90° out of phase with the EMF applied to it.

_____5. The ac current in a pure capacitance lags behind the applied EMF by 90°.

_____6. For a given peak value of the applied EMF, the ac current in a pure capacitance is proportional to the capacitance.

_____7. The ac current in a pure inductance lags 90° behind the applied EMF.

_____8. For a given peak value of the applied EMF, the ac current in a pure capacitance is proportional to the inductance.

_____9. The steady-state ac current in a circuit containing inductance, capacitance, and resistance has a frequency intermediate between that of the applied EMF and the natural oscillation frequency of the circuit.

_____10. The impedance of a series LRC circuit is maximum at the resonance frequency.

_____11. In a phasor diagram, the angles between vectors representing different quantities are equal to their differences of phase.

_____12. The Q value $\omega_0 L/R$ of a series resonant circuit is independent of the capacitance in the circuit.

_____13. The average power dissipated in a pure inductance is zero.

_____14. Transformers must be designed to minimize the mutual inductance between primary and secondary coils.

_____15. A transformer whose primary has 10 times as many turns as its secondary coil provides an output current about 10 times larger than the input current.

40.4 QUESTIONS

1. Inductive and capacitative reactances in series subtract rather than add. Why?

2. Electric power for domestic use is transmitted at high voltage, then stepped down near the point of consumption. Why?

3. The reactance of a capacitor decreases with increased frequency, while that of an inductor increases. Why?

4. At a certain instant, the current in a series LRC circuit is zero. In general, the power being supplied by the generator is not zero at this instant, even though no energy is being dissipated in the resistor. Where is the energy going?

5. A capacitance is to be used directly across the ac power line $(V_{eff} = 117 \text{ V})$. What maximum voltage must the capacitor be able to withstand?

6. In a circuit consisting of a resistor and a capacitor in series, an ac ammeter reads a certain current. An inductor is added to the circuit, in series with the other two elements, and the ammeter reading is unchanged. Explain why.

40.5 EXAMPLES

1. In the circuit sketched at right, find the voltage across the inductor as a function of the generator frequency. What is $\mathcal{E}_L$ at f = 50 Hz? At f = 5000 Hz? An LR circuit is frequently used in electronic circuitry as a <u>filter</u>. Why?

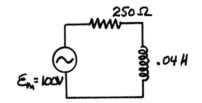

2. In the circuit sketched at the right, let L = 0.01 H, R = 260 Ω,
    C = 0.1 μF, and $\mathcal{E}_m$ = 150 V. At a frequency
    of 1000 Hz, what power is being supplied
    by the generator? What power is being
    dissipated in the resistor? Should these
    be equal?

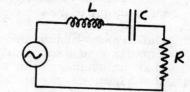

3. In the circuit sketched at the right,
    with arbitrary values of R, L, and C,
    show that the current has <u>half</u> its
    maximum value at frequencies (angular)
    given by

$$\omega = \omega_0 \; \frac{\pm\sqrt{3}\,\omega_0}{2Q}$$

    provided only that Q is large compared to 1. Thus the Q of a circuit
    is a measure of the "sharpness" of its resonance peak.

4. In the circuit sketched at the right, let
    R_g = 5000 Ω and R = 2.5 Ω. What must be
    the turns ratio of the transformer in
    order to deliver the maximum possible
    power to the "load" R?

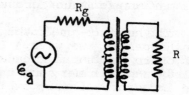

40.6   ANSWERS

True or False?

1. True.

2. True - although not necessarily in phase with the applied voltage.

3. False - $\mathcal{E}_m = \omega NBA$; it's proportional to the frequency.

4. False - it's in phase; this is just Ohm's law.

5. False - it <u>leads</u> the applied EMF by 90°.

6. True - $I_m = \omega C \mathcal{E}_m$.

7. True.

8. False - inversely proportional: $I_m = \mathcal{E}_m/\omega L$.

9. False - in the steady state, it has the frequency of the applied EMF.

10. False - it's minimum, because at resonance X_C and X_L cancel.

11. True.

12. False - ω_0 depends on C.

13. True.

14. False - mutual inductance between the coils is the whole point of a
    transformer.

15. True - this is a "step-down" transformer.

Questions

1. In series connection, the current through the two elements must be
    the same, while the voltage drops "add." But the voltage across a
    capacitor lags the current through it, while that across a capacitor
    leads the current, by 90°. Thus the voltage across inductor and

328

capacitor are 180° out of phase with each other - they tend to cancel.

2. It saves on wire. The smaller the current, the higher the resistance of the transmission line can be and yet keep the power loss (I^2R) to an acceptable value.

3. As the frequency increases, less charge has to be moved on and off the capacitor plates, so the voltage required to cause a _given_ amount of current - and so the reactance - decreases. But for a given amount of current in an inductor, at higher frequency a given magnetic field in the inductor has to be set up and taken down more rapidly, so the voltage required, and the reactance, increase.

4. The power supplied by the generator has to equal that dissipated in the resistor, on the average - but not instantaneously. At this instant the energy supplied would be going into charging up the capacitor or setting up the magnetic field in the inductor - or both.

5. The maximum voltage across the line at any instant is $\sqrt{2}\ V_{eff} = 165$ V.

6. It must be that the total impedance of the circuit is unchanged; that can happen in two ways. If the inductance is very small, its contribution to the total impedance may just be unobservable; or, if its value is precisely such that $X_L = 2X_C$, then $(X_C - X_L)^2$, and therefore the impedance of the combination, is unchanged.

Examples

Partial Solutions (1)

1. It is instructive to work this through for yourself, but of course you can get the impedance of the circuit just by setting $X_C = 0$ in the formula (in your text, or below) for a series LRC circuit.

2. The generator and resistor power should be equal, since no energy is dissipated (on the average) in a pure inductor or capacitor. The first thing you need to find, of course, is just the total impedance of the combination at the given frequency.

3. The impedance of an LRC circuit is given by

$$Z = \sqrt{(X_C - X_L)^2 + R^2}$$

At the frequencies at which I_m has half its maximum value, what must be the value of the impedance?

4. If the primary/secondary turns ratio is n, then

$$\mathcal{E}_{m2} = n\ \mathcal{E}_{m1}$$

where $\mathcal{E}_{m1}$ and $\mathcal{E}_{m2}$ are the peak EMF values in primary and secondary loops, respectively. What is the current ratio? Using this, just set up the two (Kirchhoff) loop equations and find an expression for the power in R.

Partial Solutions (2)

1. To set this up, let the generator voltage and the current in the circuit be

$$\mathcal{E}_g = \mathcal{E}_m \sin \omega t \qquad \text{and} \qquad I = I_m \sin (\omega t + \phi)$$

And Kirchhoff's loop equation for this circuit is

$$\mathcal{E}_g = \mathcal{E}_R + \mathcal{E}_L = IR + L\frac{dI}{dt}$$

So

$$\mathcal{E}_m \sin \omega t = \omega L I_m \cos(\omega t + \phi) + R I_m \sin(\omega t + \phi)$$

which you would solve by expanding the trigonometric functions on the right, in terms of the sine and cosine of a sum, and solving for I_m and ϕ.

If we just put $X_C = 0$ in the LRC circuit formula, we get

$$Z = \sqrt{\omega^2 L^2 + R^2}$$

2. The impedance is

$$Z = \sqrt{(X_C - X_L)^2 + R^2}$$

and the phase

$$\phi = \tan^{-1}\left[\frac{X_C - X_L}{R}\right]$$

Here

$$\omega = (2)(1000\ \text{Hz}) = 6280\ \text{sec}^{-1}$$

$$X_L = (6280\ \text{sec}^{-1})(0.01\ \text{H}) = 62.8\ \Omega$$

and

$$X_C = \frac{1}{(6280\ \text{sec}^{-1})(10^{-7}\ \text{F})} = 1590\ \Omega$$

Find the impedance and the phase of the current.

3. The impedance of the circuit at resonance is $Z = R$. At angular frequency ω, if the current has half its maximum value,

$$Z(\omega) = 2R$$

or

$$Z^2 = \left(\frac{1}{\omega C} - \omega L\right)^2 + R^2 = 4R^2$$

you have just to solve this for ω.

4. The currents in primary and secondary coils are related by

$$I_{m1} = n I_{m2}$$

if the no-load magnetization current in the primary loop is negligible. In this case, also, I_1 is in phase with the applied EMF. Thus

$$\mathcal{E}_g - I_1 R_g = \mathcal{E}_g - n I_2 R_g = \mathcal{E}_1 = (1/n)\mathcal{E}_2$$

and

$$\mathcal{E}_2 = I_2 R$$

so

$$n\mathcal{E}_g = I_2(R + n^2 R_g)$$

and the power delivered to the load is just $\frac{1}{2} I_{m2}^2 R$.

Partial Solutions (3)

1. The peak value of the voltage across the inductor is

$$\mathcal{E}_{Lm} = \omega L I_m = \frac{\omega L \mathcal{E}_m}{Z} = \frac{\mathcal{E}_m}{\sqrt{1 + (R/\omega L)^2}}$$

Here, with $L = 0.04$ H, $R = 250\ \Omega$, and $\mathcal{E}_m = 100$ V, this is

$$\mathcal{E}_{Lm} = \frac{100\ \text{V}}{\sqrt{1 + (f_0/f)^2}}$$

with $f_0 = 995$ Hz. This gives

$$\underline{\mathcal{E}_{Lm}(50\ \text{Hz}) = 5.02\ \text{V}} \qquad \underline{\mathcal{E}_{Lm}(5000\ \text{Hz}) = 98.1\ \text{V}}$$

For high frequencies, essentially all the generator voltage appears at the inductor; for low frequencies, only a small fraction of it. If a complex signal is applied to an RL circuit, it "filters" out the low frequencies and passes the high-frequency signal to the inductor.

2. With the given values we get

$$Z = \sqrt{(1527 \ \Omega)^2 + (260 \ \Omega)^2} = 1551 \ \Omega$$

$$\phi = \tan^{-1} \frac{1527}{260} = 80°.4$$

So the power being supplied by the generator is

$$P = \frac{\mathcal{E}_m^2}{2Z} \cos \phi = (7.36 \ \text{W}) \cos 80°.4 = \underline{1.23 \ \text{W}}$$

But the power being dissipated in the resistor is

$$\frac{I_m^2 R}{2} = \frac{\mathcal{E}_m^2 R}{2Z^2} = \frac{(150 \ \text{V})^2 (260 \ \Omega)}{(2)(1551 \ \Omega)^2} = \underline{1.23 \ \text{W}}$$

and the two are indeed equal.

3. We have

$$\frac{1}{\omega C} - \omega L = \pm\sqrt{3} \ R$$

which, using $\omega_0 = 1/LC$ and $Q = \omega_0 L/R$, can be written

$$\omega^2 \pm \frac{\sqrt{3}\omega_0\omega}{Q} - \omega_0^2 = 0$$

Solve this with the binomial theorem (ignoring negative roots) to get

$$\omega = \frac{+\sqrt{3}}{-2Q} \omega_0 + \omega_0 \sqrt{1 + \frac{3}{2Q^2}}$$

Since we assumed Q is large, the square root is approximately = 1 and we have

$$\underline{\omega \simeq \omega_0 \pm \frac{\sqrt{3}}{2Q} \omega_0}$$

as advertised.

4. The power delivered to the load resistor is

$$P = \frac{I^2 R}{2} = \frac{n^2 \mathcal{E}_g^2 R}{2(R + n^2 R_g)^2}$$

Setting dP/dn = 0 gives n for maximum power to the load. This gives just

$$R - n^2 R_g = 0$$

or

$$n^2 = \frac{R}{R_g} = \frac{2.5 \ \Omega}{5000 \ \Omega} = 0.0005$$

or

$$\underline{n = 0.0224}$$

CHAPTER 41
Maxwell's Equation and Electromagnetic Waves

41.1 CHAPTER SUMMARY

Our experimental knowledge of electricity and magnetism can be summarized in four equations relating the E and B fields to their sources and to each other:

$$\oint_s \vec{E} \cdot \hat{n} \; dA = \frac{q}{\varepsilon_0}$$

$$\oint_s \vec{B} \cdot \hat{n} \; dA = 0$$

$$\oint_c \vec{E} \cdot d\vec{l} = -\frac{d}{dt} \int_s \vec{B} \cdot \hat{n} \; dA$$

$$\oint_c \vec{B} \cdot d\vec{l} = \mu_0 I + \varepsilon_0 \mu_0 \frac{d}{dt} \int_s \vec{E} \cdot \hat{n} \; dA$$

The first is Gauss' law; the second, the analogous expression for the magnetic field; the third, Faraday's law; and the fourth is Ampère's law including the displacement-current generalization term. Collectively the four are known as Maxwell's equations. The source terms include bound charge in dielectrics and magnetization currents in magnetized materials, as well as free charge and conduction currents. This difficulty can be evaded by writing the fourth equation in terms of the $\vec{H}$ field, which depends only on the real conduction current; an analogous restatement can be made of the first one.

We now observe that these equations have solutions in the form of the $\vec{E}$ and $\vec{B}$ fields propagating as waves. We look at a situation in free space, in which $\vec{E}$ and $\vec{B}$ are assumed to depend only on x and t. Then we find that either of the transverse components E_y and B_z obey the equation

$$\frac{\partial^2 E}{\partial x^2}y = \mu_0 \varepsilon_0 \frac{\partial^2 E}{\partial t^2}y$$

We have already encountered this partial differential equation in Chapter 21; its solutions are waves propagating in the x direction with speed

$$v = c = \frac{1}{\sqrt{\mu_0 \varepsilon_0}}$$

The $\vec{E}$ and $\vec{B}$ fields in this situation are perpendicular to one another and to the direction of propagation; $\vec{E}$ and $\vec{B}$ propagate as two coupled transverse waves. Their amplitudes are related by $E_{ym} = B_{zm}c$.

The predicted speed of these electromagnetic waves is known, since μ_0 and ε_0 are known constants from the electric and magnetic force laws. They are found to have the speed of light in free space, and light is presently understood as an electromagnetic wave.

We define the Poynting vector as the quantity

$$\vec{S} \equiv \vec{E} \times \vec{H}$$

It is plainly in the direction of propagation of the electromagnetic wave, and the magnitude of the Poynting vector gives the wave intensity - the energy flow across unit area per unit time.

41.2 CHECK LIST

$c = 3.00 \times 10^8$ m/sec

Maxwell's equations

Gauss' law

Gauss' law for magnetism

Faraday's law

displacement current

bound charge

magnetization current

displacement vector

polarization of a dielectric

wave equation

plane waves

electromagnetic wave

transverse waves

partial derivative

polarization of a wave

Poynting vector

intensity of a wave

41.3 TRUE OR FALSE?

_____1. The lines of $\vec{B}$ are always closed curves, without beginning or end.

_____2. The charges and currents that appear as "source" terms in Maxwell's equations include free charge and macroscopic conduction currents only.

_____3. For mechanical waves in material media - such as sound waves - the velocity of wave propagation is characteristic of the medium.

_____4. For electromagnetic waves, such as light, the wave velocity is independent of the medium.

_____5. In electromagnetic waves in free space, the oscillations of $\vec{B}$ are $\pi/2$ out of phase with those of $\vec{E}$.

_____6. In electromagnetic waves in free space, the magnetic field $\vec{B}$ is at right angles to $\vec{E}$.

_____7. In electromagnetic waves in free space, both the $\vec{E}$ and $\vec{B}$ fields are at right angles to the direction of wave propagation.

_____8. The intensity of electromagnetic waves is given by $\vec{E} \cdot \vec{H}$.

_____9. The total energy density in an electromagnetic wave is equally divided between that of the electric and that of the magnetic field.

_____10. The Poynting vector is in the direction of wave propagation.

41.4 QUESTIONS

1. Which of the following are or are not included among Maxwell's equations: the law of Biot and Savart, Ampère's law, Coulomb's law, Lenz's law, Faraday's law, and Gauss' law?

2. Write out the Maxwell equations in terms of the $\vec{E}$ and $\vec{H}$ fields, in empty space.

3. What role does Maxwell's "displacement current" play in the theory of electromagnetic waves?

4. Many radio receivers use a wire loop as an antenna. How should it be oriented, relative to the direction of the tramsmitting station?

41.5   EXAMPLES

1. A circular parallel-plate capacitor is, at some instant, being charged at a rate of 5.0×10^{-4} A. At this instant, find an expression for $\vec{B}$ as a function of position, in the region between the plates.

2. A long, straight wire, whose diameter is 0.04 cm, has resistance of $1.62 \ \Omega/m$ and carries a current of 0.09 A. Calculate the Poynting vector at the surface of the wire, and from it the energy flow into unit length of the wire. How does this compare to the power being dissipated in the length of wire?

3. An isotropic light source emits light energy at a rate of 100 W. At a point 20 m from the source, find the magnitudes of the $\vec{E}$ and $\vec{B}$ fields.

41.6   ANSWERS

True or False?

1. True - they would begin or end on isolated magnetic poles, which apparently do not exist.

2. False - magnetization currents, displacement currents, and bound charges on dielectrics also act as sources.

3. True.

4. False - electromagnetic waves do not need a material medium to propagate, but in matter their velocity depends on the medium.

5. False - they are in phase.

6. True.

7. True.

8. False - by the Poynting vector $S \equiv \vec{E} \times \vec{H}$.

9. True.

10. True.

Questions

1. The first, third, and fourth of Maxwell's equations are, directly, Gauss', Faraday's, and Ampère's law (the latter including the displacement-current correction). Lenz's law is the minus sign in the third equation, but of itself is not one of Maxwell's equations. Coulomb's law and the law of Biot and Savart are the basic rules for calculating the $\vec{E}$ and $\vec{B}$ fields, respectively. They do not appear as such, although Coulomb's and Gauss' laws are equivalent.

2. They take the apparently much more symmetric form

$$\oint_s \vec{E} \cdot \hat{n} \ dA = 0 \qquad\qquad \oint_s \vec{H} \cdot \hat{n} \ dA = 0$$

$$\oint_c \vec{E} \cdot d\vec{l} = -\mu_0 \frac{d}{dt} \int_s \vec{H} \cdot \hat{n} \ dA \qquad \oint_c \vec{H} \cdot d\vec{l} = \varepsilon_0 \frac{d}{dt} \int_s \vec{E} \cdot \hat{n} \ dA$$

in the absence of sources.

3. A crucial one. In empty space (see the answer to the last question) the displacement current is the only source of the magnetic field. Without it, there could be no propagation of electric and magnetic fields as waves.

4. A loop antenna works by Faraday's law – the changing $\vec{B}$ field inducing an EMF and thereby a current in the loop. Thus it must be oriented so that there is a magnetic flux through the loop – preferably so that $\vec{B}$ is normal to the plane of the loop. This means that for best reception the direction from receiver to transmitter should be in the plane of the antenna.

Examples

Partial Solutions (1)

1. In the region between the plates, there is no conduction current; the source of the magnetic field is thus the time-changing electric field in the capacitor. You are given the rate at which the capacitor is being charged. What is the rate of change of the flux of the electric field?

2. The magnetic field due to a long, straight wire carrying current I is

$$B = \frac{\mu_0 I}{2\pi r}$$

in what direction? What is the electric field at the surface of the wire?

3. You are given that the light source is isotropic – that is, that it radiates uniformly in all directions. What is the intensity – the power across unit area – at a distance of 20 m? This is what is given by the magnitude of the Poynting vector.

Partial Solutions (2)

1. Since $Q = CV$, the charging current

$$I = \frac{dQ}{dt} = C \frac{dV}{dt}$$

If edge effects may be neglected – which you must assume – the field between the plates is uniform, and the potential difference $V = Ed$. The capacitance of parallel plates is

$$C = \frac{\varepsilon_0 A}{d} = \frac{\pi R^2 \varepsilon_0}{d}$$

So, finally,

$$\frac{dE}{dt} = \frac{I}{\pi \varepsilon_0 R^2}$$

Apply Ampère's law to get $\vec{B}$. What <u>symmetry</u> is there to this situation?

2. The electric field is along the wire; it is what "drives" the conduction current. Since the current is uniform along the wire, we may

assume the field is also. The field is

$$B = \frac{\mu_0 I}{2\pi r} = (2 \times 10^{-7} \text{ N/A}^2)\frac{(9 \times 10^{-2} \text{ A})}{(2 \times 10^{-4} \text{ m})}$$

$$= 9 \times 10^{-5} \text{ T}$$

Calculate the Poynting vector.

3. By symmetry the intensity 20 m away must be

$$|\vec{S}| = \frac{P}{4\pi R^2} = \frac{100 \text{ W}}{(4\pi)(20 \text{ m})^2} = 0.0199 \text{ W/m}$$

But since $\vec{E}$ and $\vec{B}$ are perpendicular, in an electromagnetic wave,

$$|\vec{S}| = |\vec{E} \times \vec{H}| = EH = \frac{EB}{\mu_0}$$

Be careful about one thing - what you've calculated is an <u>average</u> power. What difference does that make?

Partial Solutions (3)

1. The whole situation is symmetric about the axis of the circular capacitor plates. Thus apply Ampère's law around the path sketched:

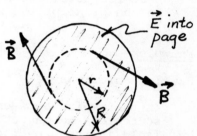

$$\oint_c \vec{B} \cdot d\vec{l} = \mu_0 \varepsilon_0 \frac{d}{dt}\int_s \vec{E} \cdot \hat{n} \, dA$$

or

$$2\pi r B = \mu_0 \varepsilon_0 (\pi r^2) \frac{dE}{dt} = \mu_0 \varepsilon_0 (\pi r^2)\frac{I}{\pi \varepsilon_0 R^2}$$

since B, by symmetry, is uniform around the curve and E is the same everywhere within the plates. Thus

$$B = \frac{\mu_0 I r}{2\pi R^2} = (2 \times 10^{-7} \text{ N/A}^2)\frac{(2.0 \times 10^{-4} \text{ A})}{(1.2 \times 10^{-1} \text{ m})}\frac{r}{R}$$

$$= \underline{(3.33 \times 10^{-10} \text{ T}) \frac{r}{R}}$$

2. The directions of $\vec{E}$, $\vec{H}$, and $\vec{S}$ are shown on the the sketch. We have

$$H = \frac{B}{\mu_0} = 71.6 \text{ A/m}$$

and

$$S = EH = (0.146)(71.6) = 10.5 \text{ W/m}^2$$

The surface area of a 1-m length of the wire is 1.26×10^{-3} m, so according to the Poynting-vector approach the energy entering unit length of the wire is

$$(10.5 \text{ W/m}^2)(1.26 \times 10^{-3} \text{ m}^2)$$

$$= \underline{0.0131 \text{ W}}$$

But the power being dissipated in 1 m of the wire is

$$P = I^2 R = (0.09 \text{ A})^2 (1.62 \text{ }\Omega/\text{m})(1 \text{ m})$$

$$= \underline{0.0131 \text{ W}}$$

3. The average value of the intensity is one-half the peak value, since it oscillates from zero to a maximum value. If the maximum value of the fields are E_0 and B_0, what we have calculated is

$$S_{av} = \frac{E_0 B_0}{2\mu_0}$$

But in an electromagnetic wave $B_0 = E_0/c$. Hence

$$S_{av} = \frac{E_0^2}{2\mu_0 c}$$

or

$$E_0 = (2\mu_0 cS)^{\frac{1}{2}} = \left[(2)(4\pi \times 10^{-7} \text{ N/A}^2)(3.0 \times 10^8 \text{ m/sec})(0.0199 \text{ W/m}^2) \right]^{\frac{1}{2}}$$

$$= \underline{3.87 \text{ V/m}}$$

and

$$B_0 = \frac{E_0}{c} = \underline{1.29 \times 10^{-8} \text{ T}}$$

CHAPTER 42
Quantization

42.1 CHAPTER SUMMARY

Maxwell's synthesis of electromagnetism and optics was a triumph of classical physics. At the same time, discrepancies in the understanding of closely related phenomena - the interaction of electromagnetic radiation with matter - led to the fundamentally different quantum theory.

Planck introduced the concept of energy quantization in his treatment of the spectral distribution of radiation from a hot object, assuming that oscillators in the walls of the object could have only certain discrete energy values. Einstein extended this in his theory of the photoelectric effect. By assuming that light could be absorbed only in fixed amounts ("photons") of energy

$$E = hf$$

he was able to explain properties of the effect which were beyond classical electrodynamics.

The light emitted from a gas discharge contains discrete wavelengths; in many cases, such as the Balmer series of lines in the spectrum of hydrogen, these display simple regular patterns. Bohr developed the first model of atomic structure capable of explaining this. He assumed the electron orbits around the central "nucleus" (the picture of the atom established by Rutherford's scattering experiments) were discrete, the only allowed orbits being those having angular momentum

$$L = n\hbar = \frac{nh}{2\pi} \qquad \text{for } n = 1, 2, 3, \ldots$$

A transition of the electron from one Bohr orbit to another would be accompanied by the emission of a single photon of appropriate energy. His treatment yielded orbits in the hydrogen atom given by

$$E = -\frac{mk^2e^4}{2n^2\hbar^2} = -\frac{13.6}{n^2} \text{ eV}$$

$$r = \frac{n^2\hbar^2}{mke^2} = (0.529 \text{ Å})(n^2)$$

which reproduced the observed spectral series in hydrogen and predicted the existence of others which subsequently were observed.

Electromagnetic radiation thus acts in many ways as a particle as well as a wave; the Compton scattering of x-rays may be treated as a billiard-ball collision between a photon and a free electron. De Broglie hypothesized that this "wave-particle duality" is a general feature of nature, that associated with the motion of any particle there is a wave propagation of wavelength

$$\lambda = \frac{h}{p}$$

where p is the particle's momentum. In this view, Bohr's quantization
condition became a standing-wave criterion: the allowed Bohr orbits
are those in which the circumference is an integral number of wavelengths.
Schrödinger's wave mechanics is the elaboration of this idea. The de
Broglie wave hypothesis was soon confirmed in the observation of
electron diffraction by Davisson and Germer.

The dual nature - wave and particle - of physical entities puts a
fundamental limitation on the precision with which they can be observed;
a wave cannot be precisely localized. This is expressed by the Heisenberg uncertainty principle

$$\Delta p \; \Delta x \geq \tfrac{1}{2}\hbar$$

42.2 CHECK LIST

Planck's constant, $h = 6.63 \times 10^{-34}$ J-sec

electron charge, $e = 1.60 \times 10^{-19}$ C

Rydberg constant, $R_\infty = 109,737.5$ cm^{-1}

Maxwell's equations

quantization

blackbody radiation

spectral distribution

Rayleigh-Jeans law

ultraviolet catastrophe

photoelectric effect

photon

work function

threshold frequency

Compton scattering

Compton wavelength

quantum theory

Bohr model

Balmer series

Rutherford scattering

Bohr orbit

stationary state

Paschen, Lyman, Brackett, etc., series

reduced mass

energy-level diagram

de Broglie wavelength

wave mechanics

wave-particle duality

uncertainty principle

42.3 TRUE OR FALSE?

_____ 1. In classical electromagnetic theory, a charged particle radiates electromagnetic energy at a rate proportional to its acceleration.

_____ 2. Newtonian mechanics fails to describe systems on an atomic or smaller scale of size.

_____ 3. A blackbody is an object which absorbs all radiation incident upon it.

_____ 4. Planck predicted the observed spectral distribution of blackbody radiation from a cavity by assuming standing waves at discrete wavelengths in the cavity.

_____ 5. Planck predicted the observed spectral distribution of blackbody radiation from a cavity by assuming oscillators in the walls could not have a frequency greater than a fixed maximum value.

_____ 6. According to Planck's radiation law, in the limit of high frequency, the intensity of blackbody radiation decreases exponentially with wavelength.

_____7. The maximum current in the photoelectric effect is proportional to the incident light intensity.

_____8. The maximum kinetic energy of ejected electrons in the photo-electric effect is proportional to the incident light intensity.

_____9. Einstein treated the photoelectric effect by assuming that the incident light is absorbed only in discrete amounts of energy $E = hf$.

_____10. In the photoelectric effect, the maximum kinetic energy of ejected electrons is proportional to the wavelength of the incident light.

_____11. On a given material, light of wavelength longer than a certain maximum value cannot cause photoelectric emission.

_____12. The change in wavelength on Compton scattering of x-rays is independent of their wavelength.

_____13. The Rydberg constant is the same for the spectra of all elements.

_____14. Thomson's model of the atom introduced the idea of the <u>nucleus</u>, a much smaller region in which all the positive charge and most of the mass of the atom are concentrated.

_____15. Bohr assumed, as his quantization condition, that the wavelength of the electron, in the hydrogen atom, must fit a whole number of times into the circumference of its orbit.

_____16. Bohr assumed that, in a transition between allowed electron orbits, a single photon of appropriate energy is emitted.

_____17. In Bohr's model of the hydrogen atom, the orbital frequency of the electron is the same as the frequency of emitted radiation.

_____18. De Broglie's idea of a wave motion associated with the motion of electrons was based on the observation of electron diffraction in experiments.

_____19. The wavelength of an electron is the same as that of a photon of the same momentum.

_____20. The wavelength of an electron is the same as that of a photon of the same energy.

_____21. For neutrons, protons, and heavier particles, the de Broglie wavelength is so small that their wave properties are unobservable.

_____22. The de Broglie wavelength increases with the speed of a particle.

_____23. Neither light nor electrons can adequately be described either as a particle or as a wave.

_____24. The uncertainty principle places no absolute limitation on the precision with which the position of a particle can be measured.

_____25. The uncertainty principle is a necessary consequence of wave-particle duality.

42.4 QUESTIONS

1. The Compton effect is essentially unobservable for visible light. Why is this?

2. In the text, the Bohr-orbit energy and radius formulas are derived

340

for arbitrary nuclear charge number Z. Does this imply that the Balmer series, or its equivalent, is to be found in the spectra of all the elements?

3. In the Bohr model, allowed energy values become more and more closely spaced as one goes to higher values of energy or orbital radius. How is this fact related to the apparent nature of <u>macroscopic</u> orbital systems?

4. The speed of a photon is known without any "uncertainty" - it is precisely c. Does it follow, from the uncertainty principle, that nothing whatever can be known about the photon's position?

5. In the classical-electrodynamic picture of the photoelectric effect, no minimum or "threshold" light frequency exists, but in certain circumstances a time lag, between turning on the light and the emission of photoelectrons, is to be expected. Briefly, explain why.

6. If light is incident upon hydrogen gas, it is possible for an atom in its ground state to absorb some energy, "exciting" the atom to a higher energy state. What is the minimum frequency of light for which this can happen?

7. Is Bohr's picture of the hydrogen atom consistent with the uncertainty principle? Explain.

42.5 EXAMPLES

1. Ultraviolet light of wavelength 2600 $\overset{\text{o}}{\text{A}}$, on a certain metal, ejects photoelectrons whose maximum kinetic energy is 1.34 eV. What maximum wavelength of light will eject photoelectrons from the same metal?

2. Photons of energy 1.16×10^5 eV (this would be in the gamma-ray region) undergo Compton scattering. What are the minimum and the maximum values which the kinetic energy of the recoiling electron may have?

3. A hydrogen atom is in the tenth Bohr state. Find the orbital frequency of the electron and compare it to the frequency of light emitted in a transition from the n = 10 to the n = 9 state.

4. Find a general expression for the de Broglie wavelength of an electron as a function of its kinetic energy. Evaluate the wavelength for an electron with $E_k = 2.60 \times 10^5$ eV. Show that, for very high E_k, the electron's wavelength is the same as that of a photon of the same energy.

42.6 ANSWERS

True or False?

1. False - proportional to the square of its acceleration.

2. True - the failure is general, as we now understand it, but is in practice observable only on the very small scale.

3. True.

4. False - the statement sounds most like the approach that leads to the Rayleigh-Jeans law, and <u>any</u> standing-wave system, of course, has discrete wavelengths.

5. False - the crucial assumption was that the energy of each oscillator could only be an integer multiple of a fundamental value proportional to the frequency.

6. False - it decreases exponentially with c/λ, which is the frequency.

7. True.

8. False - for given incident frequency, it is independent of the intensity.

9. True.

10. False - it increases linearly with the frequency.

11. True - this corresponds to a necessary minimum photon energy.

12. True - it depends only on the scattering angle.

13. False - it increases very slightly with atomic mass, due to the increase of the "reduced mass" of the system.

14. False - this is a nucleus, all right, but Thomson's model didn't have one.

15. False - the de Broglie hypothesis, and this rationalization of Bohr's quantization condition, came later.

16. True - this idea is what connects the discrete allowed orbital energies to the discrete frequencies of emitted light.

17. False - in general; it becomes true in the limit of very high n.

18. False - the experiments came later; de Broglie's hypothesis was a wholly speculative one.

19. True.

20. False - the momentum determines the wavelength, and the relation of momentum to energy for an electron (which has a nonzero rest mass) is different from that for a photon.

21. False - neutron diffraction is observable, for instance.

22. False - it goes inversely as the momentum, thus at low speeds inversely as the speed.

23. True.

24. True - it limits only simultaneous knowledge of momentum and position.

25. True - it is analogous to the relation between spatial extent and wavelength range for a classical wave packet.

Questions

1. The maximum possible change in wavelength of the scattered light (0.049 A) is so small as to be very difficult to observe for visible light with wavelength of several thousand angstroms.

2. No; it implies that hydrogenlike series should occur in the spectrum of any one-electron atom, regardless of the nuclear charge. These occur in light radiated by He^+ ions, for instance. The detailed dynamics of a multielectron atom are substantially different and are not treated in the basic Bohr approach. One objection to Bohr's theory, in fact, was just this - that there was no obvious way to extend it to atoms with more than one electron.

3. As the system - one point charge orbiting about another - becomes larger and larger, the available energy values become more and more nearly continuous. In a macroscopic system, the discreteness of energy levels is unobservable and classical dynamics predicts that any energy value is possible. As an extreme example, the earth's orbit around the sun (the force has the same form!) would be something like the $(10^{74})^{th}$ Bohr orbit.

4. No, our exact knowledge of the photon's speed says nothing about its momentum; this depends on wavelength. It is position and _momentum_ observations that the uncertainty principle relates.

5. In classical electrodynamics there is no limitation on the energy that an electron can absorb from the electromagnetic field; thus, while it may take time for a single electron to accumulate enough energy to break free of the metal, it could do so for any frequency of incident radiation.

6. From the ground state, the next available allowed state is that with n = 2; the energy required for this transition would be

$$\Delta E = hf = \frac{-13.6}{4} - \frac{-13.6}{1} = 10.2 \text{ eV}$$

and the corresponding frequency is

$$\frac{10.2 \text{ eV}}{4.14 \times 10^{-15} \text{ eV-sec}} = 2.46 \times 10^{15} \text{ Hz}$$

which is in the ultraviolet.

7. No; the very idea of a sharply defined orbit implies a simultaneous specification of the electron's position and motion - precisely what the uncertainty principle limits. Limitations intrinsic to the model (for instance, in a given state, the angular momentum is known at least within $\hbar$) produce minimum uncertainties in the electron's position, which are of the order of the whole size of the atom. All that is left of Bohr's picture is a fuzzy glob, with the electron in it somewhere.

Examples

Partial Solutions (1)

1. The threshold frequency and wavelength depend on the work function of the metal; this can be found from the data given.

2. The wavelength change in Compton scattering is

$$\lambda' - \lambda = \lambda_e (1 - \cos \theta)$$

where

$$\lambda_e = \frac{hc}{m_e c^2}$$

is the Compton wavelength of the electron. Given this, find the energy that has been transferred to the scattered electron.

3. The transition from the nth to the $(n - 1)^{th}$ state emits a photon whose frequency is

$$f = \frac{E_n - E_{n-1}}{h}$$

The orbital frequency can be found if you know the velocity, as the radius of the orbit is known. What can you use to find the orbital velocity in a given Bohr orbit?

4. For a general expression, and in particular for the value of E_k given, the relativistic relation between energy and momentum must be used.

This is
$$E^2 = (pc)^2 + (mc^2)^2$$
for a particle of rest mass m.

Partial Solutions (2)

1. The maximum kinetic energy of photoelectrons is given by
$$E_k = hf - \phi$$
This plainly cannot be negative; thus the photoelectric effect cannot happen unless
$$f > \frac{\phi}{h}$$
or
$$\lambda < \frac{hc}{\phi}$$
Find the work function from the energy at 2600 Å.

2. A photon's energy is hc/λ, so the kinetic energy transferred to the electron is
$$E_k = \frac{hc}{\lambda} - \frac{hc}{\lambda'} = \frac{hc(\lambda' - \lambda)}{\lambda'\lambda}$$
This is
$$E_k = \frac{hc\lambda_e(1 - \cos\theta)}{\lambda[\lambda + \lambda_e(1 - \cos\theta)]}$$
What are the maximum and minimum values that this expression can take on?

3. The velocity can be obtained from the orbital energy, or from
$$\ell = mvr = n\hbar$$
or
$$v = \frac{n\hbar}{mr}$$
The orbital frequency is therefore
$$f_0 = \frac{v}{2\pi r} = \frac{n\hbar}{2\pi mr^2}$$
The transition emits light of frequency
$$f = \frac{E_n - E_{n-1}}{h} = \frac{13.6 \text{ eV}}{h}\left[\frac{1}{(n - 1)^2} - \frac{1}{n^2}\right]$$

4. The total energy
$$E = E_k + mc^2$$
thus
$$(E_k + mc^2)^2 = (pc)^2 + (mc^2)^2$$
Solve for the momentum, and from that find the de Broglie wavelength.

Partial Solutions (3)

1. In the first case,
$$1.34 \text{ eV} = \frac{hc}{2600 \text{ Å}} - \phi$$
which gives
$$\phi = 3.43 \text{ eV}$$

and thus the maximum wavelength which can cause the emission of photoelectrons is

$$\frac{hc}{3.43 \text{ eV}} = \underline{3620 \text{ Å}}$$

2. Plainly at $0°$, from the expression found above, the kinetic energy transferred is zero; the maximum value occurs at $180°$:

$$E_{k \text{ max}} = \frac{2hc\lambda_e}{\lambda(\lambda + 2\lambda_e)} = \frac{hc/\lambda}{1 + \lambda/2\lambda_e}$$

$$= \frac{E}{1 + m_e c^2/2E}$$

if $E = hc/\lambda$ is the energy of the incident photon. Here we are given $E = 1.16 \times 10^5$ eV and $m_e c^2 = 5.11 \times 10^5$ eV. In this case, then, the kinetic energy transferred to the electron varies from zero to

$$\frac{1.16 \times 10^5 \text{ eV}}{1 + \dfrac{5.11 \times 10^5 \text{ eV}}{2(1.16 \times 10^5) \text{ eV}}} = \underline{3.62 \times 10^4 \text{ eV}}$$

3. We have prescriptions for the orbital radius and energy in the Bohr orbits. After a little juggling we find for the orbital frequency

$$f_0 = \frac{2E_0}{n^3 h}$$

where $E_0 = 13.6$ eV is the magnitude of the energy in the first Bohr orbit. The radiation frequency is

$$f = \frac{(2n - 1) E_0}{n^2 (n - 1)^2 h}$$

For $n = 10$, these give

$$\underline{f = 7.72 \times 10^{12} \text{ sec}^{-1}} \qquad \underline{f_0 = 6.58 \times 10^{12} \text{ sec}^{-1}}$$

They are close, but not the same. In the limit of large n these two become equal, as they should be in the classical view. This is an instance of Bohr's correspondence principle.

4. We get

$$E_k^2 + 2mc^2 E_k + (mc^2)^2 = (pc)^2 + (mc^2)^2$$

so

$$p^2 = \frac{E_k (E_k + 2mc^2)}{c^2}$$

or

$$\lambda = \frac{h}{p} = \frac{hc}{E_k\sqrt{1 + 2mc^2/E_k}}$$

The rest mass of an electron is 5.11×10^5 eV/c^2; thus a kinetic energy of 2.6×10^5 eV gives

$$\underline{\lambda = 2.15 \times 10^{-2} \text{ Å}}$$

If $E_k \gg mc^2$, the radical in the expression above approaches unity, and

$$\lambda \simeq \frac{hc}{E_k}$$

as for a photon of energy equal to E_k.